OH, CLARE!

Also by Richmal Crompton:

The 'William' Books (1922-1970)
The 'Jimmy' Books (1949-1951)
The 'Just William' BBC radio plays (2008-2010)

Novels:
The Innermost Room (1923); The Hidden Light (1924); Anne Morrison (1925);
The Wildings (1925); David Wilding (1926); The House (1926);
Millicent Dorrington (1927); Leadon Hill (1927); The Thorn Bush (1928);
Roofs Off! (1928); The Four Graces (1929); Abbots' End (1929);
Blue Flames (1930); Naomi Godstone (1930); Portrait of a Family (1931);
The Odyssey of Euphemia Tracy (1932); Marriage of Hermione (1932);
The Holiday (1933); Chedsy Place (1934); The Old Man's Birthday (1934);
Quartet (1935); Caroline (1936); There Are Four Seasons (1937);
Journeying Wave (1938); Merlin Bay (1939); Steffan Green (1940);
Narcissa (1941); Mrs Frensham Describes a Circle (1942);
Weatherly Parade (1943); Westover (1946); The Ridleys (1947);
Family Roundabout (1948); Frost at Morning (1950); Linden Rise (1952);
The Gypsy's Baby (1954); Four in Exile (1954);
Matty and the Dearingroydes (1956); Blind Man's Buff (1957);
Wiseman's Folly (1959); The Inheritor (1960)

Short story collections:
Kathleen and I, and of course, Veronica (1926)
A Monstrous Regiment (1927)
Enter - Patricia (1927)
The Middle Things (1928)
Felicity Stands By (1928)
Sugar and Spice (1928)
Mist (1928)
Ladies First (1929)
The Silver Birch (1931)
The First Morning (1936)
The House in the Wood (2022)
The Apple Blossom Lady (2023)

OH, CLARE!
and other humorous sketches

Richmal Crompton

David Schutte

First published in the United Kingdom in 2024
by David Schutte
14 Brockton : Lydbury North : Shropshire: SY7 8BA

10 9 8 7 6 5 4 3 2 1

ISBN 978-0-9564239-6-2

A CIP catalogue record for this book
is available from the British Library

Printed in England by CPI Antony Rowe

INTRODUCTION

Richmal Crompton is, of course, most well known for her 38 "*Just William*" books. In her lifetime she also published 10 volumes of short stories for the adult market, and 40 novels. Following years of research, including her own account book, I have discovered another 125 short stories published in magazines in the 1920s and 1930s which have never previously been collected in book form. I have published 25 of these in *The House in the Wood* (2022), and 27 in *The Apple Blossom Lady* (2023).

But, starting with *Punch* in 1920, Richmal Crompton also wrote over 250 humorous sketches (averaging around 720 words each) for *The Humorist*, *London Opinion* and *The Passing Show*. Her first published short story collection published in 1926, *Kathleen and I (and, of course, Veronica)*, features 52 of these pieces, with 7 more written to complete the book. Another 34 were included in the 42 sketches that make up *Enter – Patricia* published in 1927.

My researches have so far unearthed another 159 pieces that have never been reprinted, and I am pleased to present the majority in this volume for Miss Crompton's legion of fans to enjoy. Crompton tells each tale from a male point of view and so has great fun revealing the failings of these storytellers, as well as the mysteries and idiosyncrasies of their ladies.

Two of the characters that recur in a large number of these uncollected sketches are Clare and Delia. In some cases Crompton adapted the original published piece by changing the heroine's name to suit the book collection, e.g. a few tales featuring Angela, Clare, Belinda or Delia occasionally became Kathleen, and a few Clare and Delia sketches became Patricia. I have taken a similar liberty, but only with a couple of tales.

I have compiled this book in five sections, featuring Clare, Kathleen, Patricia, Delia and a pot pourri of other characters, often unnamed.

As Richmal Crompton herself implored in her introduction to *Enter – Patricia*:

To
THE READER

With a respectful recommendation not to read
all the following sketches at one sitting

David Schutte

CONTENTS

Part 1. Oh, Clare!   9

A Touch of Spring; Self-Denial; A Little Knowledge; Economy; The Old Adams; Jones' Plot; Nurse's Night Out; The Great Ballot Gamble; Life With the Lid Off; The Profiteer; Christmas Presents; Woman's Wiles; The Flu-ke; A Venus Tragedy; A Good Selection; The Object Lesson; The Pet; Clare Goes Out to Lunch; Wasn't it Sweet?; A Wireless Tragedy; The Umbrella; The Telegrams; A Question of Hats; Victory; Gathering the Holly; Coming Down To It; A Free Choice; In the Fog; Losing Clare; The Note; Easter Eggs; By Telephone; Clicking; The Picnic; A Summer's Afternoon; The Thing; The Bulbs; The First Word; The Invitations; An Autumn Diary; A Master Tactician; Mrs Jones and Me; Bad Luck; Exchange Is No Robbery; The Frozen Pipe; Alphege and Archie; Our Holiday.

Part 2. Kathleen and I   83

A Way Out of the Present Unrest; The Artists; Minus Aunt Jane.

Part 3. Enter – Patricia   87

The Power of Thought; St Martin's Summer; Feet of Clay; Going Out to Tea; Celebrating Spring.

Part 4. Introducing Delia   95

Good Resolutions; A Sign of Spring; Possessing the Power; Coming Down; The Reason Why; The Organiser; Burying the Hatchet; Our Easter Holiday; A Mean Trick; A Moving Tragedy; Daughters of Deceit; After All; A Difficulty; The Clothes Horse; Touring with Delia; Appropriate; What's In a Name!; John and Delia; The Finding of Muffles; Bob's Box; The Daily Guide; The Name; A Question of Licence; The Vase; Two to Tea; Our Country Walk; The Lift; Ancient v Modern; The Name; A Little Fortune-Telling; The Explanation; Uncle Frederick's Christmas Present; Cat and Mouse; The Clicking of Clarence; After the Thriller; Spill Fever; Our Christmas Change.

Part 5. Miss Thomson et al   156

Getting the Number; A Brief Respite; Culture and Cunning; The Title; A Strike in Fairyland; High Commerce; The Collector; In the 'Bus; Fire Eater; Seven Days; The Plot That Failed; The Gift; (Laughter.); Mrs Hawkins on the Drama; The Treat; The Method; The Riddle of the Heath; The Fall of David; The Wager; The Pendulum Swings; Cruel Uncle; The Give-away; The Rival Garage; Marigold's Double; Next-Door Neighbours; Making an Impression; The Handy Man; Clarissa Changes a Wheel; Vera Looks Out a Train; Aunt Martha and the Doctor; Simpson and the Baby; Solving a Problem; The Smoker's Cure; A Spring Walk; Car Stealers; My Holiday; Alexander; Retribution; My Seat; A Super-tax; Left in Charge.

Part 1
Oh, Clare!

A Touch of Spring
(The Humorist 26/4/1924)

"Spring cleaning," I said, "is merely a bad habit. It is the result of that restlessness and craving for change and excitement that is one of the most vicious characteristics of your sex."

"That sounds really well," said Clare, critically. "Are you going to put it in an article?"

"Yes, I'm calling it 'The Psychology of Spring Cleaning'."

"It's not psychology that worries me," said Clare. "It's dust."

"Dust," I said, "is indestructible. Nothing can be destroyed. When all is said and done, what are we all but dust?"

"Yes," said Clare, "but we don't all spread ourselves over the top of the piano and in the chinks of the furniture. It's that sort of dust I dislike. I don't mind you and me. I think you're quite a nice bit of dust."

"Don't try to turn me from my subject," I said severely. "You cannot destroy matter. Nature abhors a vacuum."

"Does it?" said Clare. "I rather like one myself for the spring cleaning. Janie's going to lend me hers."

"You go into a room," I said, warming to my subject, "and flick about with a brush and a duster, and the dust jumps up into the air and stays there till your back's turned, and then simply sits down where it was before, laughing at you up its sleeve."

"It will make a beautiful article, darling!"

said Clare affectionately. "Mrs Jones can come next Monday, and we hope to do the whole house in the week."

"Except my study," I said firmly. "I forbid you to touch my study. You promised to obey me in the marriage service, and I hold you to it."

"Y-yes," admitted Clare meditatively, "but you promised with all your worldly goods to me endow, and you simply refuse to buy me half the things I want, though I know you've got money in the bank which, according to the marriage service, is mine. I don't consider that you have with all your worldly goods me endowed, and I consider that lets me off the obeying part."

"You sophist!" I said.

"Please don't use language like that in the drawing room," said Clare, "and, considering that you're away all day, I don't see how you can stop me doing out your study."

"I shall lock my study door every morning," I said.

I did.

The rest of the house became uninhabitable. Clare and I sat in my study every evening. Every morning I locked my study before setting off for work.

The week passed. The danger passed. Mrs Jones, our corpulent and wheezy Spirit of the Spring, passed on to fresh fields and pastures new (or, in plain terms, to Mrs Jenkins in "The Limes"), and our house breathed again.

My brother came in to dinner the day after she had gone.

"I've just been reading that article of

9

yours, 'The Psychology of Spring Cleaning'," he said. "Jolly good!"

"Wasn't it?" I said modestly. "And I lived up to it, too. I didn't allow them to touch my study. It's the only un-spring-cleaned room in the house. Now come and see if you can discover any difference between my study and, say, the drawing room."

He came. He was impressed.

"Well, honestly," he said, "I think that your study looks, if anything, the cleaner."

When he had gone I told Clare.

"It's what I've always said," I remarked. "Spring cleaning annoys the dust. It puts its back up, and the last state— you know, John said that he thought my study looked cleaner than the drawing room."

"I dare say it does," said Clare. "The drawing room was done at the beginning of the week, and your study was done at the end."

I gasped.

"My study? But I locked the door every day!"

Clare carefully threaded her needle.

"Yes, darling," she murmured, "but you left the key each day in your old jacket pocket."

Self-Denial
(*The Humorist 31/5/1924*)

The sun streamed into the breakfast room. The birds were singing. The tulips and daffodils were nodding, or blowing, or whatever they do in the garden. It was spring. I knew that it was spring by the look in Clare's eyes as she came into the room. With a sudden flash of inspiration I forestalled her.

"I simply must have a new suit," I said.

She looked at me suspiciously, but my guileless look disarmed her suspicions.

"Why?" she said coldly.

"This looks so frightfully shabby now that the spring weather's come," I said.

She looked me up and down.

"I think it looks perfectly all right," she said distantly.

"It looks dreadful. And after all, as your husband, I have to dress up to a certain standard. I want a new overcoat, too."

"You *don't!*"

"I *do!* That old thing simply isn't fit to wear – and a new hat and new gloves."

Clare's indignation burst forth.

"I think it's absolutely silly to want to get new clothes just because the sun comes out. It's simply imagination thinking they look shabby!"

"Perhaps you're right," I said slowly. "Perhaps we ought to go on wearing our old clothes for a long time yet. I agree with you that the habit of buying new clothes in the spring is a foolish one. So we'll agree not to."

Of course, I'd simply got her.

"You won't get the new suit and overcoat?" she said.

"Oh no," I said. "You've quite converted

me to your idea that it's foolish to buy new clothes in spring."

As I said, I'd got her. Logically, she couldn't do anything.

I went off to the office in a glow of pride and triumph. It had really been rather a clever stroke. I carefully ignored the subject for the rest of the week.

On the Monday of the next week, Clare appeared at my office. She was dressed in a new coat and skirt with new shoes and stockings, and a new hat that made my bank book's heart palpitate. I held my head.

"Good heavens!" I said.

"Yes," said Clare calmly. "I thought I might get something really posh as you weren't going to buy anything new. It seemed to leave double for me. Or so I reasoned it."

"Reason!" I groaned. "Don't talk about reason. What did you say to me yourself only last Monday?"

"Last Monday!" said Clare. "A whole week ago! How can I be expected to remember that? But I do look rather nice, don't I?"

I didn't kill her on the spot. Nor did I write to the papers repudiating her debts. She was quite right. She did look rather nice. I took her out to lunch.

A Little Knowledge
(The Humorist 9/8/1924)

"You know," said Charles, "it's perfectly absurd to think of any well-run household without a medical reference book."

"I don't know that Clare and I set up any claim to be well-run," I murmured.

"No, but look here," said Charles, "suppose you were ill – really ill."

"I'd send for the doctor."

"Yes, but suppose you were miles away from a doctor."

"I'm not."

"Or suppose your doctor were out."

"I'd send for another."

"And suppose he were out."

"I'd die. I've made my will. We've all got to die some time."

"You won't listen to me," Charles said impatiently: "I'm trying to tell you how to avoid such a catastrophe."

"*So* kind of you to put it that way," I murmured.

"If you have a medical reference book, all you have to do is look up your symptoms in it and – well, ten to one, you won't need a doctor."

"Is it as drastic as that?" I said.

"You misunderstand me," said Charles. "You will be able to cure yourself. You'll save all doctors' fees. You'll never need a doctor. You'll catch the symptoms at once and arrest them. If you have a medical reference book you really needn't ever be ill."

"Needn't I? But I don't want to live for ever, like the Labour Government."

"Just listen to me—" began Charles, drawing a deep breath.

I put up my hands.

"Kamerad!" I said. "I'd rather buy the book."

"I simply want a medical reference book. I'm going to live for ever."

The young man in the shop looked at me pityingly.

"This is quite a good one," he said. "Illustrated."

I opened it at the picture of a spider on a large plate.

"The base of the brain," he said.

"Really?" I murmured, turning over hastily.

On the next page was the picture of a tall and graceful tree.

"That's rather pretty," I said.

"The spinal cord," he explained.

"Fancy!" I murmured, closing the book.

I read it all the way home.

"What's the matter with you?" said Clare, when I arrived. "You look blue."

"I've discovered that I'm in the initial stages of scarlet fever," I said gloomily. "It's often fatal. I've got quite a lot of ordinary minor diseases as well, according to this book."

"Let me see," she said, taking it from me.

I went upstairs to take my temperature. It was normal, but you can't always tell by that. When I came down Clare was reading the book. I looked over her shoulder.

"I say," I said reproachfully, "you might read about my disease."

"I'm reading about my own," she said. "I've got amaurosis."

"Never heard of it," I said incredulously.

"I've only just found out that I've got it. It's little spots before the eyes."

I took the book from her and settled down before the fire with it.

"I believe I've got diphtheria as well as all the others," I said, after a few minutes.

At that moment I saw Charles passing the gate. It was pouring with rain, but I ran down to him.

"I say, Charles!" I called.

He stopped.

"I'm awfully interested in what you said about a medical reference book," I said. "Have you got one yourself?"

He looked guilty.

"N-not exactly," he said. "I'm always meaning to get one."

I pressed it into his hands.

"I thought perhaps you mightn't have one. I've got one for you as a present."

"Oh, I say," said Charles. "How kind of you. But you did get one for yourself, I hope?"

"Oh, yes," I said unblushingly. "I did get one for myself."

I went back to Clare.

"I've given the book away," I said.

"Thank heaven!" said Clare.

"Do you know," said Clare late that evening. "I don't believe I've got am – am – whatever it is – after all."

"My scarlet fever and diphtheria seem to have passed off too," I said. "I've only got a slight chill through going out to Charles in the rain."

"Have you?" said Clare sympathetically. "I'll ring up the doctor."

Economy

(The Humorist 9/8/1924)

"I've spent all today being economical," said Clare.

"No!" I said with an incredulity that was born of experience.

"I have, honestly. The Sales, you know."

"Oh, the *Sales!*" I said, in a voice of resignation and hopelessness.

"You won't talk like that when you hear," she said proudly. "I wanted some lace and it was six-and-six a yard at Flemming's and I saw *just* the same advertised at D.T.Evans in town at five-and-six, so I went up for it. I wanted five yards, so I must have saved heaps and heaps of money. You can do the sum for yourself."

"I will," I said grimly, taking out a pencil and a notebook. "Fare up to town first of all. How much?"

"Oh, you know, surely," said Clare, powdering her nose. "I always forget. I just give the man a ten shilling note and take the change."

"Four shillings, I suppose," I said. "Now the lace. How much did you want?"

"Five yards."

"One pound seven and sixpence. How much did you spend on lunch?"

"Darling," said Clare reproachfully, "you surely don't grudge me that! You always say that you hate me to have nasty little snacks of tea and things when I go up to town."

"I do. I'm not grudging. I'm doing a sum in arithmetic. How much was the lunch?"

"Well, you know, the salmon seemed the only eatable thing on the menu, and it *is* a little expensive, but when you've been

working hard all morning looking at shops you don't feel like chops or steak or dull hot things like that. It came to about seven-and-six. And you know, darling, I'd have to have lunch at home."

"What would you have had at home?"

"Well – let me think. The joint was for tonight. There was only the cold meat, and I hate cold meat. I'd probably have had an egg and coffee and then some cake."

"I'll call lunch five-and-six, then, and I'm being generous."

"It's a *funny* sort of sum," said Clare. "I don't understand it."

"What did you do after lunch?"

"Well, dear, I felt so tired. I just went into a picture house to rest."

"What price seats?"

"Oh, the two shilling. I'm always afraid of germs and things in the others."

"Then tea?"

"You didn't want me to come home without tea, darling, did you?"

"Not at all. It's just for the sum. How much was tea?"

"I had a *very* economical tea. Just half a crown. I remember, because I gave a ten shilling note and forgot to wait for change. A waiter had to come running out to me with it, so I gave him an extra shilling tip."

"Well, we won't count that. Taxi?"

"Darling," said Clare. "you've often said you hated me to stand in crowded buses when I'm tired. I was *frightfully* tired, carrying the lace and everything. You *surely* don't grudge me a taxi."

"Far from it. It's only in the pursuit of knowledge. How much was the taxi?"

"It was three-and-six with the tip."

I did a little sum in my notebook.

"Do stop scribbling figures," said Clare, "and come into the garden to look at the roses. Three and a half of them have come out since you saw them last night. Darling, what a funny way you make your threes. They look like frogs. I always begin at the other end."

She did three with her finger on the bald place on my head. I ignored her.

"Listen," I said at last. "If you bought the lace at Flemming's, you'd have spent £1 12s 6d. By going to town you've spent £2 2s 6d. A difference of ten shillings."

She was so busy making threes on my bald spot that she didn't hear me.

"Umph?" she said.

"A difference of ten shillings," I repeated, closing my notebook.

She gave a little scream.

"I told you I'd been *economical*," she said. "Fancy saving *ten shillings*. I shall feel that I really *can* go bust after this. Now, stop adding up how much I've saved and come into the garden to look at the roses."

So I left it at that, and went into the garden to look at the roses.

The Old Adams
(London Opinion 20/9/1924)

It all began with a wretched little book that Clare's mother sent us for a marriage anniversary present. It was called *The Secret of Happiness*.

I shouldn't have read the thing only I'd forgotten to buy an evening paper, and it was too wet for golf, and the only things to read in the house seemed to be *The Secret of Happiness* and the parish magazine. To say that it was a choice of evils puts it too mildly.

Anyway, I settled down to *The Secret of Happiness* and hoped for the best. It was the more unknown of the two evils. I know all there is to know of the vicar's literary style.

The book was about 200 pages long – a masterpiece in its way. I always admire authors who can stretch out a sentence to fill a book; all this author had to say was that you'd be happy if you made the other person happy. When he'd finished saying it one way, he started again and said it another way. And so on. For 200 pages. With the help of a few little dots at intervals to spin it out. Thus . . . or . ⦙ . or §
. . . six in a half page space. The thing was really quite clever in its way....

Moreover, it was convincing. I'd always thought there was some catch in that idea that you'd be happy if you made the other person happy. I always thought it a bit fishy and I've never met anyone who's seriously tried it. But it certainly sounded quite convincing as the book put it. By the time I'd reached page 200 and come to the little drawing of a daisy that marked the end, I'd decided quite seriously to try it.

The next morning I received two tickets for a concert from Brown. In the enclosed letter, Brown said that they had been sent to him, but he found that he was unable to go and he hoped that Clare and I would enjoy it. One glance at the programme showed me why Brown had found he would be unable to go.

I dislike classical music as much as Brown does. It's nothing to be ashamed of. It's just the kind of soul you happen to be born with. Some people are born with one coloured hair and some with another. And some people are born with a soul that likes classical music and some aren't. I'm not. Mine's the sort of soul that doesn't like classical music – and quite a decent sort of soul as souls go.

Ordinarily I'd have chucked the tickets into the waste paper basket without a word, but now the conscience newly discovered for me by *The Secret of Happiness* raised its head and barked at me. Would Clare like to go? I handed her the tickets.

So we went.

It was a super-super-super-super classical concert. I won't try to describe what I underwent. I don't want to harrow your feelings too much. There are things that lie too deep for words – at least for words that respectable editors will pass.

Anyway, it was over at last. Clare said that she had enjoyed it awfully and I tried to think that Clare's pleasure compensated for my sufferings. I wasn't quite sure that it did, because as I said, I haven't got the really highest kind of soul. However, I felt that my new life of self-sacrifice would soon elevate it.

The next morning I went to Clare's bureau for some blotting-paper, cheaper and less trouble than buying some for myself. I had used up the last piece I had scrounged. I found, sitting on the blotting-paper, a letter from Clare to her mother. It began:

"Dear Mother,
"I went to a concert with John last night—"

I thought it might help my newly-turned leaf to read of Clare's pleasure in the concert. Moreover, Clare always says that she has no secrets from me and likes me to read her letters. So I read on.

"That little book you sent about trying to make the other person happy was so inspiring that I determined to act on it. And when John asked me to go to the concert I thought he must want to go himself, so I said 'Yes'. Well, of course, I was bored stiff, but John's pleasure almost repaid me—"

I sought out Clare and described to her in a few well-chosen words (words that no respectable editor would pass, so I will not record my speech verbatim, though it was not devoid of eloquence) my feelings during the concert.

Then we saw the catch in the thing. It's all right one trying to make the other happy, or the other trying to make one happy, but when they start trying to make each other happy, only misery and classical concerts and that sort of thing ensues. So we decided to be selfish and unselfish, in turn, week and week about. It was a good idea, but it fell through, because we both insisted on bagging the first week of selfishness to make the most of the other while the idea was fresh. So we finally decided to go back to the old Adam life. We'd really got on very well as old Adams.

We wrapped up *The Secret of Happiness* with an old pair of stockings of Clare's and an old pair of braces of mine and sent it to the village jumble sale and charged 2d for the lot.

Jones' Plot
(The Humorist 4/10/1924)

"I say," said Jones excitedly, meeting me in the street one morning, "You write, don't you?"

"I sometimes try to," I said modestly.

"Well, I've got a fine plot for you," he said. "I'll give it to you, and you can do what you like with it. I should think it would run to a novel or a short story."

"Really?" I murmured politely. "I'm afraid I'm trying to catch a train right now."

But it was useless. Every ruse *is* useless against the Joneses of this world. They have the wiliness of the serpent without the gentleness of the dove.

"I can easily come along with you to the station," he said. "It isn't far out of my way."

I tried to shake him off by hurrying, but he trotted along at my heels like an energetic spaniel.

"I thought of it in the night," he said breathlessly, "and, as I've really no time myself to waste in writing, it struck me that you were just the chap to take it on – plenty of time on your hands and nothing much to do, don't you know." (I may remark here that I am a hard-working, ten-hours-a-day journalist.) "Anyway, the main idea is that the man has a double, you know, and he's in a high office of State."

"Which?" I said. "The man or the double?"

"The man, of course. I said so. "Well, the man commits a crime—"

"What sort of a crime?"

"*Any* sort of a crime," he said, irritably; "just a crime. I'm leaving you to fill in all these minor details. I'm just giving you the broad outlines. Well, the man is arrested for it, but the man's wife is sure he didn't do it, and visits the double at midnight."

"Tut, tut," I said. "Why at midnight?"

"Surely, as a writer, you must know that it's much more dramatic to visit someone at midnight than, say, at breakfast time."

"Yes, but why not the happy mean? Why not at about 4pm, when you get in for tea if you're lucky? I mean, I shouldn't know what to offer anyone who called at midnight. Did the double make her a cup of tea in his pyjamas or give her the remains of the cold meat, or merely pass her the bull's-eye tin?"

"You know," said Jones patiently, "it's awfully difficult to keep the thread in my mind when you insist on interrupting. I've told you he was a criminal. He wouldn't have gone to bed. He'd be lying on a divan or something, smoking cocaine."

"I don't think you can smoke cocaine."

"Well, as I said, you must verify those minor details. He must be drinking cocaine, then, or inhaling it, or whatever you do with cocaine. He must be doing something sinister, because he's the villain. Anyway, he kidnaps the woman and imprisons her in a lonely country house."

"Why?"

"Oh, simply villainy. He's always doing sinister things like that out of pure villainy. Well, the next thing is that the lawyer who was defending the man is found murdered, and the man escapes from prison."

"How?"

"As I keep telling you, those are details that you must fill in yourself."

"I see. Here's the station. Thanks so much. Goodbye."

"Oh, I might as well run up to town with you just to finish it. It seems a shame to leave you in suspense."

"I don't mind. I can bear it," I hastened to reassure him.

But he was too kind-hearted for that. He dragged me past my own particular carriage where the other three of our bridge four were awaiting me. Pathetically, almost tearfully, I besought him not to waste his precious time on me, but he ignored my prayers. He dragged me into a wretched carriage labelled "non-smokers" and began again.

By the time we reached Beckenham he'd got both the man and his wife imprisoned in a lonely moated grange, and the double, in his usual sinister way, was intriguing to restore the German Emperor to the throne. At Sydenham the man and his wife were rescued by aeroplane, but no one would believe that the man was the man because the double said he was the man. At London Bridge the double had imprisoned the German Chancellor in an underground dungeon and was pursuing the man and his wife by motor car along a country road.

When the train stopped I fled like a woodland hart from sight and sound of Jones, leaving three overturned porters to mark the path of my flight.

That night Jones rang me up.

"I'll just finish that story," he said. "Well, the man had a file which he'd had built into the sole of his boot and when—"

"I'm so sorry," I said, "but I'm afraid it's no use tonight. You can't get through to me. Our telephone's out of order."

The next day he called, but I sent a message that I was just recovering from a serious illness and the doctor had said that I must see no one. He left a message that the man might be called Montmorency, and the double Rudolph.

All the next week I went to London by an

earlier train and crept down to the station by back streets. The end of Jones' plot hung like a dark cloud over my life. He rang me up, but I was always out. He came to see me, but I was always ill. He ambushed me on my way to the station, but I dodged round corners like a professional criminal evading justice. The strain, however, was telling on me. I began to have horrible dreams about the man and the wife and the double and the German Emperor and the Chancellor. Finally, Jones wrote down the end of his plot and sent it to me by post. I tried not to read it, but the thing had begun to have a horrible fascination for me. The double pursued the man and wife and the German Chancellor and the Doge of Venice (no, I don't know why he came in. I don't think Jones did, either) under the sea, all dressed in divers' costumes, and the double was swallowed whole by a whale and everyone lived happily ever after. The dreams I had that night are simply indescribable.

At this point I heard Jones' voice in the hall.

"I'm afraid he's very busy just now," Clare was saying.

"Oh, he'll see me," said Jones. "We're – er– collaborating."

He came in. I hastily drew the cover over the typewriter at which I was working.

"I hope you'll be able to use that plot," said Jones anxiously. "I took a good deal of trouble working it out."

"Oh, yes," I assured him.

"Well," he said proudly, "send me a copy of whatever it comes out in, won't you?"

So I'll send him a copy of this.

I can't help it if he doesn't like it.

Anyway, I feel I owe him one.

Nurse's Night Out
(The Humorist 25/10/1924)

"The children simply won't go to sleep," said Clare. "It's Nurse's night out, and I've been up three times. They keep wanting me to put on that comic nose that Freddie gave them."

"I hope you don't give it to them," I said sternly.

"No, I don't," said Clare. "But I *can't* get them to be quiet and go to sleep."

"All that is needed is a little firmness," I said, severely. "You coax them and bribe them, and then you're surprised that they don't do what you tell them."

"You'd better tackle them," said Clare. "You'd be far better than I. The comic nose is in Jimmy's drawer."

"I don't want to know anything about the comic nose," I said. "I shall stand no nonsense. I shall be firm."

There came a fresh outburst of sound from the night nursery. I went upstairs.

"Now, children —" I began.

They howled at me.

"Oh, Daddy, *do* put it on! It's in Jimmy's drawer."

"Certainly not! Now, just listen to me—"

"Oh, Daddy, *do!*"

"Now listen to what—"

"Oh, Daddy, DO!"

"Now look here, children—"

"Oh, Daddy, *DO!*"

"Well, if you'll really go to sleep afterwards—"

It was a large, red, bulbous, cardboard nose with a bushy moustache attached and elastic that fastened behind the ears.

It was a great success.

"Now, children—" I said, firmly, at last.

"Daddy, now be a bear!"

"Certainly not! Now listen to me—"

"Oh, Daddy, *do* be a bear!"

"I'm going to turn the light out and you must—"

"Daddy, DO be a bear!"

"Well, if you're sure you'll go to sleep *directly* after—"

I was a bear. Sheila got out of bed and pinned the little woolly mat to my coat behind. I was a great success as a bear.

"Now, children," I said at last, "that's quite enough—"

"Daddy, we *promise* to go to sleep if you'll sing the funny song with your hair made into a spike in front, like you did once before. The vaseline's in that drawer. Daddy, *do!*"

"Now listen, children—"

"Daddy, DO!"

I did. It created quite a furore of applause.

"Now, you promised—"

"Yes, Daddy, we will. And you'll come and do it tomorrow night too, won't you?"

"*No!*" I said.

I went downstairs.

"You see!" I said. "They're perfectly quiet. All they need is a little firmness. I simply went in and said to them quite firmly—"

At first I couldn't think what she was laughing at. When I realised, I went out of the room with great dignity. I went upstairs, took off the nose, unpinned the mat and unspiked my hair.

Since then I have tried to arrange pressing business appointments for Nurse's night out.

The Great Ballot Gamble
(London Opinion 8/11/1924)

"I'm not going meekly to vote just as you tell me this time," said Clare pugnaciously.

"You never do," I said. "You only pretend you're going to; then you go into your little hole and put a cross against them all for luck."

"I *don't!*" she said indignantly. "Anyhow, I'm going to decide entirely by myself this time. I'm quite without prejudice to start with. I shall read the papers and listen to the people who come to canvas me and ask them about anything I don't understand, and you needn't try to influence me in any way at all, because I shan't take any notice of you."

"All right," I said. "That's that."

When I came home from the office one evening, about a week later, she told me that a Liberal canvasser had called on her.

"How did you get on?" I said with interest.

"He was *such* a nice man," said Clare. "Baby was in the room, and he was so much interested in her. He's got a little girl just two years older and – isn't it funny? – she had whooping cough last spring when Baby had it. I told him about that tonic that did Baby so much good, and I gave him a copy of the prescription, and he told me some of the things his little girl said. They were so amusing. One day—"

"Yes," I said, "but what about politics? I mean, did he mention his party's programme?"

"Oh, I think he was just going to when the Gresham-Smiths called, so he went. But just as he was going he said that he was sure I'd vote the right way. I think that was so nice of him."

"So I suppose you'll vote Liberal," I said, "just because this fellow's infant had whooping cough the same time as yours?"

"I haven't made up my mind *how* I'll vote yet," said Clare with dignity.

The next evening she announced that the Conservative canvasser had been.

"He was perfectly sweet," she said. "I was putting the bulbs into the bowls and he helped me. He did about ten bowls. He says that most people water them far too much and keep them in the dark too long."

"Did he mention politics at all?"

"He hadn't time. Doing the bulbs took so much longer than you'd think, and he helped me carry them down to the cellar and, of course, you can't talk politics and do bulbs at the same time, and as soon as we'd finished he simply had to fly for a meeting, but just as he was going he said that he was sure I'd read their programme and it spoke for itself…. He was *such* a nice man…."

"So I suppose you're a Conservative now?" I said.

"Oh, I haven't made up my mind yet," said Clare.

A Labour canvasser came the next week.

"Did he mention politics by any chance?" I said, "or did he only tell you about his little girl and help you pot bulbs?"

"He talked politics all the time," said Clare, "but he talked so quickly that I couldn't understand. And he sat on the chair next the little table with the Chinese vase, and he kept waving his hands about, and my heart was in my mouth all the time, because you know it's *irreplaceable!*"

"So you didn't get much from him?"

"No, but I was awfully glad he didn't break the vase. He touched it once and made it wobble, and I nearly screamed."

"So you've not made your mind up yet?"

"No; there's heaps of time," said Clare.

The polling day arrived.

"Will you come to vote with me on the way to the station?" I said to Clare at breakfast.

Clare was looking rather worried.

"Who shall I vote for?" she said casually.

"Oh, I'm not going to prejudice you," I said. "You're going to judge entirely by yourself, you know."

Clare sighed.

"Yes… I know," she said.

Then, after a silence:

"I'm going to try and get a sign."

She got a book from the bookshelf and a pin from her work box. She opened the book and shut her eyes.

"Now, I'm going to put down this pin at random on this page, and if it comes to a capital 'L' it means Liberal, and if it comes to a small 'l' it means Labour, and if it comes to a 'C' it means Conservative."

"Well?" I said.

"It's a 'Z'," she said sadly.

She tried twice more. The first time it was an 'S' and the second time it was a 'T'.

"You'll be fined by the library if you puncture much more of its property," I said.

"Who are *you* going to vote for?" said Clare rather meekly.

"I'm not going to tell you," I said. "The ballot's secret."

"You're being quite a pig, aren't you?" said Clare.

"Quite," I agreed pleasantly. "I thought you were going to read the papers and find out all about it."

"I did mean to. I read those manifesto things and they all seemed so noble that there was nothing to choose between them.... I meant to read speeches and articles and things, but whenever I opened the paper I always saw something really vital in it about whether skirts were going to be longer or whether shingling was going out, and when I'd finished reading that it was time to talk to Cook about the dinner, or take Baby out or something, so I never really got into politics."

"Well, it's too late now," I said. "I'm ready. Do get your things on."

She got her things on; then drew me into the nursery. "Let's say goodbye to Baby before we go."

Baby was gurgling merrily.

"Baby help Mummy," she said. "Mummy doin' to vote. Sall Mummy vote Labour or Conservative or Liberal?"

"Yibyal," cooed Baby.

"*There!*" said Clare. She looked at me crushingly. "She's got more sense than all the rest of you put together."

"Clare," I said in horror, "do you seriously mean to tell me that you're going to vote Liberal just because this wretched infant has mouthed the word after you?"

"Of course I am," said Clare. "Isn't he a nasty rude man, darling?"

But she didn't. She saw a clean-shaven man smoking a pipe standing outside the polling place, and it reminded her of Mr Baldwin, so she took it as a "sign" and voted Conservative.

But I'm inclined to wager that somehow or other she managed to spoil her paper!

Life with the Lid Off
(The Passing Show 15/11/1924)

I am an author in a small way. That means that I write when I feel like it and not when I don't. That's the only enjoyable way of being an author.

I think it's a degradation of authorship to sit in a study on a ripping day when you might be doing something really useful in the world such as bringing down your handicap or preventing over-population among the peaches in the kitchen garden.

But Clare has other ideas. Clare thinks that the whole art of authorship is to sit at a desk in a study for so many hours a day with a piece of foolscap paper before you and a pen poised gracefully in your hand. Generally I am adamant against this idea of hers but occasionally – very occasionally – I yield. I yielded this morning.

"I don't feel like it," I pleaded. "I can't insult my public by writing when I'm not inspired."

"Darling," said Clare earnestly, "I'm sure that if you just sit quietly for a few minutes the inspiration will come."

She kissed me in rather an endearing way and then took advantage of my momentary weakness to push me gently into the study and close the door.

I had to write something so I began a kind of diary of the morning....

10 o'clock. Begin to write. Date, address, etc.

10.5. Go to easy chair and take up detective tale. Very interesting.

10.30. Return to desk quickly at sound of Clare's footsteps. Am writing this as Clare looks in. In reply to her whispered question as to whether I am getting on all right reply curtly that I am.

10.35. Hold conversation with gardener through window about prospects of upcoming football season.

11.00. Return to desk at sound of Clare's footsteps. Enter Clare on tiptoe with cup of Bovril. Thank her with expression of abstraction and annoyance at interruption. Exit Clare on tiptoe with expression of apology.

11.5. Back to armchair. Drink Bovril (quite decent stuff) and read detective story again. Am pretty sure I know who did it.

11.30. Return to desk at sound of Clare's footsteps. Am writing hard when Clare enters and do not look up. Clare takes empty cup and exits on tiptoe.

11.35. Hear Clare upstairs and sneak out into hall for golf club. Practise swing on hearthrug (Pro. advises this).

12. Break vase on mantelpiece and return hastily to desk in readiness for Clare who, however, does not come.

12.5. More practise of swing.

12.30. Break another vase. Return again to desk. Enter Clare. I look up from desk, hand to head, as if exasperated at interruption. Clare apologises and retires without further investigation.

12.35. Finish detective story in armchair. Was quite wrong as to who did it.

1 o'clock. Lunch bell. Exit from study.

Conversation during lunch.

Clare: "You've had a lovely long morning's work, darling, haven't you?"

Me: "Yes. It does take it out of one!"

Clare: "Did you finish what you were doing?"

Me: "Yes. It wasn't the butler after all."

Clare: *"What?"*

Me: "Oh, I'm sorry. I mean, yes, I did. I'm getting a bit mixed."

Clare: "Is it a romance or a drama of real life?"

Me (quite truthfully): "It's a drama of real life."

Clare: "How nice! I love that sort of thing! Do you think it will be accepted?"

Me: "Oh, I don't see why not."

I don't either. But I hope Clare won't see it if it is.

The Profiteer

(London Opinion 22/11/1924)

As I came home, I saw him standing at our gate, looking very aggressive and very dirty and with a repulsive cast in one eye.

"You live 'ere?" he said pugnaciously.

I admitted that I did.

"Then it's your kid's knocked me down with 'is blinkin' bike – down in this 'ere blinkin' road – a'ruinin' of me clothes an' me nerves."

"I say! Really?" I said, aghast.

Ronny has just been promoted from a scooter to a bicycle and he certainly has the instincts of a Jehu.

"Yus, *I* say, too," he said with biting sarcasm. "Look at me trowsers – *spoilt*, that's wot they are. 'Oo d'you think's goin' to wear these 'ere trowsers now?"

I looked at his trowsers. They were nondescript garments uniformly faded and patched and covered with dust.

"*Look* at 'em," he said, "would *you* wear 'em?"

"Certainly not!" I said, with some indignation.

"Then why should I? All rolled in the dust by your blinkin' kid. While the shock to me nerves —"

"I'll just go in and inquire," I said, and walked firmly up to the front door. I went into the drawing room.

"Is Ronny in?" I said to Clare.

"No, darling. He's out somewhere on his new bicycle," she said.

"Yes," I said sternly, "and he's just knocked a man down on his nice new bicycle."

"Oh, yes," she said. "He came to tell me

about it – the man did – he's got such funny eyes and—"

I held up my hand.

"I know what you're going to say," I said. "You took the boy's part, of course. You always do. Probably told him that you hadn't got a boy and that if you had, he hadn't got a bicycle and that if he had, he hadn't knocked him down."

"Oh, I didn't put it like that," she said. "But—"

"No," I said firmly, "I'm not going to be drawn into any discussion. This is the sort of situation that needs a man to deal with it."

"All I was going to say—" began Clare, but I went back to the dingy gentleman at the front gate.

"Now," I said with a brisk man-of-the-world manner, "I'm sorry my boy knocked you down. Will ten shillings put things right?"

"Ten shillings!" he repeated indignantly. "Look at me clothes – I *ask* you – I shall want noo trowsers *an'* a noo coat. Well, *you* know what gemmen's clothes corsts nowadays. Could *you* buy a noo shute for ten bob – I *ask* you?"

A crowd of village children was beginning to collect around us.

"Fifteen shillings?" I said hastily.

"A quid," he said firmly. "A quid's the least I can take for me noo shute, Guv'nor. As I says, *you* know's well's I do what noo shutes corsts."

The crowd of gaping children was growing. I gave him a pound note and turned to go.

"Then there's me nerves," he said.

"*What?*"

"Shock to me nerves," he said calmly. "Me nervous constitushun' abs'lutely in an uproar with this. I'm a nervous sens'tive man, Guv'nor. Tonics, doctors – you've gotter think of them – not to mention compensation throwin' me out of work through shock to me nerves."

"What is your work?" I demanded.

"Lookin' for work," he said. "Bin lookin' for work for years an' years. Well, I'd bin bound to 'ave found it soon now 'f it 'adn't bin for this 'ere blinkin' accident upsettin' me nerves – I won't be fit for work for months an' months with the shock to me nerves—"

I handed him a ten-shilling note.

"A quid, Guv'nor," he said. "You can't value the nerves of a 'ighly strung gemman like meself at less'n a quid."

The vicar's wife was coming down the road with a determined look upon her face. I knew that in a minute she would be upon us, demanding to know what was the matter, taking the matter in hand in her best Mothers Meeting style, and trying to march both of us off to the vicar. I took another note from my pocket, gave it to him, and went quickly indoors.

"Well?" said Clare.

"You have to deal tactfully with these people," I said. "It's no use getting their backs up. It's no use saying you simply won't listen to him, as you did."

"But I didn't," said Clare. "I kept on trying to tell you. I gave him a pound for his clothes and a pound for his nerves. That's what he asked me for."

"*What?*" I said.

Just then Ronny came in. I turned on him.

"You young blackguard!" I said. "What do you mean by knocking people down in the road?"

"Oh – him!" said Ronny. "It was young Jones who knocked against him – not me –

I was on in front. He hardly touched him anyway."

Without a word I took my hat and set off to Jones' house. I wondered how much of the four pounds I could get back from Jones.

Jones himself opened the door.

"Good afternoon," I said, "sorry to bother you, but do you know that your boy knocked a man down—"

"Oh! Yes," he said. "The man came round as soon as it happened. Got two pounds out of me, too. What's the matter?"

I did not answer. I was running full speed down the road.

Yes, you've guessed right – he'd completely disappeared.

If any reader meets a man with a cast in his eye, who looks as if he'd just spent three pounds on his clothes and three pounds on his nerves, kindly detain him and let me know.

Christmas Presents

(The Humorist 6/12/1924)

"Let's talk about what we're going to give each other for Christmas," said Clare.

"All right," I said without enthusiasm. "What are you going to give me?"

"Well, I wasn't thinking of that so much," said Clare, "as of what you're going to give me. I'm literally dying for a long jade necklace."

"I'm sorry," I said. "The news is literally a great shock to me. I'll try to provide a decent show for your funeral. Do you want the children to be brought up as Liberals, or Labour, or Conservative? Give me your dying wishes before it's too late."

"But you can buy me a long jade necklace," said Clare, "and then I'll be all right."

"No, I can't," I said sternly, "that's just where you make a mistake."

"I suppose I'd better come down a peg, then."

"I should."

"What about a new evening dress?"

"Well, what about it?"

"One of those very cheap ones. I mean about six guineas."

"Well, what about it?"

"I mean, could you rise to that for my Christmas present?"

"We've been talking for hours about my Christmas present to you. Now let's talk about yours to me for a change."

"All right," she said in a bored kind of voice. "You seem to have everything you really need. I suppose you wouldn't like some pale mauve notepaper?"

"Your supposition is quite correct," I said. "I wouldn't. I never use coloured notepaper."

"I know. That's why I thought it could be so useful. I do— Oh, very well! Would you like some new cushions for the drawing room settee?"

"Not in the least. The idea leaves me quite cold. I'd like a new razor."

"But, my dear man, what on earth good would a new razor be for me?"

"But I thought we were talking about *my* Christmas present."

"Yes, but it seems such a waste of money to give you something that I shall never want to borrow. What about a nice leather travelling blouse case? You could use it for your shirts if ever I didn't happen to need it."

"A razor," I said firmly. "A really superior razor in a handsome leather case."

She sighed resignedly.

"All right. Find out how much they cost and let me have a cheque for the amount."

"Why?"

"So that I can buy it for you, of course. You don't want me to spend the money I've saved by the sweat of my brow, do you?"

"Yes, I certainly do."

"You're a bit mean about Christmas presents," sighed Clare.

The next day the rent demand note came in and my bank balance began to shrink like Alice in the pool of tears.

"I'm not sure that I can manage a whole dress," I said to Clare. "I'll give you the collar or the flounce or the sleeves or something."

"Very well," said Clare quite pleasantly. "And I'll give you a nice razor case."

The next day the rates demand came in and my bank balance began to need a magnifying glass to see anything at all.

"You know, you don't really need an evening dress," I said to Clare. "You look absolutely topping in that yellow thing."

"Apricot," murmured Clare.

"Well, you look topping in it. It would simply break my heart to see you in any other. Suppose I give you a pair of stockings? They're always useful."

"All right," said Clare, still quite pleasantly. "And I really don't think you need a new razor. They're nasty, dangerous things. You'd look simply topping in a beard – a nice yellow beard. It would be a pity to give you a razor. I'll give you a pair of shoelaces. They're always useful."

The next day, the children's school bills came in. I'm always rather eloquent when the school bills come in. I say quite clever and cynical things about education. I'm really quite worth listening to. When I'd finished being clever and cynical, I said:

"I don't see how I'm going to have a penny left over for Christmas presents. You don't need any more stockings, you know. You've got a drawer full. I may get you a pair of shoe buckles – something nice and quiet in steel. They're always useful."

"Yes, darling," said Clare. "And I don't think you really need any new shoe laces. Those you have look very nice and strong, and you can always darn them when they break into holes. I think I'll give you a nice quiet steel hairpin all of your very own to clean your pipe with. It will always be useful. It will last for years and years with proper treatment."

Then I found the lists that the children had written for Father Christmas. I handed them to Clare with a groan.

"Look!" I said. "They've inherited your

extravagant tastes. If the bank will give me an overdraft, I may be able to get the mildest of them – not the 'lif siz moter' or the 'monky' or the 'reel airoplane' – but the toy 'engun' and the doll and the 'noersark' and a few things like that; but you and I will have to give up all idea of giving each other presents."

"Oh, dear," said Clare, "is it as bad as that?"

It wasn't quite as bad as that.

We did give each other Christmas presents.

I gave Clare new mantles for the gas brackets in the drawing room and Clare gave me new castors for the dining room sofa.

Woman's Wiles

(London Opinion 13/12/1924)

"I want you to have your photograph taken before Christmas," said Clare casually.

"I know," I said. "You always do, but you never get it."

"It's about ten years since you had it done," she said reproachfully.

"About," I agreed.

"Well, I want to have one in the drawing room and another on my writing-desk."

"I prefer both the drawing room and your writing-desk without them. I don't want to make myself cheap by having my photograph stuck all over the place. I don't want to stoop to the level of a matinée idol. If people want to know what I look like they can come and look at me. They can stand at the gate and watch me when I go off to work in the morning.

"If they won't take the trouble to do that, they can do without knowing what I look like. I'm not going to pander to their laziness by having photographs of myself stuck up everywhere."

"You're simply talking nonsense," said Clare sternly. "You can't give me a single decent reason why you shouldn't have one taken."

"I can. I can give you heaps. I'm afraid it won't do me justice. It won't reproduce my pretty colouring or the vivacity of my expression or the charm of my rare smile. My rare smile wouldn't come for a mere cameraman. It's too rare. Besides, I've taken a lot of trouble over my moustache lately, trying to get it just the right size, and it would probably look too big or too small in a photograph and that would discourage

it, and it would stop trying."

"*Don't* you talk nonsense," said Clare.

"Don't I," I agreed. "Anyway, I'm not going to have my photograph taken."

"Well, let's have Baby done instead, then."

"All right," I said. "She'd be a better subject. She hasn't my self-respect or dignity or modesty or proper pride. She wouldn't realise what an outrage was being done on her. But you know what she's like since she went to the dentist. He destroyed her faith in human nature."

"She'll be all right if you come too."

"Oh, I don't mind coming to help," I said condescendingly.

"It won't hurt, darling," I said soothingly.

"It won't hurt, pet," said Clare soothingly.

"It won't hurt, kiddie," said the photographer soothingly.

"It will. I *know* it will," said Baby. "I won't thit in the theat an' I won't open my mouth for it. I *won't!*"

"You needn't open your mouth for it, darling," I said. "You just sit in the chair and watch the funny man."

The photographer looked at me rather coldly.

"No, I *won't!*" said Baby. "It'll thoot at me if I thit right in front, it will."

"It won't, pet," said Clare. "Now look here." She winked at me. "Daddy will be done first, then you'll see it doesn't hurt."

"Right you are!" I said, winking at the photographer, and taking my place in the chair. "Daddy's being done now, and you see it doesn't hurt."

The man did some quite realistic business with his curtains and camera. It struck me that quite a good actor was lost in him. Then I got up.

"You see," I said. "Now, Baby—"
But Clare was gathering up her wraps.
"I say!" I said. "What—?"
"Oh, we've got *heaps* of Baby," said Clare calmly. "It was you I wanted. I think he got rather a nice one of you…."

No, I didn't wreck the place and murder the man and Clare and Baby as they deserved. I went home quite meekly. But I'm going to get my own back. I'm going to keep one of those photographs and give it to Clare unframed as a Christmas present.

The Flu-ke
(London Opinion 28/2/1925)

We had accepted the invitation, but when it came to the point, we didn't want to go. You may know the feeling. Jones says, "Can you and your wife come to dinner with us on Monday?" and you think, "How nice and friendly!"

Then Monday evening comes, and you feel quite different. It's an awful fag having to turn out into a cold wet world. The Joneses when all is said and done are terrific bores. You are in the middle of an exciting detective story which ought to go back to the library tomorrow. You haven't had time yet to look at the evening paper.

But I was just going to be noble and manly when Clare said:

"I wish you hadn't said we'd go. I don't want to a bit."

"Why don't you?" I said sternly.

"Well, I've nothing to wear for one thing, and it's such a beastly night for another, and I don't feel like going out and being polite to them. I'd rather stay in and be rude to you. And – do you want any more reasons? I could give you heaps."

"No," I said, "that's quite enough. I sympathise with you about them all, only I don't see how anything but sudden illness could be any use now. We're due there in half an hour."

"Sudden illness?" said Clare, brightly. "I could easily be suddenly ill if that's all you want. Everyone's having 'flu. It's a perfectly good sudden illness to have."

"They'd know we hadn't had a doctor."

"Well, let's have the doctor, then," said Clare.

"But what about the temperature?" I said.

"Put me a hot-water bottle somewhere handy and I dare say I can manage it."

I looked at her sadly.

"You must have been a great trial to your parents when you were a child," I said.

"I was," she agreed. "They were frightfully relieved when I married— I say, is that the doctor's car outside the Browns'?"

I went to the window. It was.

"A-ha!" hissed Clare. "Fate's on our side. All will be well. Only trust me. Fly and get me a hot-water bottle." I flew out and got her one. "Now arrange me nicely on the sofa." I arranged her. "Now put the bottle under the cushion." I put it. "Now cover me with a rug. It looks better." I covered her. Then she assumed an expression suggestive of a rough Channel crossing. "Now go upstairs and hail the doctor out of the landing window when he comes out of the Browns'. Please speak softly and move on tiptoe. Remember the agony I'm suffering."

I went up to the landing window. The doctor was just getting into his car. I waved a wild arm at him. He waved a reassuring one at me, swept up our small drive and rang our bell. I ran down to let him in.

"Good evening, Doctor," I began. "My—"

I was just going to tell him about Clare's influenza when he interrupted me.

"I promised Mrs Jones to let you know at once," he said. "They're both down with the 'flu, so they're afraid you'll have to put off your visit."

I tried to turn my sudden grin into a facial contortion expressing concern and disappointment.

"Won't you come in?" I said. I knew

Clare must have heard. He followed me into the drawing room. Clare sat on the sofa, looking rather flushed, disposing as quickly as she could of the rug and hot-water bottle and expression of agony.

"You don't want me yourself, by the way, do you?" said the doctor. "I wasn't sure whether you were beckoning to me or waving a friendly greeting."

"Oh, a friendly greeting," I said hastily.

"Oh, yes, only a friendly greeting," said Clare, giving the rug and hot-water bottle a final kick under her chair.

A Venus Tragedy
(London Opinion 7/3/1925)

Uncle John's birthday is the great family event of the year. I don't quite know who first started its mode of procedure, but it was well established when I was but a mawling child, as poets say.

Everyone in the family is invited to tea, and Uncle John receives them in the drawing room. In the hall between the doors of the dining room and the drawing room is set a table, and on to this table each member of the family deposits his or her or its present (according as it is man, woman or child) before he, she or it goes into the drawing room, carefully taking off the wrappings first.

Uncle John is one of the few people left in the world who thoroughly and wholeheartedly enjoy their birthdays. He takes a delighted interest in every one of his presents.

To continue – we all gradually assemble in the drawing room and talk to Uncle John. There is no mention of presents, but there is tense excitement in the air. Then, when the clock strikes five, Uncle John looks round on us all with mingled affection and anticipation, and says:

"Ah! — five o'clock! Tea-time, eh? Shall we adjourn to the dining room?"

We surge into the hall *en route* for the dining room.

Uncle John encounters table full of presents!

Surprise and delight of Uncle John!

Great moment!

This gives you some faint idea of the importance and excitement of Uncle John's birthday. You will gather that the main difficulty lies in the choosing of the present. When a person has reached Uncle John's age and has celebrated a birthday and Christmas with gusto every year of his life he is apt to possess by that time most of the things that naturally suggest themselves as presents. Pocket books, paper cutters, tobacco jars, leather slippers, writing-cases, blotters, tie-pins, petrol lighters – Uncle John possesses them all – on a wholesale scale.

So the person who evolves something really original for Uncle John's present is the hero of the day.

This year Aunt Jane (who doesn't really come into the story, so you needn't remember her) gave an All Hallows E'en party and invited every member of the family. I don't know why she did it, so I can't tell you. Anyway, we bobbed apples and roasted chestnuts and threw things over our shoulders at midnight, and did all the other idiotic things that one does on All Hallows E'en, and Uncle John held forth. Wherever Uncle John is, he holds forth. Uncle John loves to hold forth, and any tag will do for Uncle John to hold forth. This time it was his first visit to Paris which took place in the early sixties.

"Never to be forgotten, never to be forgotten," boomed Uncle John. "Never shall I forget it – the Louvre – that exquisite Venus de Milo – exquisite. One's first visit to Paris can only come once in a lifetime."

"Thank God!" piously murmured Aunt Jane, who is a bad sailor.

About two months later Clare and I began to discuss Uncle John's birthday present.

"What about an inkstand?" said Clare brightly.

"He's got about two dozen put away somewhere," I remarked gloomily.

Clare pondered deeply.

"Or a nice leather pocket-book," was the result.

"Too original, darling," I said sarcastically.

Then I had the bright idea.

"Do you remember what he said about the Venus de Milo at Aunt Jane's party?" I said. "Why not give him a photograph of it framed. No one will have thought of that."

"Topping!" agreed Clare. "And you can make a frame of tooled leather or fretwork."

"Or *you* could make a frame," I said coldly, "out of – er – batique or something."

"Idiot! That's only for scarves and things like that."

"Well, you can batique him a Venus on a nice warm scarf."

"Don't be funny, dear," she said patiently.

In the end we got quite a jolly photograph of the Venus de Milo framed in dark oak – not too big and not too small. We were frightfully proud of ourselves. We expected to be the star turn of the party.

The day arrived. We got there rather late, were shown into the hall and began to unwrap our present in the usual furtive way to place it upon the table with the rest. Then we turned pale, and looked at each other wildly. The table was full of Venuses de Milo (or should it be Venus de Milos?), Venus de Milo in biscuit china, in plaster, in ebony, in cardboard. There was an almost life-size painting of her in green and pink signed by cousin Frances. It looked more like the boy in the "You Dirty Boy!"

advertisement than Venus, but cousin Frances is notoriously optimistic and short-sighted. We put ours with the others because we couldn't think what else to do with it (it was too large for the waste-paper basket), and just as we turned towards the drawing room door Harold came in jauntily by the front door carrying a small parcel. He couldn't see the table because we were in front of it.

"I say," he said excitedly, "I bet I've beat you all this year. I've got the old chap a little Venus de what-do-you-call-it carved in wood. Do you remember he was talking about it at Aunt Jane's? A-ha! You never thought of that."

We gave a hollow groan and passed into the drawing room without answering. A moment later Harold entered, looking rather pale and depressed. Everyone was looking rather pale and depressed. Uncle John did not notice. He was holding forth again.

"No," he was saying, "I always maintain that reproduction on a large scale cheapens a thing – a style in clothes, a motor car, a painting – or anything. Take that statue I was telling you about as an example. An exquisite thing – exquisite – but cheapened by constant reproduction. Cheapened. I wouldn't have one of the things in my house if you paid me a thousand pounds…."

At that moment the clock struck five, and the familiar look of affection and pleased anticipation overspread Uncle John's face.

"Ah!" he said. "Tea time, eh? Shall we adjourn to the dining room?"

We all slunk into the hall.

A Good Selection

(London Opinion 2/5/1925)

"I want a new hat," said Clare.

"Again?" I groaned.

"Darling," said Clare. "It's years since I had one."

"*Literally* years, I suppose?" I said.

"Literally" is an adverb that adorns all Clare's exaggerations.

"*Quite* literally," said Clare calmly.

I considered for a moment. I saw the light of battle in Clare's eye. I am, and am not ashamed to own it, a man of peace.

"All right," I said, "but for heaven's sake, don't run to more than two guineas. Remember that it's just possible that we shan't win the Hospital Ballot Competition First Prize."

The light of battle died from Clare's eyes.

"You're rather nice," she said happily. "I'll try to get just the sort of hat you'll like."

"You'll get one costing about six-and-eleven-three, then," I said brutally.

The next evening I returned to find four new hats on Clare's bed.

I staggered back.

"Good heavens!" I ejaculated, my hand at my brow.

"It's all right, dear," said Clare soothingly. "They're only to choose one from. I want you to help me."

I sank into an easy chair and assumed my famous Early Christian Martyr expression.

"Fire away!" I said.

Clare put on a yellow thing.

"How do I look in this?" she said.

Clare looks outrageously pretty in anything, but for the good of her soul, I occasionally refrain from telling her so.

"All right," I said casually.

"It's the cheapest of the lot," said Clare.

"It looks perfectly *ripping!*" I said hastily.

I quite like it myself," said Clare judicially. "The only thing against it is that it would look awful with my green dress."

"Would it?" I said.

"Of *course* it would," said Clare firmly.

"Well, what about that?" I said, pointing hopefully to a black one. "Black goes with anything, doesn't it?"

Clare put it on.

"*Awfully* nice," I said.

"Y–yes," said Clare doubtfully. "But with a very summery frock, black looks just a little ghoulish."

"Does it?" I said. "I'm not up in ghoulishness, so I don't know. What about that red thing?"

"Cerise, darling," murmured Clare, in a pained voice as she put it on.

"Ripping," I said.

"Y-yes," said Clare, "but it would kill my pink dress."

"Would it?" I said, startled. "Murderous creature!"

"It would look sweet with my white one, of course."

"Try the last," I said. "Blue's a jolly colour and goes quite well with things."

She stuck it on.

"Ripping!" I commented.

"With this dress, y–yes," said Clare. "But my other blue dress would simply kill it."

"I'd no idea that they were so bloodthirsty," I said, deeply shocked. "They look so innocent. Well, where are we?"

"We're at the point where they all looking ripping with some things, and awful with others, and I particularly wanted one that would go with all my things."

"Of course," I said. I looked at them all despondently. "But they all seem such murderous creatures, and to keep the whole lot—"

I was going to add "is out of the question", but Clare interrupted me.

"How *sweet* of you to suggest that!" she said, pleased and excited. "You really are the most *generous* man!"

There was a short silence. In it I accepted the inevitable.

"Yes, I am, aren't I?" I said rather sarcastically.

"And you said not more than two guineas," said Clare, still pleased and excited, "and not *one* of them costs more than that."

I happened to pass the hat shop the next morning on my way to the station and thought I might save them the trouble of sending up for the hats.

I went in and remarked to the languid goddess behind the counter:

"My wife will be keeping all those hats you sent up yesterday."

"Yes," drawled the languid goddess languidly. "Moddom said so when she ordered them."

The Object Lesson
(London Opinion 20/5/1925)

Charles and Gladys were most interested to hear of our new car. They have a new car themselves, and we discussed gadgets and horse power and the superiority of our makes of car over every other all the afternoon. Then Charles said:

"What about cleaning it?"

"Well, we haven't really had it long enough to clean it yet," I said. "We only got it last week. I suppose the garage will do it."

"My dear boy," said Charles, shocked, "that's a wicked waste of money. Gladys and I clean ours ourselves. It's quite easy. I do the paint part and Gladys does the metal part. You and Clare ought to do it that way."

"By the way, we ought to be doing it now," said Gladys. "Charles, go and do your part while I entertain John, then I'll do my part while you entertain John."

"Right, dear," said Charles.

He rose with alacrity and made his way down to the garage. Gladys and I discussed tennis and motoring and the weather.

Soon he returned.

"I've done the bonnet part, dear," he said. "You can go and shine up the radiator now before I go on with the rest. It's too hot to do much at a time."

"All right," said Gladys. She rose with alacrity in her turn and made her way down to the garage. Charles and I discussed the weather and tennis and motoring. Soon she returned.

"I've done it," she said. "Now you can get on with the rest of it."

"Right, dear," said John, and left Gladys to discuss the Derby with me.

He returned quite soon, looking indignant.

"You've left a streak of metal polish all over the paint I've just cleaned," he said. "I've had to wash it off."

"I'll go and see," she said, leaving John to discuss Ascot with me.

Soon she returned.

"You've *covered* the radiator I've just cleaned with water," she said angrily. "I've had to dry it and polish it up again."

He went off to the garage. And she and I talked of the prospects of the fruit season. But conversation was not easy. The atmosphere was becoming strained. He returned, looking rather pale.

"Metal polish again," he expostulated. "A great streak all over my polished paint. I've had to wash it again. It's really the limit."

She darted off to the garage. Charles and I talked of the fraying effect that perpetually having to wash streaks of metal polish off paint that one had sweated one's soul over has upon the nerves.

Gladys returned pink with fury.

"You've done it again," she said. "I'm sick of drying it."

He dashed off to the garage. She and I discussed the harrowing effect that the perpetual drying and polishing of metal has upon the soul.

He returned like one distraught.

"You've done it again," he screamed. "Metal polish."

She darted off. He and I did not speak. She returned, wringing her hands. "Water again!" she sobbed, "and all my polishing rags are *soaked!*"

I won't go on with it. By tea time they were not on speaking terms. By the time I went, they'd got no farther than the bonnet, and divorce hovered in the air.

When I reached home, Clare said:

"What shall we do about cleaning the car? I met Gladys this morning and she says it's quite easy. She and Charles do it together. Charles does the paint work and she does the metal work."

"I know," I said. "They were doing it this afternoon."

"Shall we do it that way, too?"

"I think not!" I said.

"But it's so expensive to have it done at the garage."

"I'll pay, dear," I said. "I won't grudge it."

The Pet

(The Humorist 1/6/1925)

"I want a pet," said Clare.

"What sort of a pet?" I asked.

"A household pet," said Clare.

"What about me?" I suggested.

"I mean an intelligent pet," said Clare.

I rose with dignity.

"I'm going home to Mother," I said.

"Yes, do," said Clare pleasantly. "It's her At Home day. You'll just be in time to hand round the cake-stand."

I sat down again.

"About this pet," I said magnanimously. "What exactly do you want?"

"Oh, something that will be a companion to me when you're out," said Clare. "Something to take your place. Something—"

"Let's have no personalities, please," I said, firmly.

I spent all the next morning hunting for kittens, and in the end got one that seemed to possess every virtue. Then in the afternoon I went puppy-hunting and finally secured one that was intelligent and manly and courageous and sympathetic, and one that would be an ideal companion and a perpetual reminder of me to Clare in my absence.

I took them home to Clare.

"You must choose the one that you think will fill my place most completely, Clare," I said, "and we'll dispose of the other. The kitten is aristocratic and intuitive and light-hearted, and – er – and entertaining. The dog is faithful, and brave, and sympathetic and – er – and faithful. Which will you have?"

"Oh, I'm so sorry," said Clare. "You're too late. I only want one pet. I've just been out and bought a tortoise!"

Clare Goes Out to Lunch
(London Opinion 19/5/1925)

Clare came into the room looking very guilty.

"Darling," she said, "do you mind *frightfully* if I go out to lunch? Mrs Smith has just rung me up. She wants me to help her with a dress she is making. She's got all tied up in it."

"Oh no," I said, "do go and untie Mrs Smith. "I'd hate to think of Mrs Smith being tied up in a dress indefinitely."

"B–but I don't know what you'll do about your lunch," went on Clare, looking worried.

We were in our usual state of stafflessness. A smartly-shingled silk-stockinged hussy had looked in on us last week, stayed three nights, then gone away because she didn't like our geyser. I think the real reason was that we only have a crystal set and she was used to a seven-valve. Anyway, she went off with a jumper of Clare's I've always disliked, so I felt that all had not been in vain. But we were once more in the state when Clare cooks and does the housework and I clean the shoes and knives and go to the post and feed the rabbits and read the paper and make myself generally useful. I'm really a very domesticated man, though Clare always pretends that I'm not.

"B–but can you manage, darling?" said Clare. "I'd just made a beef-steak pie and was going to put it in the oven."

"Oh, I can see to that," I said.

"Are you sure?" said Clare doubtfully. "Remember that rice pudding."

That annoyed me. I don't like remembering that rice pudding.

Clare once made a rice pudding and put it in the oven and put me in charge of it and I forgot all about it. Quite an easy thing to do. Anyone might do it. But women do harp on these things so. So I said with dignity:

"My dear child, of course I'm perfectly capable of seeing to a simple thing like a beef-steak pie."

"Well, all you have to do is put it in the oven and leave it there for an hour and twenty minutes, and then it will be ready to eat."

"Of course," I said, still hurt by the reference to the rice pudding.

"Then there's Toodles," went on Clare. "I don't think I'll take her with me because Mrs Smith has such a nasty, savage fox-terrier. But you'll be kind to Toodles, won't you?"

Now, Toodles is Clare's Pom. She is as spoilt, vain, whining, bed-tempered a quadruped as you'd find on the face of the globe. Toodles is the only thing about Clare that I dislike, and I've often told her so. In fact, when we do quarrel, which isn't very often, it is always about Toodles. If you asked my opinion, more homes have been wrecked by Poms than by drink or any other vice. I looked at Clare with great dignity (I was still annoyed about the rice pudding) and said:

"Clare, have you ever known me to be unkind to a dumb animal?"

"No, darling," said Clare, "but I've never known a dumb animal. They all seem so far from dumb – even darling Toodles. But I want you to say a kind word to her now and then as I do" (I may remark here that Clare's "kind words" take the form of "Sweetums" and "Duckkums" and "ickle baby doggie" and other futilities that I wouldn't soil my pen by repeating), "and give her her dinner nicely and coax her a bit if she's not hungry. You will, won't you, darling?"

"What time are you going to Mrs Smith's?" I said.

"I ought to be going now," said Clare, "because she's getting into an awful state about her dress – an hour and twenty minutes for the beef-steak pie, don't forget – goodbye my pessus lickle Toodles – Daddy look after you."

When Clare had gone, I put the beef-steak into the oven and then went into the morning room to read the paper. Toodles joined me there. You'd never believe how that creature pirouetted about trying to attract my attention. She was simply determined that I should say "Duckkums" or "Sweetums" to her, and I was equally determined that I wouldn't. She posed on one chair against a green cushion; then she posed on another chair on an orange cushion; then she began to bang herself against my legs. I took absolutely no notice of her. Then she began to yap, so I took her by the scruff of the neck and dropped her outside the door.

When I'd finished the paper I went to do a little gardening. Then I suddenly remembered the beef-steak pie and looked at my watch. It had been in the oven for two hours and a half. I went hastily to the kitchen. The beef-steak pie was a black mess in a black dish.

I turned the gas out and then took the whole thing into the garden. I dug a nice deep hole and buried it, dish and all. I wasn't going to have Clare bringing up that beef-steak pie against me year in year out as she had done the rice pudding.

Toodles stood by and watched me with interest. Then I remembered that she

hadn't had her dinner, so I went in and got a dog biscuit for her. I threw it at her and said: "You can eat that or not as you like, you little rapscallion!" You should have seen that dog's look of fury. Then I sneaked down to the village inn.

"Have you any beef-steak pie for lunch?" I said.

And they had. Wasn't that luck? I always say that Providence helps those that help themselves. I had a very good lunch and then returned home and spent quite a pleasant afternoon, reading and ignoring the injured Toodles.

Then Clare returned.

"Was the beef-steak pie nice?" she said.

"Delicious," I said, quite truthfully. "Did you untie Mrs Smith?"

"Yes – oh, look at darling Toodles. Isn't she sweet? I think she wants to show me something. What is it, sweetheart? What does it want to show its missus, then?"

Toodles, yapping wildly, led her to the place where I'd interred the cremated pie, and, if you'll believe me, that vindictive dog began to dig up the earth till she'd laid bare the whole thing. Then she stood aside and looked at me with a triumphant look on her face.

"What is it?" said Clare, bending down; "it looks like coal in a black dish."

"Er – I think I'll just go down to the station," I said hastily, "and see if the evening paper's come in yet."

I'm going to buy a dog. I don't see why Clare should be the only person in the house with a dog. I'm going to buy a very big dog – a St Bernard or a Great Dane.

It needn't be a pedigree dog, and it needn't be especially well-trained. But it must dislike Poms.

Wasn't It Sweet!
(The Humorist 10/10/1925)

It ambled in at our front door, very small and fluffy and adorable.

"A puppy!" screamed Clare. "Isn't it sweet!"

"But whose is it?" I said.

Clare had snatched it up and was burying her face in its fur.

"Isn't it perfectly sweet?" she said again.

"But whose is it?" I repeated, following them into the drawing room.

"I don't care whose it is," said Clare, kissing its ears. "It's lost, anyway. I'm going to keep it. Finding's keeping."

"Not in the law," I objected.

"It hasn't got a collar. That means it doesn't belong to anyone. And I've found it. So it's mine."

It made a playful dart at Clare's necklace and she kissed it on the nose.

"Isn't it absolutely sweet!" she said.

"Do stop saying that for a minute," I said patiently. "You'd better give it to me and I'll take it to the police station. We've no right to keep it."

"Isn't he a nasty cruel man?" said Clare to the puppy. "They shan't send you to a nasty police station, so there! You're *my* sweet little puppy-dog now, aren't you?"

And she kissed the middle of his back.

"Clare, you've no sense of civic honour!" I said. "Someone's lost that dog."

"They haven't. They've just turned him out because they didn't want him. And he's come here because he thought he'd have a good home – and so he shall, the pet!"

And she kissed the top of his head.

"But suppose everyone kept everything they found belonging to other people. If you found a diamond brooch, for instance, you wouldn't want to keep it, would you?"

"Well, I've got a diamond brooch," said Clare, "but I haven't got a sweet little puppy like this."

She kissed him just beneath his chin and he playfully patted her cheeks with his paws.

"Isn't he a lamb?" said Clare.

"No, he's a dog," I said, "and you can't keep him. Think of his master and mistress looking for him, broken-hearted."

"Nonsense," said Clare. "They've probably got his father and his mother and dozens of little brothers and sisters. They'll hardly miss him."

"He may be valuable."

"He's not. He's just a dear, adorable, fascinating little mongrel."

And she kissed him again.

"It would be most dishonourable to keep that dog without making enquiries."

"All right. We don't mind being dishonourable, do we, angel? We think kindness to animals comes before anything, don't we?"

And she kissed it on the tip of its tail.

Just then Horace came in. Horace is Clare's brother.

"Horace, do look at my sweet little dog," said Clare.

Horace adjusted his monocle and looked at it.

"Jolly little beggar, isn't it?" said Horace. "I thought so when I saw it down the road a few minutes ago."

"*Did* you?" said Clare ecstatically. "What was it doing, the lamb?"

"It was in somebody's dustbin, almost covered with flies, worrying some remains of fish."

Clare hastily put the lamb down. I

noticed that she was surreptitiously rubbing her lips with her handkerchief.

"John's just going to take it to the police station," she said. "Do hurry up, John."

"Clare wants to keep it," I said, "and I really think she might, after all."

"Oh," said Clare, "I – er – d-don't think I'd better, dear. I think you were quite right. As you said, its master and mistress might be looking for it, broken-hearted."

"No," I said judicially, "I think you were right. They probably have the rest of the litter and wouldn't notice it."

Clare was still rubbing her lips.

"B-but, darling," she said, "I think you were so right about civic – civic honour and all that sort of thing. I'd hate to do anything dishonourable."

"But kindness to animals comes before anything," I reminded her.

"I don't know that it does, really," said Clare, still rubbing her lips. "You know, what you said about dishonourableness and diamond brooches quite convinced me. I think you were so right. Do take it to the police station, darling."

"I'm afraid I haven't time now," I said. "You wouldn't let me when I wanted to."

"Horace," said Clare, "do take it to the police station."

Horace gathered it up into his arms.

"Righto!" he said.

Clare heaved a sigh of relief.

"Thanks so much," she said. "I'd love to keep it, but John's made me think that it wouldn't be quite honourable."

She heaved another sigh of relief as Horace and the puppy vanished from sight.

"Well," she said casually, "I'll just run up and have a wash. But wasn't it sweet!"

A Wireless Tragedy
(The Humorist 27/2/1926)

I don't know how it is, but nowadays women despise you if you don't know all there is to know – and more – about wireless.

I think that the attitude is absurd. They don't expect all men to sing or play the ukulele or wriggle their ears or solve crossword puzzles. They know that these are natural gifts and if you've got them you've got them, and if you haven't you haven't, and that's all there is to be said about them. But they do expect all men to understand wireless and to be able to put their sets right for them at a moment's notice just as easily as they clean their pipes or fix in their studs.

They seem to look upon it as a natural male asset. They seem to think we're all born to it just as we are to trousers and a bald middle age. They never know anything about it themselves and yet they expect us to ooze wireless knowledge, so to speak, from every pore.

I used to be quite honest and say that I didn't understand the things, but it wasn't worth it. Even Clare wasn't sympathetic about it. She said that she felt ashamed of telling Mrs Jones and Mrs Brown and Mrs Robinson that I didn't understand it when apparently Mr Jones and Mr Brown and Mr Robinson can fix up a set merely by flickering an eyelash. So gradually a fiction grew up (carefully nourished and cherished and tended by Clare) that I was just as good at wireless sets as Mr Jones and Mr Brown and Mr Robinson. In fact much better.

I did my best, of course, as a loyal

husband should, to support the fiction. I mugged up a few wireless terms and when people said "I hear that you're a great authority on wireless" I smiled modestly and said (quite truly) "Oh, I wouldn't say that", and when my own set went wrong I sent for the man under cover of darkness and when anyone came to ask me to put their sets right I was always out.

There's a certain expression on people's faces that means they're coming to ask you to put their sets right and you can generally see it in time from the drawing room window as it comes up the drive, and be out. It's quite simple. So my reputation grew and grew and grew. Until last night.

Last night Clare asked Mrs Jones and Mrs Brown and Mrs Robinson in to supper and after supper we listened to the wireless. It was highbrow music and people always pretend to want to listen to highbrow music away from their own homes. I don't know why. I suppose it's just human nature. The thing was going quite nicely when suddenly in the very middle of a highbrow flourish, it stopped.

"Something's gone wrong," said Mrs Jones intelligently. I played for time.

"I don't think so," I said. "It's just a dramatic pause. They have them in all the best music nowadays. They're – they're effective, you know."

We waited in silence. So did the wireless.

"It's rather – *long* for a dramatic pause," said Mrs Brown at last.

"I think there *is* something wrong," said Mrs Jones, still more intelligently.

"I don't suppose it will take you a minute to put it right, will it?" said Mrs Robinson, looking at me. "That's the best, isn't it," she murmured to Clare, "of having a husband who understands wireless?"

Driven to bay, so to speak, by this speech, I got up and with an air of frowning concentration and deep knowledge began to twiddle little handles. I twiddled all the little handles I could see and suddenly the flood of highbrow melody came swelling into the room, just as if it had never stopped. I sat down with a superior smile.

"That didn't take you long," said Mrs Jones, admiringly.

"Oh, no," I said, "it was quite a simple matter."

"What was it?" said Mrs Robinson.

"Oh – er – the insulator had got – er – disconnected," I said, taking a bold plunge.

They all looked admiringly at me and enviously at Clare.

"Well," said Mrs Brown, "I don't think that John's ever put ours right in that time. He takes hours and turns the whole thing out all over the place."

"It's just a knack," I explained kindly, "just a knack of spotting at once what's wrong with the thing, that's all."

The music died away. The announcer spoke.

"I really must apologise," he said, "for the few minutes' break in the transmission during this item—"

I murmured something about "letters to write" and crept from the room.

The Umbrella

(The Humorist 10/4/1926)

"She's taken my umbrella!" gasped Clare.

"Who?" I said, waking up.

"That woman who's just got out of the carriage – the woman in the green hat. Look, there! She must have taken it off the rack. It's my carved ivory one. Oh, *do* go and get it back."

I'm essentially the man for crisis, so I leapt out of the carriage and hurried across the platform after the green hat. It was unfortunate that my own train, containing Clare, glided away at that moment. If I had leapt back agilely I might have caught it, but I had decided to retrieve Clare's umbrella at all costs. As a man and a husband I wasn't going to have women in green hats calmly walking off with my wife's umbrellas without so much as a "By your leave"!

The woman in the green hat had crossed the platform and got into another train. I followed her. Just as I reached the door of her carriage the train began to move off, so I jumped in with her. It seemed the only thing to do. I sat down opposite her and wondered how to begin. She hadn't got a very encouraging face, and she was clutching Clare's umbrella firmly with both hands. Before I'd made up my mind exactly how to frame the sentence the train slowed down at the station. I took the bull by the horns – I mean, the umbrella by the tassel – and said nervously:

"Excuse me, but—"

She glared at me (she had a snaky sort of eye) and flicked the umbrella away, and said: "Excuse *me*, young man!" And she didn't say it kindly, either.

You may call me a coward if you like, but the fact remains that I simply hadn't the courage to say, "That's my wife's umbrella. You stole it five minutes ago." Her eye had demoralised me. I kept trying to say it, but whenever I'd screwed my courage to the sticking-point (as somebody or other says in English literature) I met her eye and went to pieces again.

There are eyes like that. It's a physical impossibility to tell their owners that they've stolen your wife's umbrella. I didn't know what was going to happen. I was determined not to go home without it.

Then I saw that she was growing drowsy. Her snaky eye fluttered and drooped. She breathed heavily. She nodded. And just then, by good fortune, the train drew up at a station.

I took the umbrella from her nerveless grasp, shot out of the train and bolted into another train which was just starting off. I didn't know where it was going till I found myself at Margate an hour later, and had to wait two hours for a train back to town. It was a horribly long and expensive journey. But I didn't mind. I'd got the umbrella. I'd justified my character as a man and a husband. I went home with the umbrella in my hand and a shining halo round my head.

"*What* a time you've been!" said Clare.

I handed the umbrella to her.

"Here it is!" I said simply, striking a manly attitude.

Clare took it and examined it.

"It is *frightfully* like mine, isn't it?" she said.

"Isn't it yours?" I said blankly.

"No. I found mine at home when I got here. And then, of course, I remembered that I hadn't taken it out with me. But I saw her getting out of the carriage with an umbrella just like mine and that made me think for a minute that it *was* mine.... Well, if you meet her again, you'll just have to apologise and give it her back."

But I won't, because she'll have hypnotised me with her snaky eye and given me in charge for theft long before I've opened my mouth.

That's why, whenever I see a woman in a green hat now, I bolt down the nearest side street. And such a lot of women seem to be wearing green hats this spring. It's a very wearing life.

The Telegrams
(The Humorist 19/6/1926)

We live in the country, and our Post Office is our General Stores, and also our Intelligence Department.

Mr Miggs keeps the Post Office and exercises a beneficent rule over all the village.

He delivers the telegrams himself, and makes suitable suggestions and arrangements for their recipients, according to their contents.

When we had a wire telling us that the Browns, who were to have spent the weekend with us, couldn't come, he brought it up and said to Clare, who opened the door:

"They're not coming, 'm. So I called at Mr Jenks and told him you wouldn't be wanting the large joint you'd ordered after all."

Mr Jenks is our butcher.

When we had a wire offering us some rooms at Margate that we'd been trying to get for a long time, Mr Miggs arrived with the wire and literally prevented our accepting them. He said that Margate was too cold at that time of year, and he stood at the gate arguing about it till it was too late to send the wire.

Another time when we wanted to go to Torquay and had written a postcard to an address we'd heard of, Mr Miggs, instead of sending off the postcard with the rest of the mail, brought it back to us in a state of great agitation, pointing out that Torquay would be too relaxing for us that month, and that he knew someone in the village who had been to those rooms last year and found them uncomfortable. He simply wouldn't let us wire an acceptance.

When we had a wire telling us that Aunt Jane was dead, he called at the florist's on the way up with it and told them to make a wreath just like the one we had the year before when Uncle Joseph died.

"I supposed that that was what you'd want done," he said, with dignity.

Mr Miggs has a very grave and dignified face, with a white beard like a fringe all the way round it. When he comes on these errands with our telegrams in his hand, he looks like someone on whom all the cares and responsibilities of the world rest. Clare and I always watch him with delight from behind the dining room curtains as he comes up the drive.

When Clare went to stay with her mother for a fortnight, she said to me:

"I must keep dear old Miggs occupied while I'm away. I'll think out some really thrilling telegrams for him. Don't be alarmed, whatever comes!"

I received the first wire two days after she had gone. It ran:

"Come at once urgent Aunt Martha."

Now Mr Miggs knows that Aunt Martha is the rich and autocratic head of our family, and that I have expectations from her, and that she punishes the slightest disobedience to her commands by crossing you out of her will, and that I'm one of the very few people left in it. So Mr Miggs had looked out a train for me and ordered a cab before he brought the telegram. He couldn't understand my mirth and my refusal to obey Aunt Martha's supposed command.

The next telegram was:

"Can let you have cottage for August offer open till Monday wire Jones."

Now, we'd been trying to get the Jones'

cottage at Liscombe for August for years, and Mr Miggs knew it. I thought it was rather clever of Clare to have thought of that. Of course, Mr Miggs was terribly concerned and most anxious to wire at once and settle it. He couldn't understand my refusal.

The last telegram came a few days later.

"Sell out Hawaiians. Slump coming."

I thought that that was really rather unkind of Clare. It perplexed poor old Miggs horribly and gave him a sleepless night.

When Clare came home at the end of her fortnight, I said: "Your telegrams were masterpieces. They kept old Miggs' mind occupied beautifully and exercised all his talents for leadership and organisation."

Clare looked blank.

"What telegrams?" she asked.

"The three you sent. You know. Aunt Martha and the Jones and the Hawaiians. I thought they were a lovely selection."

"But I didn't send any telegrams," said Clare. "I quite forgot about it."

43

A Question of Hats
(London Opinion 14/8/1926)

"It's awfully nice, isn't it?" said Clare, holding it out at arm's length.
"Isn't it?" I agreed.
It really was.

August 14, 1926.

LONDON OPINION

2ᴰ

The Age of Innocence

"And quite ridiculously cheap," she said. "Only a guinea."

"Fancy!" I agreed with appropriate surprise.

"I'd love to wear it at the garden *fête* this afternoon."

"Well, why not?" I said cheerfully.

Her radiance clouded over.

"There's a dark said to it," she admitted sadly; "there's a thorn in the ointment; a fly in the rose—"

"On the rose, dear," I corrected.

"Don't interrupt. You see, the window was full of them and it's *possible – horribly* possible – that someone else may have bought one and may go to the *fête* in it."

"I can't understand you," I said. "You wear those little brown felt hats everywhere – *all* of you – *exactly* the same and you don't mind – you seem to like it."

"Yes, dear," said Clare sweetly, "but a trimmed straw hat is quite different."

"*Why* is it different?" I said wildly; "*how* is it different?"

"Of *course* it's different," said Clare, "it's quite different."

"Give me one reason," I pleaded. "I ask it merely as a logician and a student of psychology."

Clare explained quite kindly.

"Because a felt is one thing and a trimmed straw is another." She held it out at arm's length again and frowned at it critically, her head on one side. "It *is* so nice and it would just match the dress I'm wearing this afternoon but – *dare* I? Suppose someone else has one just the same?"

I entered into the spirit of the quandary.

"Couldn't you alter it a bit?" I said; "take the flower from the front to the back and – and – and turn up the front brim or something. That would fairly disguise it."

She frowned at it for some time, then, looking as if she had steeled herself to do or die, with a few tense movements she tore off the flower, pinned it behind and bent up the brim at the side front.

"There!" she said, putting it on.

And miraculously it suited her even more than it had done before.

"Now it won't matter if someone else has bought another," I said, striking a 'something attempted, something done' attitude, "and never call me a useless male again."

"Darling," she said. "I think you're simply *wonderful*."

I basked in it.

Brown was in the train. He seemed unusually talkative and pleased with himself.

"Your wife going to the *fête*?" he said.

"Yes, is yours?" I said.

"Yes – she bought a new hat for it this morning."

I felt a shade of anxiety; then remembered our *chef d'œuvre* of camouflage.

"So did mine," I said casually.

He was eyeing me closely.

"At Monks'?" he said.

"Yes," I admitted, still casually, "my wife bought hers there too."

He was still eyeing me.

"A straw one with a flower in the front," he went on, "twenty-one shillings."

"Yes," I said.

I looked at him knowingly and reassuringly. The poor fellow would be dreading the contretemps of the meeting of Monks' guinea headgear. I'd put him out of his misery. I knew what wives were. But suddenly it struck me that he was looking at me in just the same way.

"It's all right," he chuckled, "don't you worry, old son, though why they mind beats me. Your bowler's just the same as mine, but neither of us turns pea-green and has hysterics over it. However, my wife's rather a cute little woman and she realised that someone else might possibly have gone into Monks' this morning, so she moved the flower round to the back – just to alter it a bit – then she said it made the front look a bit flat and I said – I'm really rather an artistic sort of chap, though I don't look it – I said, 'Try turning the brim up a bit at the side just near the front, you know', and she did and, upon my word, the thing looked even better than before we started messing about with it – what's the matter, old chap?"

"They'll have started now, won't they?"

"Yes – why?"

"Oh, I thought of pulling the communication cord and sending a wire, but it's too late."

He gaped at me.

"I say, you aren't supposed to do that unless it's a matter of life and death."

"It is a matter of life and death," I said tersely.

He gaped at me again.

"Feeling the heat, old chap, aren't you?" he said kindly.

"Yes, that's it," I said.

I bought her a box of chocolates and a bunch of roses, but it didn't really make much difference.

And I need hardly say that she blamed me.

The next time I meet Brown I shall tell him exactly what I think of him.

Victory
(The Humorist 27/11/1926)

It always begins quite two months before Christmas. Clare says: "What would you like for your Christmas present?"

And I reply, guardedly: "What would you?"

And that's the end of the first round, and the matter lies dormant for a week or two.

In the next round we come to closer quarters.

"Would you like something for the house for your Christmas present?" says Clare, persuasively.

Thinking of the time when I guilelessly said "Yes" to this and she bought me a lovely fitted work box on a sort of pedestal to stand by her chair in the drawing room, I say firmly:

"No, thank you."

"Would you like something personal, then?" says Clare.

Thinking of the time when I guilelessly said "Yes" to this and was presented with a pale blue embroidered dressing gown, which turned out to be so much too small for me that she kindly wore it instead so that it shouldn't be entirely wasted, I say:

"No, thank you."

"Something for your games, perhaps," suggests Clare, kindly, in the tone of one who is doing all she can think of to give pleasure to another.

Thinking of the time when she presented me with just the golf clubs which she was in need of herself, and which I never saw again after Christmas Day, I say, very politely:

"I think not, thank you."

And Clare says: "Well, think it over, will you?"

And I say: "Yes, and you think over what you'd like, too, will you?"

And Clare says "Yes", and that's the end of the second round.

We are now at closer grips, but the real struggle has not yet begun. It's no use to avoid the subject or to pretend to have forgotten all about it. I did that once, and Clare bought herself a glorious jade necklace from me and thanked me for it so profusely that, metaphorically speaking, I had to swallow it.

Of course, I always have to pay for my Christmas present from Clare, but the whole act of the game is to try to get something that she won't find useful. Every wife at Christmas tries to get two presents from her husband – the one he gives her, and the one she gives him. And every husband worth the name is determined that she shan't.

The third round opens a week or two later. We come down to definite suggestions then.

Clare says: "Well, have you thought what you'd like for a Christmas present yet?"

And I say: "Well, what about a new pocket-case?"

Clare, of course, couldn't possibly use my pocket-case.

"N-no, I don't think so," said Clare. "That's so dull, and I don't think you really need a new pocket-case. Your old one will do for quite a long time yet. How about some nice silk handkerchiefs?"

Clare loves my silk handkerchiefs, especially the more lurid jazz effects she buys for me herself. She wears them as scarves underneath her coats. She commandeers the whole supply when she has a cold. She even trims her hats with them.

"I think not," I said. "I've got as many as I need. Do you know, dear, I think it would be so nice if just for the sake of sentiment we gave each other the same presents we gave each other the first Christmas of our married life."

That was rather clever. On the first Christmas of our married life we'd just got to the end of my gratuity and there didn't seem to be anything else in view, so I gave Clare new castors for the drawing room sofa which we'd just bought second-hand, and Clare gave me a frying pan.

But Clare was equal to the occasion. Clare is an antagonist of anyone's steel.

"Oh no," she said, with great firmness. "I think that those should be kept sacred. I think it would be a sacrilege to repeat them."

"Perhaps," I agreed. "What about a new pipe?"

"I don't feel competent to choose a pipe," said Clare. "I don't know enough about the points of a pipe."

"I'll choose it for you," I offered kindly.

"No," said Clare, unblushingly, "because that would destroy the sentiment of the thing. I think," she said, coming out into the open, "that it would be rather nice to get you a new cake-stand for the drawing room."

"But I don't want a new cake-stand for the drawing room," I objected.

"I'd find it awfully useful," she said.

"I thought we were discussing your present to me. If you want a new cake-stand for the drawing room, I'll buy you one for your present."

"Oh, no. I thought you might like one, that's all. I want a new handbag for my Christmas present."

"That's settled, then."

"Yes, but we haven't settled what I'm going to give you yet."

I thought for a few minutes, then I said very firmly: "Clare, you may give me what you like for a Christmas present, on one condition only. It must be something that I can use and you can't."

Looking rather baulked, she agreed. I was so pleased with myself for thinking of this that I bought her a really magnificent handbag.

And you'll never guess what she bought me.

She bought me a pair of silver-plated clippers for trimming the more inaccessible part of her shingle.

So now you know what I usually have to do on Sunday mornings.

Gathering the Holly
(The Humorist 4/12/1926)

"It's Christmas next week," said Clare, "and we haven't any decorations."

I didn't dispute the fact.

"And we must have some," went on Clare firmly.

"I don't see the necessity," I said equally firmly. Clare grew yet more firm.

"We *must*," she said. "Everyone always does."

"That's no reason," I said, but already my firmness was weakening before Clare's.

I took up another line of self-defence.

"All right," I said, "if you must have decorations, I suppose you can get them somewhere."

But I knew it was useless.

"I never heard of such a thing," said Clare, with spirit. "Everyone knows that it's the business of the master of the house to see to the decorations. I see to the turkey and the plum pudding, and you see to the decorations."

I considered this in silence.

"All right," I said at last. "I'll buy a box of those green paper festoon things."

Clare almost stamped.

"You won't," she said. "You'll get some holly."

I heaved a sigh of resignation.

"Very well," I said, "I'll leave an order at the florist's today. Or ought one to go to a nursery gardener?"

Clare looked as though she were trying to be patient.

"You must go into the woods and *pick* it," she said. "I wouldn't have *bought* holly in the house at Christmas for anything. It's a horrible idea – almost as bad as *buying* the plum pudding. There's *lots* of holly in the woods this year. Take the car out and get some."

Then she hurried away in the mean way women do when they're determined to have the last word. She reappeared, however, a few minutes later and said, coaxingly:

"Get me some holly from the wood, darling, and I'll make you a savoury omelette tonight."

Now, Clare can make savoury omelettes as can no one else in this world, and not infrequently, as on the present occasion, she takes unfair advantage of the fact.

After a moment's silent struggle (the struggle was between my pride and my love of savoury omelettes) I went out to get the car.

There is a road right through the wood,

and on this road I found another car unattended and its dicky packed with bunches of holly. You, of course, would simply have transferred the holly from its dicky to yours and driven off, but I'm more subtle than that. Moreover I knew the car. It belonged to George and Edith. George is my cousin.

I dismounted and made my way into the wood. I came upon them very soon. George, looking red and exhausted, armed with garden shears, and Edith holding an armful of the stuff tightly to her bosom. Now, Edith is very superstitious and, like most superstitious people, pretends not to be. I watched them for some time. Then I said:

"Evidently you're not superstitious."

"Of course I'm not," said Edith sharply, and added after a moment's pause: "Why?"

"Never heard the old saying that it's unlucky to pick holly on a Thursday?" I asked, casually. "It goes something like this:

They who holly pluck
On Thor's day
Shall have ill luck
Then and alway."

Unfinished, I admit, and the metre open to criticism, but not bad for an extempore effort.

A look of horror stole over Edith's face.

"But, of course, you aren't superstitious," I said, carelessly, "so it doesn't matter."

"N-no," said Edith, "I'm not a bit superstitious, but – I think we've got enough. Don't cut any more, George."

I accompanied them back to the car. Edith was very silent. She eyed the dicky full of holly with shrinking and distaste.

"Do you know," she said at last, "I – I

don't think it's very nice holly after all. I – I think we'll scrap this lot and come for some more tomorrow. I think we could find some – er – finer bits than these tomorrow. Let's – let's just chuck it out and leave it."

"I don't think you'd better do that," I remonstrated. "You might get into trouble for littering the woods up with cut stuff like this."

She looked at me helplessly.

"What *can* I do with it, then?" she said. "I don't want to take it home."

"I tell you what," I said, generously, "I'll take it and be responsible for disposing of it for you, shall I?"

She heaved a sigh of relief.

"Oh, thank you so much," she said, gratefully.

Clare gave a scream of delight when I drove up with my booty.

"Oh, you darling!" she said. "What *lovely* holly, and how quick you've been! Was it very hard work?"

"Not very," I said, truthfully.

Then she made me an omelette that one might hope for all one's life and never meet.

Of course, she may run into George or Edith tomorrow, but in this imperfect world one always has to take some risks.

And anyway, I've had the omelette.

Coming Down to It
(London Opinion 25/12/1926)

"I suppose you're going to the fancy-dress dance?" said Jones.

"Yes," said Clare, with a sigh. "Whenever I have a new and particularly fetching evening dress I always get an invitation to a fancy-dress dance. I suppose it's just Life."

"What are you going as?" said Mrs Jones.

"Columbine and Harlequin," said Clare.

"I look rather nice as Harlequin," I admitted.

"Well, we've got the costumes," said Clare, apologetically. "And after all, if one has nice legs one ought to show them."

"Are you referring to yours or mine?" I asked.

"To mine," said Clare.

"I see. But you needn't talk as if fancy-dress dances were an excuse to show your legs," I said, sternly. "You show them all the time nowadays.

"That's why fancy-dress dances have lost their charm. When a woman normally wore skirts to her ankles she liked fancy-dress dances because they gave her a chance to show her legs. She could go as Rosalind (they loved going as Rosalind) or Columbine or a page boy or a ballet dancer or – well, it didn't matter a bit what they went as so long as for that one glorious evening they wore skirts up to their knees, or, better still, no skirts at all. Well, now that you dress that way normally, the fancy-dress dance has lost its charm. Of course, there might be a certain thrill in going with your skirts down to your ankles – you can go as Portia or Queen Victoria or somebody like that, but it's hot and impedes dancing. I don't know why people have fancy-dress dances nowadays. They never even pretended to be anything but an excuse for a woman with a nice leg to show it to the world, and now that women have decided to dispense with the need for an excuse, it's time they dispensed with the fancy-dress dance as well. It's an anachronism."

"You don't mind his talking, do you?" said Clare, apologetically to Mrs Jones. "He has so few pleasures, and he does enjoy it so."

"Not all all," said Mrs Jones, politely. "We like it. At least, we're used to it. But a Columbine and Harlequin! My dear, it's so *ordinary*. It's almost as banal as Pierrot and Pierrette."

"I know," said Clare. "But we have the dresses."

"We have Pierrot and Pierrette dresses," said Mrs Jones, "but nothing would induce us to go in them."

"What are you going as?" I asked.

"We haven't *quite* made up our minds," said Mrs Jones. "We decided to beg, borrow, or steal something *really* old."

"My uncle has a suit of armour that I thought would do for me," said Jones.

"And didn't it?" I said.

"It nearly did," said Jones feelingly. "I could get *into* it all right—"

"It took half an hour to get him out," said Mrs Jones, pityingly. "Poor boy! He *suffered* so!"

"I'm still bruised," said Jones; "there's something so *unyielding* about a suit of armour. And you can't dance in it or move in it or sit down in it or breathe in it. You might just as well be imprisoned in the Tower of London."

50

"But we'll find *something*," said Mrs Jones with determination.

We met them again the next week.

"How go the costumes?" I asked, cheerfully.

A worried look flitted over Mrs Jones's face.

"It's terribly *wearing*," she said. "After enormous trouble we did manage to get hold of some *really* old costumes. We borrowed them from friends. We had a dress rehearsal in them last night."

"How lovely!" said Clare.

"No, it wasn't," said Mrs Jones, shortly. "They must have made shamefully poor material in those days. It was all Percy's fault. First, he must needs step on my train—"

"One's lost the knack of leaping over trains in these days," murmured Percy. "The thing kept getting under my feet."

"And it fell to pieces," said Mrs Jones, and repeated, dramatically, "simply fell to pieces – the whole thing. Percy looked very nice in his, but he must needs—"

"My dear," protested Jones, "I had to sit down."

"Yes, but you needn't have sat down *carelessly* and split them from top to bottom like that."

"And I suppose we shall have to pay for the beastly things," said Jones, morosely, "now that we've spoilt them."

"So what are you going to do?" I said.

"Well, I think that after all I shall *make* something," said Mrs Jones. "I shall get some *rich* looking material, you know, and make costumes for us as Henry the Eighth and Anne Boleyn. Not as original as we'd hoped, of course, but those things are quite easy to make with a pattern."

I met Jones in the train the day before the fancy dress dance.

"Costumes ready?" I asked.

A harassed look came into his eyes.

"It's extraordinary," he said. "My wife took no end of trouble over them, but there must have been something wrong with the patterns. We can't get them on. But it will be all right. She's altering them today."

We entered the ballroom. There was a bewildering maze of multi-coloured dancers.

"Seen the Joneses?" I said to someone.

"Yes. They were here a minute ago."

"What have they come as?" I asked.

"Pierrot and Pierrette," he answered.

A Free Choice

(The Humorist 1/1/1927)

Although it is Clare who has chosen the furniture for the rest of the house, I have always insisted on choosing everything that is in my own study. I am considered to have very good taste (for a mere man), and visitors always say that the things in my study are every bit as nice as the rest of the things in the house which are chosen by Clare.

I used to have a green tile kerb in front of the gas fire to match the green tiles on the hearth, and it always looked very neat and tasteful. Till lately. Lately it has ceased to look clean and tasteful. Experts say that the heat from the gas fire has cracked the cement. Be that as it may, the fact remains that this winter the thing suddenly began to shed its tiles in all directions.

I'd find the tiles lying about on the hearth and on the rug. Patiently I'd stick them on again. Impatiently the thing would fling them off again.

Then I began to paint the gaps the same green as the rest. I thought that was rather clever of me. It certainly nonplussed the creature for a short time. But it soon evolved a plan. It began to make big white cracks in every square I'd painted green. I realised that I was beaten. So about a week ago I said to Clare:

"Clare, I shall simply have to buy a new kerb."

Clare looked at the loose green tiles that lay scattered all over the hearth, and then at the green painted squares with the big white cracks in them, and then at the gas stove which was sniggering at us maliciously and triumphantly. She sighed.

"I'm afraid you will, dear," she said.

Yesterday she came in to me with the Stores catalogue open at the kerb page.

"Suppose you choose one now, dear," she said, "and then I can send it with my order."

I surveyed the page critically.

"I'll have this one," I said at last, with great firmness.

Clare looked at it with her head on one side.

"Wood," she commented doubtfully. "They do scratch so, darling."

"Surely not," I said. "I don't mean a wild one, of course. Couldn't we get a nice tame one that wouldn't scratch?"

"I mean," she said, "you just put a foot on them absent-mindedly and they never look the same again."

I examined the page again.

"This one, then," I said, still firmly.

Clare looked at it, her head still more on one side.

"It looks so *forbidding*," she said. "Just as if it were saying 'Trespassers will be prosecuted'. I do like a kerb that sort of invites you to put your toes into its hearth, and doesn't look as if it were trying to keep them out."

"I believe you're right," I said. "What about this one?"

"Copper," commented Clare doubtfully. "Y-yes – it's pretty – but all the fittings of your gas stove are a silvery colour."

There was only one other on the page. It was a pewter one.

"What about that?" I said.

Clare looked at it with interest. "Yes, that's a dear little thing," she said. "I like that."

"I'll have that, then," I said.

Just then came a loud knock at the door. Clare went to answer it. In a few minutes she returned looking slightly confused, carrying the pewter I'd just chosen.

"It was the Stores," she explained. "It's your kerb."

I gaped. "But—" I began.

"I only ordered it yesterday," said Clare. "I didn't think it would come till tomorrow at the earliest."

I held my head.

"But, Clare," I said, "I've only this minute chosen it. You couldn't *know* that I'd choose that one."

Clare looked demure.

"I – I sort of thought you would," she said.

In the Fog
(The Humorist 8/1/1927)

The fog was so thick that we couldn't see an inch in front of us. The bus had crawled at a snail's pace from the town and deposited us at our own special corner. All we had to do was to grope our way home. Clinging to each other, we groped.

Now fog has a curious effect upon the human brain. It seems to destroy the sense of direction. At least it seemed to destroy Clare's. I was quite sure where I was.

"We turn to the right just here, Clare," I said. "We're in Queen Charlotte Street."

"What nonsense!" said Clare's voice through the fog (although she was clinging to me I couldn't see her). "We turned to the right out of Queen Charlotte Street ages ago. We're in Pope Street now. We turn to the left just here."

"Rubbish, Clare!" I said. "We're in Queen Charlotte Street, and we turn to the right."

"The fog," said Clare kindly, "seems to be affecting your brain, my poor boy. We're in Pope Street, and we turn to the left."

"You may go where you like, Clare," I said. "I'm going to turn to the right."

"And I," said Clare, equally firmly, "am going to turn to the left."

I often wish I'd lived long enough ago to have married one of those nice, yielding Victorian wives one reads about in books. She'd have gone just where I wanted her to go in a fog. Sometimes, when I think about those women, I wonder whether there was a catch in it anywhere. I think there must have been. It sounds too good to have been really true.

But to return to Clare. Her voice came to me faintly from a distance on my left.

"Goodbye, old thing," it said, cheerfully. "I'll get the water nice and hot for you, so that when you come home chilled to the bone at midnight you can have a nice hot bath. And if you aren't back in time for breakfast I'll ring up the police about it."

"Clare!" I called.

Her voice drew nearer.

"I know what you want to say," it said. "You want to say you're sorry you said we were in Queen Charlotte Street, and that you admit we're in Pope Street, and that you're willing to rely entirely on my superior judgment, and come home with me."

"I do *not!*" I said with dignity. "I want to tell you that I'm going to make some mark on the pavement just here that we can find in the morning—"

"I'll try not to say 'I told you so'," murmured Clare.

I ignored the interruption.

"And I'll give you ten shillings if we find that it's in Pope Street."

I found a piece of chalk in my pocket and I drew a chain of crosses across the pavement.

"And now," I said distantly, "you may imagine yourself in Pope Street and go to the left if you like. I happen to know that we're in Queen Charlotte Street, and am going to the right."

Clare gurgled provocatively.

"I'll buy a pair of gloves with the ten shillings," she said.

Then we disappeared in different directions through the fog.

I wandered on and on and on and on. The fog seemed to grow thicker.

Moreover, our house seemed to have disappeared completely. A baker's shop stood where I knew our house had stood earlier in the day. And it was early closing day, so I couldn't go in and buy a penny bun and casually ask where I was.

I hunted for our house high and low, and then gave up the search. I didn't meet anyone. I seemed to be the only person left in the world. I wondered wistfully if Clare were safe at home. Perhaps – perhaps after all it *had* been Pope Street. I walked on through the fog. I wasn't looking for our house now. I was looking for someone – anyone – who might tell me where I was.

Suddenly I saw a vague blur, undoubtedly resembling a human being, approaching me through the fog. It drew nearer. I cleared my throat.

"Excuse me," I began politely, "but could you kindly tell me—"

Simultaneously the other figure was saying equally politely, in a well known voice:

"Excuse me, but could you kindly tell me—"

We stopped short, dropped our politeness, and clung to each other again.

"Where are we?" said Clare hysterically.

I struck a match to see whether I could see any landmark, and there on the pavement at our feet was a row of white chalk crosses.

"We're back again where we were," screamed Clare, "in Pope Street."

"In Queen Charlotte Street," I contradicted, fiercely.

Another figure loomed through the fog. It was a policeman.

"Good evening, constable," I said, pleasantly. "Thick, isn't it? We're in Queen Charlotte Street, I believe."

"No, Pope Street, aren't we, constable?" said Clare, coaxingly.

The deep, reassuring voice which members of the police force use to instruct and pacify ordinary mortals came through the fog.

"No. You're in High Street. Half a mile from either of 'em."

He took us home.

We gave him ten shillings.

Losing Clare
(The Humorist 19/2/1927)

"I'll meet you for lunch at Oxford Palace Hotel," said Clare, after the Joneses had sent us tickets for a matinée, "and then we'll go on to the theatre together. Let's say half-past twelve."

So we said half-past twelve.

I was there early. I arrived by the side door, and took up a strategic position from which I could see the front door, the side door, and the restaurant. And no Clare came. My neck got a sort of Charleston crick from perpetual revolutions from the front door to the side door and from the side door to the restaurant. And still she didn't come.

Innumerable people surged in continually from the side door and front door, but none of them was Clare. It was a revelation to me. Somehow I'd never realised before how many people there are in the world besides Clare and me. I began to feel lonely, as well as hungry, and I began to hate all these people who weren't Clare with a most deadly hatred. There was one woman whom I hated in particular. She was sitting behind a pillar opposite the front door, and I could only see her shoes and hat, but they were *green! Green* shoes and hat! I took a most intense dislike to her.

My thoughts went back over my past life and I thought of all the times when I'd been hard and unsympathetic to Clare. Poor Clare! It was nearly half-past one and still she hadn't come. I thought of all the accidents one reads of in the papers. I wished I'd been nicer to Clare about that coat of mine she'd given to a tramp last week. A woman, of course, couldn't be expected to know what an old coat means to a man. When I thought of Clare lying white and still in a hospital I couldn't help wishing that I'd been kinder about lots of little things.

My loneliness and anxiety increased. People were surging along in a never-ending stream. There were quite a lot, too, who looked maddeningly like Clare in the distance, but who turned out to be quite ordinary women when they got up to me.

Quarter to two! It was terrible. I went to a telephone and rang up our maid. Yes, Clare had left home before eleven. I then rang up the police to see if there'd been an accident that morning. They seemed rather unsympathetic but, of course, they didn't know Clare personally, and they probably thought of her as just an ordinary woman.

Then – at two o'clock – I took a taxi and flew round to all the other places where we sometimes meet for lunch, because, though Clare is the most wonderful woman in the world, I can't deny that she's sometimes a little absent-minded. But she wasn't at any of them. Then I went home. Clare was at home. She was just putting on a pair of black patent leather shoes.

"I've just come back," she said. "I waited for you and *waited* for you. And I'd made myself look so nice with new green shoes and a new green hat that I'd never told you about, and—"

"*What!*" I shouted. "Were *you* the woman?"

"I got there very early and I just sat by a pillar where I thought you could see me as you came in by the front door."

"I didn't go in by the front door."

"Then I thought you must have got run over, so I came home and changed my clothes, because it seemed so awful to be wearing green shoes with you dying in a hospital."

"Did you ring up the police about me?"

"No, because they were so unsympathetic when I lost Fluffles last week."

"That's all you care about me," I said. "I rang up the police about you quite an hour ago. I thought you'd been run over. If I knew you were the objectionable woman in green shoes sitting concealed by a pillar a few yards away from me—"

"I was sitting where you could see me as you came in at the front door."

"I keep telling you I didn't come in at the front door."

"And I was thinking about you all the time. I kept wishing that I'd been nicer to you about dropping cigarette ash on my new cushions yesterday. I only thought that, of course, when I thought of you as dying in hospital. Now that I know you're not dying in a hospital I think that I was absolutely justified, and I think you were just as nasty to me about that old coat and that old pipe."

"I was absolutely justified about that old coat and lots of other things, too," I said, firmly, "but – but were you sorry I was run over, Clare?"

"Yes. And were you sorry I was run over?"

"Awfully. It's too late for the play, so what shall we do?"

"Let's go and have a good meal somewhere, and then go to the pictures."

So that's what we did.

The Note

(The Humorist 5/3/1927)

I looked at the note on the block where I always keep little notes to remind me of anything I must particularly remember to do during the day. I looked at it again and again and again. It was Victoria 1230.

I couldn't for the life of me remember whose telephone number it was, or what I'd wanted to ring them up about. Still, it must be important or I shouldn't have put it down on my little block. It was obviously a situation requiring tact and initiative. After a few minutes hesitation I pulled myself together and, cheering myself, as it were, over the top, I took off the receiver.

"Number-r-r-r, please," trilled the fairy at the other end.

"Victoria 1230," I said firmly.

Soon a female voice spoke. It was business-like and rather alarming. It hadn't any of the sympathy and tenderness which poets associate with the female voice. It said, "Yes?"

I cleared my throat and hurled myself to the attack.

"Er – who is it speaking?" I said ingratiatingly.

"Mrs Frankson," she replied shortly.

"Oh, yes," I said in the tone in which one greets an old and valued friend. "This is Mr Smith."

I'd hoped that my name would awaken memories. But it didn't.

She said "Yes?" again, in a cold, expectant voice, and there was a painful silence.

"Er – is Mr Frankson in?" I asked desperately. Men are always easier to deal with than women, and perhaps I'd promised to ring him up on some business matter.

"Yes," she said. "Do you want to speak to him?"

"Yes, please," I said, mopping my brow.

Soon another voice came – a manly one this time – but as lacking in sympathy and encouragement as the female one. It said "Yes?" in words, but in tone it said, "Who the dickens are you and what the deuce do you mean by disturbing me like this?"

I wasted my most pleasant smile on the mouthpiece and said propitiatingly, "It's Mr Frankson, isn't it?"

"Yes," he said curtly.

I could tell by his voice that he wasn't the sort of man to try to help one out at all.

"This is Mr Smith," I said in a tone that I thought must make him recognise me as one of his friends. It didn't. He said "Yes?" again, and his tone was no kinder than before.

There was another long and painful silence. Then he said "Yes?" again very impatiently. I've never come across anyone who could make the innocent word "Yes" sound so disagreeable as these Franksons.

I cleared my throat again and said:

"Er – you asked me to ring you up, didn't you?"

"Certainly not," he said.

"Oh, no," I said, laughing deprecatingly. "It was the other way round, wasn't it? I promised to ring you up, didn't I?"

"I've no recollection of it."

The situation was growing desperate.

"Er – you are Mr Frankson, aren't you?" I said, to gain time.

"Yes," he said again coldly.

"Well, I'm Smith," I said.

"So you said before," he said nastily.

"Well, what I wanted to ask you—" I began, and had just stopped, praying my subconscious mind to reveal to me what it was I wanted to ask him, when I heard a taxi at the door. It was Clare coming home. Clare had been spending the weekend with her mother.

"Hold on a minute," I said, and laid the receiver on the table. Perhaps Clare would be able to tell me what I'd wanted to ring him up about.

Clare burst in.

"You brute!" she said. "You promised to meet me at the station and you never did."

"Did I promise?" I said. "I don't remember doing so."

"No, you wouldn't, with your memory," she said unkindly. "But you made a note of it specially.

"What train was it?" I asked.

"Twelve-thirty at Victoria," said Clare. "I *know* you made a note of it. On your little block."

"One minute," I said. "I must just explain to Mr Frankson."

"Whoever's Mr Frankson?" said Clare.

"A new friend of mine," I said as I took up the receiver.

"Hullo," I said cheerfully.

But my new friend had rung off.

Easter Eggs
(The Humorist 16/4/1927)

"I notice," said Clare, casually, at breakfast, "that you haven't yet asked me what present I'd like for my Easter egg."

"I haven't yet asked you what present you'd like for your Easter egg, Clare," I said in a kind tone of voice, "because I don't want to know what present you'd like for your Easter egg. I'm not going to give you a present for your Easter egg."

"But you *must*," said Clare, aghast. "You *can't* let Easter go by without giving me a present."

"You underestimate my powers, Clare," I said, still kindly, but firmly, as I reached out for the marmalade. "I can."

"Do you mean that at *Easter*," said Clare, in a tone of quivering horror, "that at *Easter* – the time when *everybody* gives presents to *everybody* – you're going to give me nothing?"

"No, Clare," I said, "I'm not going to give you nothing. I'm going to give you an egg. I'm going to give you a nice little dyed egg. All for your very own. That's what people used to give to each other for presents at Easter in the good old days of yore. We've wandered too far from the straight path of those dear old simple days – wandered into deep morasses of silk stockings and wristwatches and pearls, and even garters. It's wrong. I'm convinced it's wrong. We must get back to the grand old simple days of long ago. Your grandfather gave your grandmother an ordinary hen's egg dyed some festive shade at Easter, and it is being borne in upon me more and more that he was right."

"Last year," said Clare, "you gave me a crêpe de Chine scarf."

"Last year," I said, "I was unregenerate. I hadn't seen the error of my ways. It was very wrong of me indeed to give you a crêpe de Chine scarf. I ought to have given you a hen's egg dyed blue or purple, or something. By the way, what's your favourite colour?"

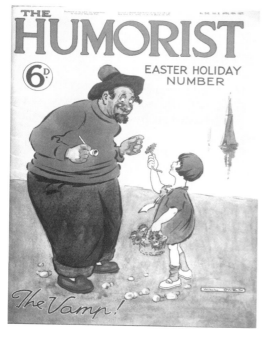

"I haven't one – in eggs," said Clare, coldly.

"That doesn't matter," I said, generously. "I'll choose one for you."

"Before you started all this silly talk about eggs," said Clare, "I was going to suggest that you got me a new handbag for an Easter egg."

"No, Clare," I said. "My conscience won't allow me to. An Easter egg is an Easter egg – not a handbag or a crêpe de Chine scarf, or a pair of silk stockings, or anything else. What has made us the nation we are? Calling a spade a spade and an egg an egg."

"A leather handbag," said Clare, "with a nice big inside pocket."

Now, I knew that we had a dozen eggs in the house, so on Easter Saturday I waited till Clare had gone out then I made my preparation. I was going to dye Clare's egg red. I'd got a nice little bit of red stuff, and I was going to boil the egg in it. It would be a lovely red egg. When I'd got everything ready I went to the larder for the egg and – I couldn't find a single egg anywhere. I searched all through the larder, and then I searched all through the kitchen.

Soon I discovered that I was growing very, very tired of looking for eggs. It may have been with catching my finger in a mousetrap on the top shelf of the store cupboard, or it may have been the strain of picking up hundreds and hundreds of tin-tacks whose tin I upset on to the floor from the bottom shelf, or it may have been the taste of the vinegar I drank in mistake for elderberry wine (Clare had – very carelessly, I consider – put vinegar into the elderberry wine bottle and omitted to alter the label).

But, whatever it was, at the end of an hour I felt so bored with eggs in general, and Easter eggs in particular, that I walked straight out of the house and bought a handbag – leather, with a nice big inside pocket.

Yes, of course, you've guessed what had happened to the eggs.

Clare gave them to me on Easter morning – the whole dozen of them – *dyed green.*

By Telephone

(London Opinion 28/5/1927)

"I'm going to tea to Mrs Robinson's, darling," said Clare, persuasively. "Won't you come with me?"

"No, I won't," I said shortly. "You know perfectly well that I have to do the garden. It's in a disgraceful condition. Besides, I don't want to go to tea with Mrs Robinson."

"Well, just walk with me there, then."

"No," I said firmly. "It will take me every minute of my time to dig over these beds. I wonder you don't offer to stay at home and help me. A really good woman would."

"No, she wouldn't," said Clare, calmly. "Digging is Adam's business, not Eve's. Adam delved, you remember, and Eve span. Will you come and fetch me home? About six."

"*No!*" I said savagely. "I won't. I've got the beastly garden to dig over and I won't have a minute, a *second*, till it's too dark to see."

"All right," said Clare, sweetly unperturbed as ever. "Goodbye, darling."

I dug and dug and dug and began to feel more and more sorry for myself. I don't like gardening. I don't like bending double for hours on end digging away at the hard, hard earth, extracting stones and slugs and worms, and planting seeds which will probably never come up because already dozens of birds have collected on the nearest tree and are laughing up their sleeves at me.

"The poor mutt!" says a sparrow to a starling, and the starling wipes its eyes and replies, weakly: "Isn't he a *scream?* But they look quite decent seeds."

But the last straw was when I discovered that Jobbins hadn't sent the weed-killer. I'd ordered it the week before and it hadn't come. I went into the house in a raging temper (pursued by titters from the birds) and rang him up. A sweetly feminine voice answered me. My fury died away.

"Is that 2719?" I asked.

"No," said the sweetly feminine voice. "You've got the wrong number."

It was really one of the most exquisite voices I've ever heard.

"Hold on a minute," I pleaded. I simply had to hear more of it.

"Yes?" it said.

"I say," I said, "isn't it a nice evening?"

"Isn't it?" it replied. "I do love these early summer evenings, don't you?"

It was distinctly encouraging. I felt tremendously bucked. It was the very first telephone flirtation I'd ever indulged in, but I felt so fed up with slaving over dull clods of earth hour after hour, and I did think it was rotten of Clare to go out to tea without even offering to stay in and help me.

"Rather!" I said then. "I say, are you dark or fair?"

"Tut! Tut!" said the sweet voice. "I shall ring off if you ask leading questions."

"If you do," I said, "I'll go straight out and poison myself."

"What with?"

"Weed-killer. I haven't got any in the house, but I can soon get some. Don't be cruel. You've got such a kind voice."

"Have I?"

"Yes. A perfectly adorable one. I guess that you're dark and slim and—"

"Well, in a quarter of an hour I shall be outside the Town Hall, so you can see for yourself if you like."

Now, I'm not a philanderer, and I'm quite aware that the world doesn't hold another woman as nice as Clare, but – well, I was simply sick of slaving over that beastly garden, and I did think that Clare might have stayed at home to help me, and I did want to see what the owner of the adorable voice looked like. After all, I thought, I needn't speak to her. I could just walk along and look at her. She wouldn't know it was me and – I could see whether she was as nice as the voice.

So I went to the Town Hall and there was nobody outside it but Clare.

"Hello," she said. "I thought you were so busy that you wouldn't have a minute, a *second*, till it was dark."

"Oh," I said nonchalantly. "I just came out to post a letter."

"Did you?" she said, and added: "I do love these early summer evenings, don't you?" She gurgled. "But you weren't *quite* right, darling. I'm auburn, not dark."

"*Clare*" I said.

"Yes," she said. "I was at Mrs Robinson's, and she'd just gone upstairs to get her new hat to show me, and the telephone bell rang, and she called down to me to be an angel and answer it for her, and so I was, and I recognised your voice, but you didn't recognise mine, and I simply couldn't resist it, so I—"

"Goodbye," I said very distantly. "I'm going down into the town."

"What for, darling?" said Clare, still gurgling.

"*Weed-killer*," I said viciously.

Clicking
(Windsor Magazine June 1927)

"I'm tired of going to dances and dancing every dance with you," said Clare. "It was all right when I first knew you, but for seven long years—" She sighed.

"Well, it's just as bad for me as it is for you," I replied. "I dance with you quite as much as you dance with me. It must be quite as trying for me."

"Let's strike," said Clare.

"'Ear! 'Ear!" I said in a vulgar manner.

"We'll part the minute we get there tonight," she said. "You can find the prettiest girl in the room and I'll find some young Adonis and have a real holiday from you."

"Thank you," I said.

We parted as we had agreed as soon as we entered the room. I found an M.C. leaning limply against the wall. I knew him vaguely at the club.

"Look here, old chap," I said, "do me a favour. Find the prettiest girl in the room and introduce me to her."

He came to life with a start.

"Right!" he said. "I spotted her a few minutes ago. She's a peach."

He took me across the room to a tall girl in black and silver, murmured some unintelligible words meant to be an introduction and drifted away.

"I didn't quite catch your name," I said to her politely.

"I didn't catch yours either," she said. "Does it matter?"

"Not a bit."

"Are you going to ask me for a dance?"

"I'm going to ask you for them all."

"How dull!"

"Not at all. And we can sit some out."

"But I don't think it's quite proper. You didn't catch my name."

"As you said, names don't matter. Let's find a nice place to sit in."

We found a very nice place and sat in it.

I looked at her left hand.

"You're married," I said sternly.

"Yes, Sherlock, dear, I am."

"He must be very nice or you wouldn't look so happy."

"I don't. I only pretend to. He isn't nice at all. He doesn't appreciate me."

"The brute! I mean, I'm sure he does really."

"He doesn't. And he's so bad-tempered. Only this week he got into a foul temper about the spring-cleaning."

"Yes, but, dear – I mean, Mrs M-m-m-m-m, someone left some soap at the bottom of the stairs and he slipped on it…. I mean, I dare say someone did that."

She looked at me coldly.

"Are you taking his part?"

"Not at all," I said hastily. "I think he's an unmitigated brute."

She softened.

"Are you married?" she said.

"Yes."

"Is she nice?"

"Generally. Sometimes she's a bit – unreasonable."

She stiffened.

"Is she?" she said coldly.

"Why should you mind?" I said.

"I don't," she snapped. "Your wives are nothing to me. But – how is she unreasonable?"

"The things she wants…. She's always wanting new clothes and she's always wanting to go up to town and she has

people to dinner and won't let me wear my nice comfy bedroom slippers for them and she does crossword puzzles all over the place and keeps asking me for words of so many letters meaning so-and-so when I want to read the paper."

The vision was with difficulty keeping calm. Here she interrupted me.

"All this only shows," she said, "how thoroughly selfish you are."

"But why should you mind?" I said.

"I don't," she said again, "but I can't help being sorry for your poor wife."

"Ah," I said, "if I'd married you…."

She smiled.

"Do you think I'd make a nice wife?"

"Adorable," I said. "And do you think I'd make a nice husband?"

"You'd have your faults, of course," she said judicially. "But on the whole" – she bent towards me in a very forward manner and kissed the tip of my ear – "on the whole you'd be quite a duck."

I closed my eyes.

"Do that again," I said.

"No," she said. "I want to dance now."

We danced together all the evening. At the end of the last dance the M.C. drew me on to one side and whispered:

"I say, I did find you a peach, didn't I? And, by Jove! You do seem to have clicked."

"She's married," I said.

"Hard lines!" he murmured.

"N-not really," I said. "You see, it's me she's married to. We clicked seven years ago."

Then I went on and left him wiping his brow.

The Picnic

(London Opinion 18/6/1927)

"I told Charles that we'd go to his picnic next Saturday," said Clare.

I stared at her in amazement.

"But *why*, Clare?" I said. "You know that no one ever goes to picnics except people who are either engaged or just going to get engaged. You know what a picnic is. It's either miserably cold and you can't hear a word anyone says to you because your teeth are chattering so, or it's miserably hot and the midges eat you and the wasps sting you and spiders swim about in your tea and the milk turns sour and the sun beats down upon you and you have to play rounders.

"Picnics exist solely for those in love, so that they can sit together under a tree and spread each other's bread and honey, and take spiders out of each other's tea and caterpillars out of each other's hair, and tell each other that no one ever really understood them till they met each other.

"Because, as you perhaps remember, when you're in love you don't mind midges eating you and wasps stinging you and spiders swimming about in your tea; you don't even mind playing rounders, because when the ball gets lost you can look for it with each other and tell each other yet again that no one ever understood you till you met each other. What on earth made you say we'd go to it?"

Clare looked demure.

"Well," she said, "I met Mr Robinson yesterday, and he said that he was going to Charlie's picnic and that he hoped I was."

"Woman," I said, indignantly, "are you carrying on a clandestine flirtation with the man?"

"Not exactly," said Clare, with a wistful sigh, "but it's rather nice after all these years of married life that a man takes an interest in one."

"Balmy" June

I was so angry that I went straight out of the house and banged the door. In the street I met Miss Franklin. Miss Franklin is very pretty. She smiled at me (she smiles very nicely) and said, "Are you going to Charles's picnic on Saturday?"

"I haven't quite decided," I said.

"Oh, do go," she said; "I'm going."

I went home to Clare.

"Clare," I said, "I think that you were quite right to tell Charles that we'd go to his picnic on Saturday."

"Why?" said Clare.

"I've just met Miss Franklin," I explained, casually, "and she said that she was going to it, and she wished I would."

"I've never understood what people see in Miss Franklin," said Clare, distantly.

"Oh, I have," I said, fervently, "and it's so nice after all these years of married life that another woman can take an interest in one."

We approached the picnic ground and looked about us. It was a bitterly cold day. A real east wind cut like a knife. The very trees were shivering.

"I expect he'll be on the look-out for me," said Clare, with chattering teeth.

"She'll be waiting for me somewhere," I replied, with a shiver.

"He's such a charming man!" chattered Clare.

"She's so delightfully pretty!" I shivered back.

We walked across the field and suddenly we came upon them. They were sitting under a tree together, and they were so much engrossed in each other that they didn't even see us. He was just taking a caterpillar out of her hair and she was taking a spider out of his tea, and they were telling each other that no one had ever really understood them till they met each other.

"*Well!*" I shivered indignantly to Clare.

And Clare chattered back, "*Well!*"

"Clare," I shivered, "no one's seen us. Let's creep back to the road and make a dash for it to the station and go home."

So we did, and when we got home we went to the pictures.

They were very nice pictures, and in the intervals I told Clare that after all no one really understood me except her, and she told me that after all no one really understood her except me.

And we had quite a nice afternoon.

A Summer's Afternoon
(The Humorist 6/8/1927)

"Look at the bit of blue sky," said Clare, cheerfully.

"Where?" I demanded.

"There," said Clare, pointing to a particularly black spot.

"You're colour-blind," I said, bitterly, and we walked on again in silence.

After about a quarter of an hour, Clare said, determinedly:

"I don't think it's quite as cold as it was, do you?"

I turned up the collar of my coat to keep out the biting wind and made no reply.

We walked on again in silence.

At last Clare said:

"I *really* don't think it's coming down quite so heavily now, do you?"

I turned my face experimentally up to the skies, then hastily withdrew it under the shelter of my hat brim again and tried to blink the rain out of my eyes.

"Do you?" said Clare again.

"I'll be honest, Clare," I said, coldly, "I do. So do you in your soul. You know perfectly well that it's pouring as hard as ever, and I consider that this habit of looking at the bright side when there isn't a bright side to look at is merely one of the signs of the decadence of a decadent age."

Clare sighed.

"Well, here we are, anyway," she said.

Charles and Horace waved their rackets in hilarious greeting.

"It's looking brighter, isn't it?" said Charles, cheerfully.

"It's going to clear in a minute," said Horace. "Let's begin, shall we? It's only a shower. Toss for partners."

We walked through a steady downpour to the tennis court.

"It's running down my back," I said, pathetically, but no one took any notice of me.

"The clouds are beginning to break over there," said Horace, with patent untruthfulness. "Come on. We'll take this side. Toss for service. Rough or smooth?"

I tried to tell him, but a gust of piercing east wind and a mouthful of rain had deprived me temporarily of the power of speech.

"We'll play till tea-time at any rate," said Charles, "and if it hasn't cleared by then we'll – well, we'll see what it's like. Fire away!"

So we played tennis till tea-time. It wasn't a game. It was a nightmare. Clare said she enjoyed it, but women have strange standards of enjoyment. Under foot was a thick squidge of porridge. They laughed whenever I fell down. Overhead was the blackness of a total eclipse. The rain was still trickling down my back. The east wind cut through me like a knife. The tennis balls were sodden.

We had tea on the veranda. The tea, of course, would have been comforting had it not been that both the east wind and the deluge, having free access to the veranda, cooled it considerably.

When we'd had tea, Horace said, doubtfully:

"Well – it hasn't cleared—"

But Charles said:

"I think there's a break in the clouds over there. Let's finish the set, anyway."

So we finished the set and played two more, and then it was time to go home. It was still pouring. We went indoors and stood for some time dripping in the hall.

"It's been a topping game," said Charles. "Thanks so much for coming."

"It would have been silly to stop just for a bit of rain," said Horace.

Just then their mother came into the hall. She was wearing a lovely warm, woolly shawl.

"Had a nice game?" she said.

"Topping," said Charles. "What have you been doing all afternoon?"

"Sitting by the fire, dear," she said.

"We hoped you'd come out for tea."

"No, dear," she said. "It was so nice and warm indoors and I wanted to have toast for tea. It gets cold so quickly out of doors."

"Horace," I said, when she'd gone, how old is your mother?"

"Seventy," said Horace.

I walked home through the rain with Clare in silence, but it was a more cheerful silence. I felt that I'd got something to live for. *I* shall be able to stay indoors by the fire and have toast for tea all the summer when I'm seventy. It's most decidedly something to live for. I shall count the years till it comes. I may even cheat a little and begin at sixty-nine. It isn't so long to wait, after all. I'm nearly forty.

"Only twenty-nine years," I said, happily.

"What's only twenty-nine years?" asked Clare.

But I didn't tell her.

The Thing

(London Opinion 20/8/1927)

"How often do you take your tyre pressure?" said Horace.

"Once a week," I replied.

"I'll lend you my thing," said Horace, with an air of munificent liberality.

"What is your thing?" I asked, mildly.

"It's a mechanical pump," said Horace. "You fix it on to the engine."

"Thanks awfully," I said, hastily. "But we've got a foot pump and it's quite all right. We're used to it. We do it in turns. I do it every other Friday and Clare does it every other Friday."

"But my thing's *much* less trouble," protested Horace, who is always officiously and irrepressibly generous. "I'll bring it round and show you how it works, and then I'll send it along to you every Friday."

"How kind of you," I murmured, "but really, you needn't trouble."

Horace, however, insisted on troubling. He came round the next day with the thing – a complicated instrument – which he fixed on to the engine of our car. Then he started the engine, and the thing proceeded to pump the tyres.

"You see how it fixes on and works, don't you?" he said to me.

Clare was looking at me with an irritating sort of smile, so I said, with great dignity, "Of course." I wasn't going to have Clare thinking that I couldn't understand a simple little thing like that. I looked at Clare and said, "Do you?"

"Of course," said Clare, rather coldly.

"Good!" said Horace. "I'll send the thing round next Friday."

So next Friday it came. It happened to be my Friday. I took it into the garage and managed very nicely. Then I went back to the garden to Clare.

"Done them," I said.

She looked at me admiringly.

"I heard the engine going," she said. "Did you manage quite easily?"

"Perfectly," I said. "Do you think you'll be able to manage next week?"

"Perfectly," said Clare, but she looked rather thoughtful.

The next Friday Horace sent the thing round again, and Clare retired to the garage with it. I heard her set the engine going. Then I crept round to watch her through the window.

She was doing exactly what I'd done the week before.

She'd set the engine going and was pumping the tyres with the foot pump.

The Bulbs

(The Humorist 29/10/1927)

"Darling," said Clare, "do be an angel and take this home and see to it. I've got to call at Mrs Smith's, and I do want them put in at once."

It was a small paper bag of bulbs for indoor planting that she had just bought.

"You'll find the bowl and the fibre stuff all ready," she went on. "You *will* be an angel and do it, won't you?"

I am a weak man, so I promised to be an angel and do it. As a matter of fact, I rather fancy myself at planting bulbs. I think that I have a knack with bulbs. So I took the little bag from Clare and started off home alone.

I had quite an uneventful journey. I met Jones on the way from the station, and we just called to see how Brown was getting on after the 'flu. We didn't stay long. Brown was downstairs and feeling deeply interested in himself. He insisted on us seeing his temperature chart. He's frightfully proud of the time it went up to 104. I think he's going to have the chart framed as soon as he's well enough to take it into the village.

We escaped as soon as we could and went our different ways. I went straight home and planted the bulbs. We put them in the dark, of course, but we peeped in to watch them anxiously every day.

"I do so love the moment when the first green tips appear," said Clare, "and when there comes that first faint fragrant perfume."

Soon there came a day when Clare said rather doubtfully: "There – there are some little green tips showing."

And there came a day when she said yet more doubtfully: "There – there *is* a faint perfume."

And the next day she said, not doubtfully at all: "There's something funny about those green tips."

And I replied: "There's something funnier still about that faint perfume."

We waited a few more days, and then there wasn't any doubt about it.

"They're *onions!*" said Clare, furiously. "They aren't bulbs at all. What on earth have you done to them?"

"Nothing," I said. "They must have made a mistake at the shop."

"Nonsense!" snapped Clare. "I wasn't given these at the shop. I know onions when I see them. I suppose that this is your idea of humour."

"You are mistaken, then," I said, very distantly. "My idea of humour, though somewhat crude, is not quite so crude as that. These are what you gave me in a bag to bring home and plant."

"They are *not*," Clare contradicted me, rudely.

We discussed the matter with some heat till it got to the point where it wouldn't bear discussion any longer, and then we were very cold to each other for several days. But during those days I began to think, and when next I met Jones I said to him:

"By the way, do you remember the day we came out of the station together and called to see how old Brown was getting on?"

Jones remembered perfectly.

"Had you anything with you?" I asked, casually.

"No," said Jones, "except a small bag of onions I was taking home."

"You – you didn't lose it by any chance,

did you?" I inquired.

"No," said Jones, surprised, "of course not: I got home with it quite all right. To tell you the truth, my wife was out and the maid was away, and I was going to make a stew for my supper. I'm rather a pro at stews," he added, modestly, "but they do need onions."

"Did it taste all right?" I ventured.

A peculiar expression came over Jones's face.

"It's funny you should mention it," he said. "No, it didn't. It had a most strange and unpleasant flavour. I ate it because there was nothing else, but I – I didn't enjoy it. Why do you ask?"

But I didn't tell him. I thought it kinder not to.

The First Word
(The Humorist 5/11/1927)

We are conspiring to deceive an innocent child. It sounds very wrong, but we have given deep thought to the matter, and have decided it is the only thing to do. But I will begin at the very beginning.

When our daughter was born, someone sent Clare a handsome leather-bound book with one side of each page left blank for snapshots, and on the other some little spaces to be filled in by the parent, giving information as to the weight of the child each month, and the date at which it first got its toe into its mouth, first crawled, stood, fell, pulled the cat's tail, and all the rest of it. You know the sort of thing.

Most of us on arriving at years of discretion have surreptitiously stolen some such record from our mothers and privately burnt it lest she should show it to our friends. But this was a super-record-deluxe, with Morocco binding, gold edges, and heavy vellum paper. As I said to Clare:

"It's terrible to expect a child to live up to that. It will handicap it and depress it all its life. I mean, any child brought up on a book like that would feel that it was expected to be Prime Minister at least."

"And how do you know she won't be?" said Clare, with spirit.

The book was the apple of Clare's eye. She took innumerable snapshots (which all looked exactly alike to me, but, of course, I daren't say so), and filled in all the little spaces most religiously. But the most important space was "Baby's First Word". She was longing to fill that in. I told her frequently that she could fill it in any time now, because Baby's first word had been "Goo", followed closely by "Sptmn", but she said it meant the first intelligible word – such a word as might be found in a dictionary. She had, of course, privately decided that it must be "Mum". She held long conversations with her daughter after this fashion:

"Say Mum, darling."

"Goo-oo-oo-oo."

"Mum, Mum, Mum, Mum. Say Mum."

"Ger-r-r-r."

"Say Mum, pet."

"Sptm-m-m-m-m."

After enduring this for some time patiently, it suddenly occurred to me to set up an opposition camp. Hang it all, I was the father! I didn't see why "Dad" shouldn't be the first word, So I joined the fray.

"Say Dad, baby."

"Goo-oo-oo-oo."

"Say Dad, Dad, Dad, Dad."

"Ger-r-r-r. Sptm-m-m-m."

In the end, the rivalry between us grew fast and furious, and still our daughter clung to her own limited but vigorous vocabulary. I am convinced that she is going to turn into a very strong-minded woman. I'm not at all sure that Clare isn't right, and that she won't end by being Prime Minister. But that is by the way.

The climax of the story comes when two young nieces of mine came to spend a weekend with us. They are called Hester and Nell. Hearing of the frenzied rivalry between us for the first word they decided to join in.

"Say Hester, darling."

"Goo-oo-oo."

"Say Nell."

"Ger-r-r-r."

Of course, we could afford to smile, because it wasn't likely that she would say either of these names. But suddenly she began to listen attentively, gazing from one to the other.

"Hester."

"Nell."

"Hester."

"Nell."

Then she gathered her forces and made a sudden might effort.

And our daughter uttered her first word.

She said, quite distinctly, "H–ell!"

As soon as they'd gone I got out the book and took it to Clare.

"Fill it in," I said, simply.

"I *can't!*" said Clare, wildly. "Just *think* of it! Think of showing it to people. Think of her seeing it in later life. It will be a terrible handicap to her. It will throw a cloud over her whole life to know that that was the first word she ever said. Besides, what sort of persons will people think we are for her to be picking up that sort of language almost before she can speak?"

"Very well, then," I said. "We must put down something else. To leave it blank will only arouse her suspicions. I suggest 'Dad'."

"Certainly not," said Clare. "We'll put 'Mum'."

We ended by drawing lots for it, and it came to "Mum".

So Clare wrote "Mum" in her best handwriting.

That is the story of how we came to conspire to deceive an innocent child. I think we were justified, don't you?

An Autumn Diary
(The Humorist 26/11/1927)

2.30.   Clare has just asked me to sweep the leaves in the garden. She asked me so nicely that I promised before I quite realised what I was doing. I shall have to do it now because I have the reputation of being a truthful man. In fact, I'm so transparently truthful that I've never even claimed to have swum the channel. Clare herself has to go out to a meeting.

2.35.   Have nerved myself to look out of the window to see what has to be done. Horrible sight has met my eyes. Lawns and beds completely covered with fallen leaves. Probably yards deep.

2.45.   Have got besom from shed and begun. Quite jolly work and not as deep as it looked from window. Jolly exercise for chillish autumn day.

3p.m.   Have swept leaves half-way down lawn. Gust of wind disperses heap, so that lawn looks exactly as it did before I began. Remind myself of Bruce's spider and Nelson and Wellington and Grace Darling and Mussolini, and other inspiring examples, who would have gone back to end of lawn and started again. Go back to end of lawn and start again.

3.10.   Have got almost to end of lawn. Gust of wind disperses heap over lawn again, completely covering it. Hope that children playing in next-door garden have not heard comments on situation that rose involuntarily to my lips. Sudden interested silence suggests that they have. Go back to end of lawn and start again.

3.30.   Have brushed leaves to very end of lawn quite successfully and then wind once more blows them all back to their original positions.   Don't care whether next-door children hear or not. Start again.

3.45.   Happen to look back when swept half way down lawn. Space brushed clear now completely covered by continually falling leaves. Make note in diary. "Cut down all trees in garden before next autumn." Decide to go into house for necessary rest and refreshment. Am convinced that Bruce's spider, Nelson, Wellington, Grace Darling and Mussolini would have done so long ago. Take up morning paper to clear brain and recover sense of proportion. See following paragraph:

"What can be more beautiful than the carpet of golden beech leaves that meets the eye at every turn this autumn?"

4 p.m.   Have typed several copies of above sentence and pinned them up on front gate and front door and on all trees in garden so that they may meet Clare's eye when she returns from meeting. Set out for golf club.

A Master Tactician
(The Humorist 3/12/1927)

"I t's Christmas next week," said Clare. "I know it is," I said. "You needn't rub it in."

"What are you going to do about it?"

"What do you mean – what am I going to do about it?" I said, suspiciously. "What can I do about it with the Income Tax what it is and my salary what it isn't? I mean – well, I mean, what can one do about it?"

"I want you to promise not to give me a

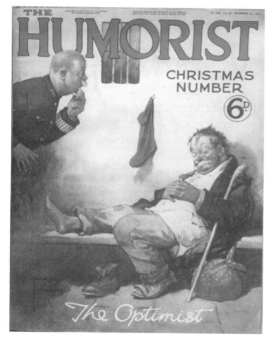

present this year," said Clare, very sweetly.

I was taken aback.

"Why ever not?" I said.

"Well, because of what you said just now, you know, about the Income Tax being what it is and your salary what it isn't, and

all that sort of thing."

I was deeply touched.

"But, Clare, my dear," I said, "that is no reason why I should not give you some little memento of the occasion. I mean – dash it all! I can't let Christmas pass without – I mean, I appreciate your attitude more than I can say and, of course, it needn't be anything expensive. I mean – I didn't mean that I was absolutely on the rocks."

"No, I'd rather you didn't give me anything," persisted Clare.

"Oh, I must give you *something*," I retorted. "As I said, it needn't be anything much. By the way, what are you giving me?"

"A new pair of braces, dear," said Clare.

"Good! Then I'll buy you a new pair of garters."

There was a silence – the sort of silence that means Clare is thinking.

Finally she said, very firmly, "No, I *insist*. You mustn't give me *anything*."

I yielded with a good grace.

"Very well, Clare," I said, "if you absolutely insist."

Again she was silent.

"Of course," she said at last, "I do see your point about not wanting to let Christmas go by without— and I *quite* see that you mightn't like to accept the braces without— well, without *some* little – well, you know what I mean."

It was my turn to grow thoughtful.

"I dare say I could conquer my feelings about that," I said at last. "Pride is, after all, a sin. And I don't suppose the braces will cost you much, will they?"

"It isn't the value," retorted Clare. "It's the *thought* behind them."

"Of course," I said; "and I'm still quite willing to—"

"No," said Clare, as firmly as ever; "I'm not going to let you give me *anything*."

There was another short silence – a very thoughtful silence. Then Clare said:

"But, of course, I do see that some little *thought*— By the way, Mrs Jones asked me to go to a course of dancing lessons with her. She says they're awfully good, and they keep one up to date so."

"Yes?" I said, very pleasantly. I was quite glad to have the subject changed.

"But I told her," said Clare, very casually, "that I couldn't possibly afford it. It's three guineas for the whole course."And then, of course, I began to see light. The subject hadn't been changed. I rose. Even Clare admits that, as a husband, I have my points.

"Well, Clare," I said, "as you won't let me give you anything, suppose you let me pay for this course of dancing lessons for you?"

Clare gazed at me in well-simulated delight and surprise.

"You darling!" she said. "What a lovely idea! Do you really mean it?"

"Certainly," I said, striking my famous attitude of magnanimity. "You may sit down at your writing-table this instant and write to Mrs Jones and tell her that you can come to the dancing lessons because I'm paying for them instead of giving you a Christmas present."

I put a sheet of paper ready for her on her writing-table, and drew out her chair with a flourish.

"Oh," said Clare, slightly – only very slightly – discomposed, "I – I wrote and told her so last night."

Mrs Jones and Me
(London Opinion 24/12/1927)

I'm writing this because I want to tell you my story before Mrs Jones gets in with hers.

You might meet Mrs Jones any day, and if I've not got in with my tale first – well, I hardly like to think what you'd think of me.

To go right to the beginning, it's Clare's fault, of course. Clare never goes anywhere without leaving everything she's carrying behind her, and so I never follow Clare out of any tram or bus or carriage or shop or restaurant or "place" of any sort without casting an eye round to see what she's left, and gathering it up for her. The thing has become second nature to me.

Well, when I was shopping with her about a month ago and she went out of the village shop with her parcel, I glanced behind as usual to see what she'd left behind and collect it. And there on the counter I saw her bag. At least I thought it was her bag. It turned out to belong to Mrs Jones, who was also in the shop. And Mrs Jones took it from me with a very nasty look. There was no need of words to tell me that Mrs Jones put the worst possible construction on the episode.

After that an evil fate began to dog me. I had tea with Clare in the little café near the station the next week, and when we came out, Clare said:

"I've left my mac there. Do get it, there's a darling."

I went back and there was a red mac just like Clare's, hanging on a hook, and I was just claiming it when Mrs Jones's cold voice once more turned my blood to ice. It wasn't Clare's. It belonged to Mrs Jones, who was having tea just near it. I tried to explain, but her nasty look paralysed me, and no criminal caught red-handed can ever have looked the part more than I did.

I rejoined Clare.

"There's only Mrs Jones's mac there," I said.

"Oh, yes," said Clare, carelessly. "I remember now. I didn't bring mine out."

Well, those two incidents had such a devastating effect on my nerves that if there'd been anyone else at all on the station bus I wouldn't have rescued that umbrella. But it was where Clare had been sitting, and we were the only people on the bus, so just as she was getting out I darted back for it. I forgot to mention it till we'd got home, then I gave it to her and said:

"You left it in the station bus, but I rescued it as usual."

"I didn't," said Clare. "I noticed it by the seat, but it isn't mine. Someone must have left it there before I got in. It's a very nice one. It's practically new."

"I'll take it along to Scotland Yard or somewhere sometime, then," I said, vaguely.

But of course I never did.

This brings us to the whist drive. I didn't want a whist drive. I didn't see why we should have a whist drive, but Clare said that we had to have one to ask back the people who'd asked us to their whist drives. I pointed out that this policy of an eye for an eye and a tooth for a tooth was wrong and un-Christian, and that we ought to forgive our enemies, but she wouldn't listen. She insisted on having a whist drive. She bought a pocket case for the first gentleman's prize, and a vase for the

first lady's prize, and I nearly broke my back carrying tables.

Mrs Jones was among the guests. She gave me the usual nasty look, and then glanced round at all the ornaments in the room as if wondering where I'd pinched them. And, of course, she won the first prize. Such people always do. Clare went out to fetch them while I engaged people in conversation. Mrs Jones began to tell us about a new umbrella she'd left in the station bus the first time she took it out. She said that someone must have stolen it because she'd made inquiries about it afterwards without any result.

Perspiration stood out on my brow. Then I heard a crash outside, and I knew that Clare had dropped the first lady's prize. Then I heard frantic sounds as of Clare searching round for something to put in its place. Mrs Jones went on describing her umbrella.

Then Clare entered. She looked awfully pleased with herself as if she'd done something awfully clever.

She made a nice little speech and presented Mrs Jones with her lost umbrella as the first prize.

So you'll understand why I want to get in with my story before you hear Mrs Jones's. If you meet her, you might try to explain – but no, on the other hand, perhaps not.

The Invitations
(London Opinion Christmas 1927)

Both Clare and I belong to hospitable families. By that I mean that every Christmas both Clare's Aunt Maud and my Aunt Martha invite us to spend Christmas with them. So far we have followed the line of least resistance. When Clare's Aunt Maud asks us first, we accept her invitation and write and tell my Aunt Martha that we're so sorry we can't come to her but we received Aunt Maud's invitation first, and when my Aunt Martha asks us first, we accept her invitation and write and tell Aunt Maud that we're so sorry we can't come to her but my Aunt Martha asked us first.

In short, we have a high ideal of family duty and in consequence spend extremely dull Christmases. At my Aunt Martha's there is always a Christmas tree dressed by Aunt Martha's husband Frederick. No one can ever complain of the quantity of presents on Uncle Frederick's Christmas tree. Uncle Frederick's Christmas tree is literally weighed down by presents.

Uncle Frederick collects his presents by a very simple and original process. Throughout the year he searches magazines and newspapers for offers of free samples of goods, and sends for them, and then when Christmas comes he hangs them on the Christmas tree and distributes them among his family with an air of bland generosity. If you're lucky you get a microscopic tube of toothpaste and if you're unlucky you get a cure for asthma. Last year Clare got a cure for obesity (Clare weighs just under eight stone) and a sample number of "The Rabbit Keeper's Monthly", and I got a tiny packet of suet and (they were beginning to run out then) a little book on how to double your income by joining someone's correspondence course.

Aunt Martha's is worse because Aunt Martha is a vegetarian. She panders to popular convention at Christmastide by having her little proteid and macaroni abominations made up into the shape of cutlets with a little bit of holly on each.

Now flesh and blood will stand this sort of thing up to a certain point and not beyond, and we'd reached that point by this time, and though I know that Clare had a strong sense of family duty I wasn't at all surprised when Aunt Martha's usual invitation came, to hear her say:

"We're *not* going. I don't care what happens, but we're *not* going."

"We'd better be careful," I cautioned, for both Clare's and my families are families where one had better be careful – the sort of families that cut you out of their wills if you forget to send a picture postcard to Great Aunt Susan on her birthday.

"I know," said Clare recklessly, "but I simply don't care. We're *not going*."

And the next day Aunt Maud's invitation arrived.

"I know what I'm going to do," said Clare. "I'm going to be very – what's the word? Is it Marconi or Macaroni? You know – the word meaning cunning?"

"I think you mean 'Machiavellian'," I murmured.

"That sort of thing," said Clare vaguely. "I knew it was that more or less. Anyway, I'm going to be it."

So she was it. She wrote to her Aunt Maud to say that we were so sorry we couldn't come to her but we had already received an invitation from my Aunt Martha, and she wrote to my Aunt Martha to say that we were so sorry that we couldn't come to her but we had already received an invitation from her Aunt Maud.

"*And*," she said virtuously, "it's perfectly true, too. At least it's what *I* call true."

I did not take up the challenge in her voice.

"And what are we going to do for Christmas, Clare?" I asked.

"We're going to a hotel," said Clare. "I've always wanted to go to a hotel for Christmas."

We had a lovely time at the hotel and we're still there. We're still there because we daren't go home.

You see, the day after Christmas we got two letters forwarded from home.

One was from my Aunt Martha and said:

"We're going to run over to Clare's Aunt Maud's on Christmas afternoon just to have a peep at you."

And the other was from Clare's Aunt Maud, and said:

"We're going to run over to John's Aunt Martha's on Christmas afternoon just to have a peep at you."

So presumably they both ran over.

Perhaps they met half way.

Perhaps they arrived and found each other out and sat down to wait till each other came back.

Perhaps—

Anyway, that's why we're still at the hotel. We daren't go home.

Bad Luck
(The Humorist 7/1/1928)

I was talking to Jones last night and I suppose I got carried away by my eloquence, as one sometimes does. One would have thought, however, that no one – least of all one's own wife – would have been mean enough to take advantage of it.

I had been deploring the lack of exercise in modern life. One often does that without really meaning it. I'd said that there was no exercise to beat that of chopping wood. I said that there was nothing I enjoyed more than chopping wood. Most men say things like that, but everyone knows they don't mean it. Certainly Clare, who has lived with me more years than we like to think, knew that I didn't mean it. But it sounds well.

It summons up engaging visions of oneself as a strong, silent man swinging an axe and grappling with primitive nature. It's the way one does talk after a good dinner when there's no chance of anyone's taking you at your word and everyone will have forgotten it in the morning. Certainly no decent wife would remember.

Of course, I should have guessed that Clare had some plot up her sleeve by the very sweetness of her smile as she said:

"Are you doing anything this afternoon, darling?"

I thought that perhaps she was going to suggest going out in the car, or having the Browns in to bridge, or roasting chestnuts, or something like that. So, with a childlike innocence that ought to have shamed her (but didn't), I answered, "No."

"That's all right," she said, cheerfully. "I thought you weren't, so I told Jenks to leave the logs for you to chop today. I told him how much you enjoyed doing it, and they ought to be done this afternoon because we really need them. You *did* say you enjoyed chopping wood, didn't you, dear?"

I looked at her coldly.

"Of course I did," I said distantly. "I'm very glad you told him to leave them. I shall very much enjoy doing them. Where are they?"

It was a beastly situation, but that was the only possible way of meeting it.

She showed me where they were, and left me to them. I took off my coat and began to wield the axe. Now, chopping wood is all very well in novels and pictures and conversation, but in real life it's the very devil. It beats me that no one has ever invented any other way of doing it. It is amazing to think that we still chop up our fire logs as Adam and Noah presumably chopped theirs.

I think that something might be done in the way of intensive culture of woodworms. I think that a highly-trained pack of woodworms would do the thing in no time. They're intelligent animals. They'd be unleashed at one side of the log; then, at a given signal, they'd start to gnaw their way through and be out at the other side in no time. A carrot or a piece of cheese would be placed at the other side to encourage them. I'm going to buy a few, at any rate, and start training them.

Anyway, I'd soon had enough of the axe method. I'm made differently, I suppose, from those great creatures in virgin forests who fell mighty trees with great sweeping strokes hour after hour, day after day, week after week, year after year. Ten minutes was quite enough for me. But I wasn't going to have Clare jeering at me. So I

crept to the gate and looked up and down. A gentleman of the road was coming along. He was a revolting-looking specimen, but I only just refrained from falling on his neck and embracing him.

"Would you like to earn five shillings?" I whispered over the gate.

He intimated huskily that he would.

"Come in, then," I said, "and chop this wood."

I admitted him in a conspiratorial manner, and he set to work with a will. He'd got quite a good idea how to set about it. But he said that it was harder wood than he'd thought it was going to be when he agreed to five shillings, and he'd have to charge seven-and-six. I sat and watched him contentedly from a distance. Next time I talk about chopping wood I shall be careful to emphasise the pleasure of watching other people doing it rather than doing it oneself. Certainly if Clare is present, I shall.

It was long after tea-time when he'd finished. I gave him ten shillings (it had risen to ten shillings because he said he'd strained one of his shoulder muscles) and went indoors.

"Finished?" asked Clare.

"Yes," I said, still rather coldly.

"Enjoyed it?"

"*Rather!*" I said, enthusiastically.

"Miss Mallings called and had tea," she said.

I was sorry to have missed Miss Mallings. She's a very pretty girl and I only know her by sight. I've never been introduced to her.

"I've never met her," I said, wistfully.

"No. She said she didn't know you by sight. I told her to go to the window and she'd see you chopping wood."

"Did she?"

"Yes."

"Er – did she say anything about me?"

"No. She seemed rather quiet after that and went away early. What did you say?"

I didn't say anything. I was thinking.

I was thinking that Life is very hard on us men.

Exchange is No Robbery
(The Humorist 11/2/1928)

I'd had that scarf for years, and I'd worn it till it was literally dropping to pieces. Even so, it was not without long and serious consideration that I decided to get a new one. It's not that I am mean. I'm not mean. But I get fond of old things. I hate new things. And that scarf had been a very, very good one.

Still, I couldn't go on wearing a few strands of ravelled silk (that was about all that was left of it) much longer, so after careful consideration, as I said, I decided to buy a new one. And, of course, as soon as I'd decided to buy a new one I never got an opportunity.

I had an unusual rush of work, and as soon as I'd finished it I had to dash home because I was going out somewhere with Clare. I might have been marooned on a desert island for all the chance of shopping I seemed to get. And so I went on wearing those strands of silk till one morning, as I was putting them on, Clare said:

"Do you mind if I don't go out with you again till you've got a new scarf? You look as if a kitten had been playing with a ball of silk round your neck when you're wearing that one."

"Clare," I said, with great dignity, "I'm aware that I need a new scarf. I'm willing to buy a new scarf. In fact, I've been trying for the past few weeks to buy a new scarf. You have a good deal of time on your hands—"

She broke in with a passionate protest. Nothing annoys a woman with a lot of time on her hands so much as to be told that she's a lot of time on her hands. I raised my voice to drown her passionate protest.

"I repeat, Clare," I said, "you've got a lot of time on your hands. If you want me to have a new scarf, why not go up to town and buy me one? I never seem to be open when the shops are."

An ecstatic gleam came into Clare's face.

"I'd meant to go up tomorrow in any case," she said, "because it's the last day of the Sales, and they're selling off all their hats at 5s.11d. each at Terry and Parker's. I'll get the hat and the scarf in the morning and meet you for lunch, shall I?"

It seemed a perfectly good arrangement, so I gave her thirty-five shillings for my scarf, told her exactly what to get and where to get it, wished her good luck with the hat, and set off for the office.

She met me for lunch, looking perfectly charming. She was wearing a new hat. It was one of the prettiest hats she'd ever had.

"Good!" I said, looking at it. "You must have been well in the van of the scrum to get that!"

"Oh, it wasn't one of the 5s.11d. ones," said Clare, carelessly. "They were all awful. *Perfectly awful!* I wouldn't have been seen dead in any of them. So I gave it up and went to the shop you told me to go to for your scarf, and just next to it I found a perfectly adorable little hat shop, and they had some perfectly adorable little hats at thirty-five shillings each. And I suddenly remembered that at Terry and Parker's they had got some men's silk scarves – *frightfully* nice ones – reduced to 5s.11d. each, so I got the thirty-five shilling hat for me, and I went back to Terry and Parker's and got the 5s.11d. scarf for you. I wouldn't have done it, of course, if I hadn't considered it quite fair. You see, it's a *frightfully* pretty one, much prettier than

your old one. Here it is."

She opened a parcel and took it out.

I threw it one glance and then ordered a stiff brandy.

I gave the scarf to the first tramp who paid us a visit on our return home.

I'm still wearing my strands of silk, but Clare looks really awfully pretty in her new hat.

The Frozen Pipe

(The Humorist 18/2/1928)

"The water pipe's frozen," said Clare, tragically. "What *shall* we do?"

"Wait till it thaws," I suggested.

She seemed irritated. Sensible answers always irritate a woman.

"But how shall we get *water*?" she snapped.

"Borrow it," I said. "If none comes at all. Perhaps Mrs Jones next door will lend us some."

Certainly none came at all through our taps, so that's what we did. We borrowed it from Mrs Jones – buckets and buckets of it. Water seemed to come through Mrs Jones's pipes all right in spite of the frost. Every now and then Clare would moan:

"And when the thaw comes and it bursts we'll be *deluged!*"

But the thaw came and we weren't deluged. In fact, still no water came. Everyone else's pipes thawed and deluged and became quite normal again, but not ours. Ours remained frozen and waterless though by this time it was quite warm.

"It's the *strangest* thing," said Clare. "It doesn't seem possible somehow. I think I'll send for a plumber tomorrow. I'm beginning to feel absolutely ashamed of sending in to Mrs Jones for water like this. She'll begin to think the company's cut us off."

And then suddenly in a flash I remembered. The night the frost came I'd turned the water off at the main. I'd completely forgotten all about it till Clare said that.

I crept out and turned it on again.

A few minutes later Clare called out joyfully:

"It's thawed *at last*! It's coming! But isn't it *mysterious* that it's taken all this time to thaw?"

In fact, she's still telling people how mysterious it is.

Alphege and Archie
(The Humorist 21/4/1928)

"I've lost Alphege," said Clare, mournfully.

Alphege is Clare's dog. He's called Alphege because she found him on St Alphege's Day (I don't know who St Alphege is, but then, I don't think anyone else does, either). Alphege is not the sort of dog one buys or is given. He's essentially the sort of dog one finds. And, of course, he's always getting lost.

"He came back from the golf links with you this morning, didn't he?" said Clare, anxiously.

"Oh, yes," I said, trying not to look guilty, because though he *had* come with me all right from the golf links, I wasn't particularly anxious to talk about the golf links. You'll see why in a minute.

"It's an unlucky day," moaned Clare. "First your scarf, and now Alphege."

Now we come to the scarf. Clare had given me that scarf for a birthday present. It was, as she truly said, a nice bright scarf. It was the sort of scarf one christens "Archie". At the age of seventeen I should have loved it. But when you've attained a certain age and a certain weight you lose your taste for clothes that leave a trail of motionless people staring after you wherever you go.

Besides, when you have a dog like Alphege tagging after you everywhere, that's quite enough strain on your dignity. I keep trying not to wear the thing. I keep trying to sneak out of the house without it, but whenever I do, Clare calls out:

"You've forgotten your scarf, darling. Do put it on. There's such a nasty east wind."

So I come back and put it on. I've got my fair share of courage, but I'm not a cave man. I couldn't tell Clare that I didn't like that scarf.

So ever since my birthday I've gone on wearing it daily. Till today. And today I made a bold bid for freedom. I went up to the golf course as usual with Alphege and Archie. As usual, I'd rather have gone without either of them, but Clare insisted on Archie, and Alphege insisted on Alphege.

As a matter of fact, I simply hate Alphege's coming with me when I go to golf. There's something in that dog's expression when I miss the ball that I don't like at all.

Anyway, this morning I didn't put in much golf. I took a trowel in my pocket, went far out into the rough, dug a little hole and buried Archie. Then I filled up the little hole so that you would never have dreamed that it was anyone's last resting place.

Then I went home and told Clare that I'd lost Archie. She was frightfully upset and rang up the caretaker of the golf house – of course, without avail. I think that if it hadn't come on to pour with rain she'd have gone out to look for it herself.

"Someone must have stolen it," she said, sadly. "It was such a beautiful scarf. It *was* careless of you. But you'll call at Scotland Yard about it, won't you?"

"Yes, darling," I promised, brightly. "I'll certainly call at Scotland Yard about it."

I was rather relieved that Alphege got lost in the afternoon because it took her mind off Archie.

"It's simply a day of ill luck," she said, sorrowfully. "And all in this terrible rain. If he doesn't come in before night I shall ring up the BBC and ask them to broadcast him."

"They won't, Clare," I assured her.

"I don't see why they shouldn't," she said, with spirit. "I've often heard them broadcast things like that. Missing from his home since – well, since this morning, in Alphege's case – and then a description."

"You can try, of course," I said, noncommittally, "but I expect he's really gone off to seek his fortune somewhere. He's a born adventurer. He's probably gone to the White City to see if he can win a race or two."

"Don't be silly. He isn't a greyhound."

"He's as much a greyhound as anything else," I retorted. "There isn't a single breed of dog that you can definitely say he isn't."

She was standing by the window gazing mournfully out at the rain. Suddenly she grew rigid.

"He's coming!" she gasped. "It is him, isn't it? He's so covered with mud that it's difficult to tell. And he's *bringing* something. What is it? Is it a dead cat?"

But, of course, I knew what it was even before I joined her at the window. It was Alphege perpetrating the supreme *faux pas* of his existence.

There he was struggling along with it through the wind and the rain, dragging it behind him through the mud. It was Alphege bringing home Archie.

Our Holiday
(*The Humorist 7/4/1928*)

"A caravan?" I said, doubtfully.

"Yes," said Clare, eagerly, "a caravan. The Browns did it last year. You hire one. With a horse."

"A *horse*?"

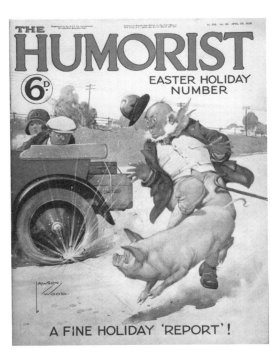

A FINE HOLIDAY 'REPORT'!

"Of course, darling. It's no fun except with a horse. The real old-fashioned caravan holiday."

"Y-yes," I said, doubtfully.

Clare continued with zest:

"It's the *greatest* fun! Mrs Brown was telling me all about it. Of course, it's a bit mouldy on wet days because you can't have really comfortable chairs in a caravan, and the food's a bit of a problem, but it's the *simplicity* of the whole thing that's its great charm."

"Y-yes," I said, still more doubtfully.

"They had some awfully amusing times with farmers who said they were trespassing on their land when they put up for the night. And one night their horse got loose and they had to spend all the next day looking for it. Once it was ill, too, and Mr Brown had to walk ten miles for the nearest vet. But, of course, you have to take the rough with the smooth, and it's all such a complete change from one's ordinary life that it's a sort of tonic."

"It's a change from one's ordinary life all right," I admitted, without enthusiasm. "What sort of weather did they have?"

"Oh, not bad," said Clare, carelessly. "Mixed, of course, as it always is. They had rather a hot spell, and the nights in the caravan were a bit stuffy, but when they tried sleeping out the cows were such a nuisance. They had a cold spell, too, and their oil-stove went wrong, but it didn't really matter much because, anyway, an oil-stove smells hateful, doesn't it? She said it was the *greatest* fun altogether and it did them a world of good. They were quite different beings when they came home."

"I can believe that part of it," I said.

"Well, look here, darling," went on Clare, "I'll ring up Mrs Brown tomorrow, shall I, and find out just where they hired the caravan and all about it?"

"If you like," I said, rising carelessly. "I'll just go and write a letter."

And I went a wrote a letter engaging rooms at the sea for the whole of my annual holiday. Then I sneaked out of the house and posted it.

When I came back, Clare was telephoning. She was evidently telephoning to Mrs Brown.

"No, darling, I *know* you never had a caravan holiday. I *know* you'd hate it. So would I. I made it all up. That's what I keep trying to tell you. I *had* to do something. Every year I badger him and badger him to engage rooms early and he always puts if off till the last minute. I had to do something drastic this year. Yes, it's been *absolutely* successful. He wrote the letter at once. He's just gone out to post it now."

I'm going to write quite a long book about women one day.

I've started making notes for it already.

Part 2
Kathleen and I

A Way Out of the Present Unrest
(Punch 22/9/1920)

"A penny for your thoughts," I said to Kathleen.

"I like that," said Kathleen indignantly. "A penny was the market value of my thoughts in 1914. Why should butter and cheese and reels of cotton go up more than double and my thoughts stay the same?"

"Twopence," I offered.

"I said more than double," she remarked coldly.

I plunged.

"Sixpence," I said.

"Done!"

"I'll put it in the collection bag for you next Sunday," I added hastily.

"Well, I was thinking of Veronica's future. I was wondering what she was going to be."

"When we went to the Crystal Palace," I said gently, "I rather gathered that she wanted to be the proprietor of a merry-go-round. They were dragons with red plush seats."

"She might go into Parliament," said Kathleen dreamily; "I expect women will be able to do everything by the time she's grown up. She might be a cabinet minister. I don't see why she shouldn't be Prime Minister."

"Her hair's just about the right length now," I said. "And perhaps she could give me congenial employment. I wouldn't mind being Minister of Transport. There's quite a good salary attached. But of course she might have ideas of her own on the subject."

Feeling curious, I went in search of Veronica. I found her at a private dance given by the butterflies and hollyhocks at the other end of the lawn. When she saw me she came to meet me and made her excuses very politely.

"We've just been wondering what you're going to be when you've stopped being a little girl," I said.

"Me?" said Veronica calmly. "Oh, I'm going to be a fairy. You don't want me to be anything else, do you?" she added anxiously.

Even the Prime Minister's post seemed suddenly quite flat.

"Oh, no," I said. "I think you've made a very good choice."

But she was not quite satisfied.

"I shall hate going away from you," she said. "Couldn't you come too?"

"Where?"

"To Fairyland."

"Ah!" I said, "that takes some thinking about. Could we come back if we didn't like it?"

"N-no, I don't fink so. I've never heard of anyone doing that. But you'll love it," she went on earnestly. "You'll be ever so tiny and you can draw funny frost pictures wiv rainbows and fold up flowers into buds and splash dew-water over everything at night and ride on butterflies and help the birds to make nests. Fink what *fun* to help a bird make a nest! You'll *love* it!"

"Is that all?" I said sternly. "Are you

keeping nothing from me? What about witches and spells and being turned into frogs? I'm sure I remember that in my fairy tales."

"Oh, nothing that *matters*," she said quickly. "You can always *tell* a witch, you know, and we'll keep out of their way. An' if a nasty fairy turns you into a frog a nice one will always turn you back quite soon. It's all right. You mustn't worry about *that*. There won't be any fun if you don't come too, darlin'," she ended shamelessly.

I considered.

"Veronica," I said at last, "is there such a thing as Ireland in fairyland? Is there an exchange that won't keep steady? Is there any labour trouble?"

She shook her head.

"I've never heard of anyfin that sounds like those," she said. "I'm sure there isn't."

"That decides it," I said. "We'll all come. As soon as you can possibly arrange it."

She heaved a sigh of relief and ran off to tell the glad news to the butterflies and hollyhocks.

So that's settled.

I think we've made a wise decision.

After all, what's a witch or two, or even a temporary existence as a frog, compared with a coal strike?

The Artists
(Punch 27/7/1921)

"It's your birfday tomorrow," said Veronica.

Veronica was drawing giants with ears detached from their heads. Veronica's ears rarely meet the rest of the person. They are distant accessories floating in the region of the head, but never of it.

"I'm afraid it is," I sighed.

"Would you like a lion for your birfday present?" went on Veronica.

"Well," I considered, "the food question would be a great difficulty, and I've nowhere to keep it."

Veronica raised a face pink with effort from her row of giants.

"I meant a *drawed* lion," she said, "wif fur an' lots of legs to make it look pretty."

"I'd love it," I said.

The lion appeared duly on my plate the next morning. I carried him away with me and put him in the middle of the library table so as to get the best effect. He was a beautiful creature, with many legs and a splendid upright mane. His fur was wild and luxuriant. He grew on one, especially when studied sideways or upside down.

I was sitting wrapped in wonder at him when a visitor arrived, a distant relative belonging to the advanced schools of Futuristic art. He had brought some of his sketches with him and spread them out on the library table for my inspection.

"I'm just going to send those off to Kraff, the editor of the Futurist paper, you know. He wants to reproduce some of my work," he said with modest pride. "I'll let you have a copy when it comes out."

I expressed gratitude. Personally I

preferred Veronica's lion to any of them.

"You losted my lion?" said Veronica suspiciously when she came to say "Good night".

I hunted for him desperately on the table. There were several giants, but no lion.

"I must have put him away in a safe place," I said cheerfully. "He'll turn up all right."

He did.

A month later, the distant relative ran down to see me, bringing a copy of the Futurist paper.

"Here they are," he said, showing me the reproductions of his work. "They're all in; but there's one I simply can't remember doing. I sent them off from here, you know. I've absolutely no recollection of this one. It's a rather wonderful piece of work, but it's a complete mystery to me."

He pointed it out. Beneath it was the title, "A Storm at Sea".

It was Veronica's lion.

Minus Aunt Jane
(London Opinion Christmas 1924)

I found out quite by accident that Aunt Jane was going to spend the afternoon with the Randalls. Now, the Randalls are our fifth cousins seven times removed, and their relationship to Aunt Jane is still more involved, but Aunt Jane likes them, and often visits them, and when she does, she likes to pay Kathleen and me a surprise visit. She disapproves of Kathleen and me, and she finds something fresh to disapprove of every time she sees us. She enjoys disapproving of us, and she enjoys paying us surprise visits. We aren't really fond of Aunt Jane....

I got back very early from the office, but I thought I'd scout round a bit first, just in case the surprise visit had come off. I knew that Kathleen was out. I crept round to the morning room window, and peeped in cautiously. There she was, in a long black cloak, standing by Kathleen's bureau. She was probably reading Kathleen's letters. She loves reading letters and discovering unpaid bills, and finding out afresh how worldly and extravagant and generally immoral we are. Life would be a hollow mockery to Aunt Jane if she didn't disapprove of Kathleen and me. It would be devoid of all excitement and thrill. She'd have nothing to think about and nothing to talk about. I could just imagine her gloating over Kathleen's millinery and dressmaking bills and bridge invitations. I couldn't see her head, because the blind was half down, but I could see the rest of her quite plainly.

I slunk off to the bottom of the garden. I simply couldn't face her without Kathleen to support me. Where Aunt Jane is concerned I frankly own myself a coward.

I was horribly hungry, but I daren't go in even to get some tea on the quiet. Smith, our maid, is of a Christian disposition, and would have taken pity on me, but the necessary explanations would have been my undoing. Smith has a voice like a loudspeaker, and Aunt Jane has ears like microphones. I tried to get into the greenhouse, but it was locked; so I sat, cold and miserable and hungry, under the hedge at the bottom of the garden, and watched the front door, to see when she'd go. She didn't go. Hours passed.... She was evidently sitting tight, like the spider in his den, and revelling in our letters and bills and scones and cakes. I grew hungrier and hungrier, and less charitable in my feelings towards Aunt Jane. It began to rain. I crouched under the hedge, but the hedge was on Aunt Jane's side. It sent horrid little streams of water down my back. My gaze at the front door became more and more murderous, and still Aunt Jane did not appear....

It was six-thirty when Kathleen came home. I crept out of the hedge and waded to the front door to meet her.

"She's here!" I whispered hoarsely.

"Who?"

"Aunt Jane. She's in the morning room, reading your letters and eating our cakes."

"*No!*"

"She is. I've seen her. At least, I've seen her reading your letters, and I presume she's now eating cakes. I've been in hiding."

She looked at me with consternation.

"Oh, you poor dear! You *are* wet!"

"And hungry," I said pathetically, "and cross. I'm even hungrier and crosser than

I'm wet."

"Come on!" she said firmly. "Let's brave her together. She can't eat us."

"I could eat her," I whispered faintly. "I'm so hungry that I could eat almost anything."

We threw open the morning room door and entered, Kathleen summoning an unconvincing smile of welcome in the process.

In front of Kathleen's bureau was a dressmakers' dummy wearing a long black cloak.

"*This!*" gasped Kathleen. "Did you think that *this...?*"

"I couldn't see its head," I faltered. "I thought...."

"I was making it this morning," said Kathleen. "I forgot I'd left it down here... and you...."

She looked at me, wet and cold and hungry and miserable. Then she sat down and had hysterics.

I said a few terse, well-chosen words to the dummy, and then went out of the room with great dignity to find something to eat. Kathleen was still having hysterics. There's something lacking about modern wives. They've simply no idea of even the elements of wifely sympathy....

Part 3
Enter - Patricia

The Power of Thought
(The Humorist 16/1/1926)

"Patricia," I said, "will you meet me in town on Tuesday afternoon, and we'll have lunch together, and go to whatever the spirit moves us to go to?"

Patricia sighed wistfully.

"I'd rather like to," she said, "but I can't."

"Did no one ever tell you in your distant childhood, Patricia," I said, sternly, "that there's no such word in the English language as 'can't'?"

"Yes, but I never believed them; did you?"

"Why can't you come with me on Tuesday?" I said.

"Because it's my birthday."

"Your birthday?" I said, surprised. "I'd no idea. How old are you, Patricia? I beg your pardon – how young are you?"

"Twenty-two," said Patricia.

I sighed.

"I suppose there'll be a perfect queue of reporters outside your house that morning, all waiting to ask you to what you attribute your remarkable longevity. You might make a fortune out of the patent medicine people."

"Is that meant to be funny?" said Patricia.

"More or less," I said.

"Well," said Patricia, generously, "I won't be hard on you. But don't do it again."

"Thank you," I said, humbly. "Old age is having quite a mellowing effect on you, Patricia. But what I want to know is, why does your birthday prevent your coming to lunch with me? Why not *celebrate* your birthday by having lunch with me? Now, don't dismiss the idea without proper consideration. Think it over."

"It's impossible," interrupted Patricia. "I always have a party on my birthday."

"Oh," I said, tentatively, "then perhaps I may expect—"

"No," said Patricia, with a sigh. "It's always just family. It's a tradition. Cousins and aunts and uncles, you know."

I considered this in silence.

"Patricia," I said at last, slowly, "haven't you a long-lost uncle who went to America in his youth and hasn't been heard of since? I've got horn-rimmed spectacles and a big hat, and I could learn American in no time."

"No," said Patricia. "I'm afraid not."

"I know," I said, after a moment's deep thought. "I've got it! I'll go to the Herald's College and get them to trace my family back to where it meets yours. When you come to think of it, all families must meet somewhere as you trace them back to Adam. Then I'll come as a relation and it will be all right."

"No, it won't," said Patricia firmly.

"What *can* I do, then?" I said, annoyed. "I don't believe you *want* to have lunch with me."

"Honestly, I do," said Patricia, "but one can't fight against family tradition. Nothing short of the whole family's being down with 'flu will do it."

"Now *that's* an idea, Patricia!" I said. "I've been reading a book on the Power of Thought. If I think of your whole family's being down with 'flu, they'll *be* down with 'flu, if I think long and strong enough."

"What nonsense!" said Patricia.

On Patricia's birthday, I approached the house as soon as I decently could after breakfast, and the first person I saw was Patricia's mother. She was coming out of the front gate, all dressed up.

"I've just come to wish Patricia many happy returns of the day," I said, pacifically.

"Poor child!" said Patricia's mother. "We were going to have such a nice birthday party for her. Of course, we generally have a family party here, you know; but we heard a few days ago that a dear little third cousin of Patricia's is going to be christened today, so we decided to combine Patricia's birthday party with the christening party. But I'm afraid the poor girl won't be able to come after all."

"Why?" I said anxiously.

"I'm afraid she's got 'flu," said Patricia's mother. "Quite mild, but you have to be careful with 'flu, so I'm leaving her in bed."

She sailed on, leaving me thunderstruck.

I went in miserably, wrote a little note, and sent it up with my humble offering.

"Miss Patricia says the answer will be down in half an hour," said the maid when she returned.

At the end of half an hour Patricia came in, looking radiant.

"Here's the answer," she said. "Thank you so much; and now let's start and have a lovely day – lunch, and a *matinée*, and—"

"But, Patricia," I gasped, "your mother said you had 'flu."

"Oh, I began to feel better as soon as mother set off to the christening party."

"Oh," I said; "and to what do you attribute your rapid recovery, Patricia?"

A wicked smile flickered over her face.

"To the Power of Thought," she said.

88

St Martin's Summer
(London Opinion 9/10/1926)

"You call it St Martin's summer," said Patricia.

"I don't," I objected. "I call it a nasty cold winter day."

"It isn't winter."

"Well, it's a very good imitation of it, then,"

"It's St Martin's summer—"

"Why? Why is it St Martin's summer?" I persisted.

She was slightly taken aback by this.

"Well, everyone calls it St Martin's summer."

"I don't, for one."

"I suppose St Martin called it summer and the name sort of stuck."

"Do you mean to tell me," I said, "that they canonised the man simply for saying it was summer when it wasn't?"

"Oh, do stop arguing. You're quite bewildering me. What I wanted to tell you when you started contradicting and badgering me was that Mother and Father were married in St Martin's summer, and they always give a picnic, the last picnic of the season, to celebrate it," said Patricia, very demurely.

"Oh," I said, and then again after a pause, "Oh!" Then in a more friendly tone of voice I added: "Who goes to the picnic, Patricia?"

"Oh, anyone we ask," said Patricia, casually.

"Are you going to ask me?"

"I was," she said, meaningly, "before you started arguing and contradicting me."

"Are you going to be there?"

"Yes. On duty."

"What duty?"

"Entertaining the guests."

"Thanks for your kind invitation, Patricia," I said. "I'll come. As a guest. I warn you I'm the sort of guest who requires a good deal of entertaining."

"You'll take what you get," said Patricia, tossing her head. "I ought to warn you, too, that the guests always bring some little appropriate present for Mother and Father – appropriate to St Martin's summer. You needn't, but the others probably will."

"Then I will, Patricia. In St Martin's summer I always do as the Romans do."

The picnic day turned out a nasty, draughty, wintry day, but I went because I wanted to be entertained by Patricia. She didn't really entertain me very well. As soon as I'd secured a nice place out of the wind for her to entertain me in, she slipped away and began entertaining someone else. I seemed to spend all the time finding corners out of the wind and fetching Patricia to entertain me.

Then the guests made their little presentations to Patricia's mother and father. One gave a bunch of late roses, and one a parasol that was trying not to look like an umbrella, and another an electric fan, and another a flowering plant. All of them tried effectively or ineffectively to be appropriate to St Martin's summer.

But mine was the most appropriate. I gave them a hot-water bottle.

Feet of Clay

(The Humorist 1/10/1927)

"You *must* introduce me to her," said Patricia. "I'll never forgive you if you don't."

"Patricia," I said, "she's perfectly ordinary. I don't know why you want to waste your time on her."

"*Ordinary!*" repeated Patricia, indignantly. "I think she's *wonderful*. It's been the ambition of my life for *years* to meet her."

"I thought you only read her book last month," I said, mildly.

"I was using the term 'years' in its figurative sense," said Patricia, with dignity. "I've *longed* to meet her ever since I've read it, and especially since I knew that she was your second cousin twice removed."

Now, being second cousin twice removed to a famous authoress had its disadvantages. For one thing, it seems to reduce you to a nonentity. You aren't yourself any longer. You're merely "Aphra Murray's" second cousin twice removed. It makes one rather sore. And Patricia's attitude made me especially sore. I did think that Patricia might have been interested in me for my own sake and not just because I was "Aphra Murray's" second cousin twice removed.

I sighed.

"Why do you want to meet her?" I said, plaintively.

"Because I've read her book, and I want to tell her that it's the most *wonderful* book in the world, and I've seen her photograph in the newspaper, and I think she looks the most charming woman I've ever seen, and

I'm looking forward to meeting her as one of the most *wonderful* experiences of my life, and if you don't introduce me to her the minute I arrive I'll never forgive you."

"I'd rather looked forward to having you to myself for that afternoon," I murmured, sadly.

"I shan't want to talk to you," said Patricia, rudely. "I shall only want to talk to your cousin."

"Twice removed," I supplied, dejectedly.

"There are thousands and thousands of things I want to say to her," went on Patricia. "You've got to introduce me the *minute* I arrive, and I simply shan't sleep a wink with excitement between then and now."

The afternoon arrived. My second cousin twice removed was in fine form. She looked handsome and well dressed, and she was in good talking vein. Aphra loves admirers of her works, and I foresaw that I shouldn't get a single word with Patricia.

I was standing by the drawing room door when Patricia arrived.

"Introduce me quick," she said, breathlessly. "Where is she?"

The party was being held in the drawing room and conservatory.

"There she is," I said; "over there – with the vicar."

Patricia looked, and a strange expression came over her face. She turned to me.

"Well," she said, "you said you wanted to talk to me this afternoon. What did you want to talk to me about?"

"Hundreds of things," I said; "simply hundreds of things. But I thought that you had to be introduced at once to my second cousin twice removed."

"Oh, that will do later," said Patricia, vaguely, still with that strange, strange expression on her face. "You may talk to me first."

So I talked to her. I'm awfully good at talking to Patricia. I can do it for hours and hours and hours without getting tired of it. But suddenly I saw Aphra detach herself from the vicar and begin to make her way over to the drawing room.

I heaved a sigh. "Here she is," I said. "I suppose I must—"

I looked round for Patricia. She had completely disappeared. Aphra greeted me and began to talk to me. Personally I have always thought my second cousin twice removed overrated, but she likes talking, so I let her talk. Then I escaped and began to look for Patricia. I found her at the other end of the conservatory. There was still the strange, strange look on her face.

"You've missed your chance," I said. "She was over there talking to me. Didn't you see her?"

She gave a mirthless laugh.

"Oh, plenty of time," she said. "Though I'm afraid I must go home soon. Go on talking to me."

So I went on blissfully talking to her till I saw that Aphra was coming over to the conservatory again.

"Here she is," I said to Patricia. "I'll—" But suddenly Patricia wasn't there. I went in search of her and found her at the other end of the drawing room.

"I say," I said, "she was *there*. Didn't you see? You've missed your chance again. I thought you wanted to be introduced."

"I don't," snapped Patricia. "I want to go home. You can come with me if you like."

I brightened. It was more than I had expected. I'd expected to spend the afternoon miserably listening to Aphra talking to Patricia. Instead—

"Have you enjoyed it, Patricia?" I said on the way home.

"No!" snapped Patricia.

"But I did all I *could* to introduce you to her, Patricia," I pleaded.

"If you had introduced me to her I'd never have forgiven you. *Never!*" burst out Patricia.

"Why?" I said, wonderingly. "Didn't you like the look of her?"

"*No!*"

"I thought you admired her books so, Patricia."

"I don't. I *hate* her books. I'll never read another as long as I live. I'll go straight to the library now and cross them off my list. I've never had such a *ghastly* afternoon in my life!"

"W-why, Patricia?" I stammered in amazement.

"Didn't you notice?" said Patricia, furiously. "Didn't you *notice*? She'd got on a hat *exactly* like mine!"

Going Out to Tea

(The Passing Show 10/3/1928)

I felt that I didn't want to go out to tea with Mrs Green one bit, but I hadn't the moral courage to put the feeling into words when she asked me. She added that her sister was kindly lending her collection of miniatures and she thought that her friends would like to see them, so she was giving a small reception.

She took for granted that I was passionately interested in Art in all its branches, and when people do that it's difficult, if not actually impossible, to undeceive them.

I set off to Mrs Green's reception in good time, because I thought I might as well get it over quickly.

And on the way I met Patricia.

"Well, Patricia," I said brightly. "Whither away, my pretty sweeting?"

"I've told you before not to call me names like that," said Patricia, severely.

"But it's in Shakespeare," I said.

"Then leave it there," said Patricia, sternly. "If you want to know where I'm going, I'm going to Mrs Brown's. She's having a tea fight with music. Worse luck. Mother's meanly got out of it and shoved me in."

"Just like a modern parent," I said sympathetically. "They've no consciences. But I don't like to see you walking the public streets unchaperoned. I'll just see you as far as Mrs Brown's."

"I really don't want you to," said Patricia.

"It's isn't a question of what you want," I said, crushingly, "it's a question of what's good for you."

I took her to Mrs Brown's.

"I think I'll come in with you, Patricia," I said.

"You won't," said Patricia firmly. "She hasn't asked you. She doesn't even know you."

"No," I admitted, "but that's all the more reason for my going in with you. "She *ought* to know me. It's—"

"Goodbye," said Patricia pleasantly.

"One minute, Patricia," I pleaded. "I'm supposed to be going to Mrs Green's and I don't know the way."

"Don't you know the way to Mrs Green's?" said Patricia incredulously.

"No," I replied brazenly.

"But you've been there before."

"I know, but I've forgotten the way."

Patricia told me the way.

"I can't possibly follow all that," I said. "If you just come to the end of the road you can point it out to me."

Patricia came to the end of the road with me, but still I could not understand her directions. So she came a little further. Gradually, street by street, I lured her to Mrs Green's.

"Now that you're here, you'd better come in, Patricia," I said. "You can explain about miniatures to me. I understand you better than other people. I think your intellect must be more on a par with mine."

"Please don't insult me," said Patricia, with spirit. "And I certainly won't come in. She did ask me, but I quite definitely refused."

"I'd better see you back to Mrs Brown's, then," I said sadly. On the way back, I said:

"Patricia, what time do you generally have tea?"

"At four," said Patricia.

"So do I," I said, "and it's ten past now.

Don't you think we'd better do something about it?"

So we went into a very nice little tea shop. We had a nice long talk there, that was ever so much more enjoyable than Mrs Brown's music, and ate large quantities of macaroons that were ever so much more enjoyable than Mrs Green's miniatures.

We were with Patricia's mother the next day when we met Mrs Brown and Mrs Green simultaneously. Patricia's mother said effusively that Patricia had been to Mrs Brown's to tea and I had been to Mrs Green's to tea only the day before, and wasn't it a coincidence that we should all meet this morning?

For a minute I thought that the way of transgressors was going to be hard.

But it wasn't.

"You must forgive me, dear," said Mrs Brown to Patricia, "for hardly having a word with you, but there were such a lot of people that I hardly *saw* the people I wanted to."

"And I was so sorry not to have a *real* talk with you," said Mrs Green to me. "I do hope you didn't think me very rude. I did look for you after tea, but you had gone."

There's absolutely no doubt that sometimes Providence favours the wicked.

Celebrating Spring
(The Humorist 30/3/1929)

"It's spring," I said to Miss Murgatroyd, meeting her in the High Street on March 25th.

"How do you know?" asked Miss Murgatroyd.

"It says so in the calendar."

"I don't believe it."

"But it's in print, so it must be true. Besides, haven't you noticed bulbs coming up and seed catalogues arriving?"

"Of course. And a Spring Fashion catalogue came this morning. There's a duck of a hat!"

"Well, then, it must be spring, mustn't it?"

"I suppose so. What are you going to do about it?"

"What are *you* going to do about it?"

"What *can* I do about it besides buy a new hat?"

"Aren't you going to make good resolutions or anything like that?"

"Oh, no. Not after January the first. It's illegal to make good resolutions after January the first."

"But we must celebrate it somehow."

"How does one celebrate spring?"

"I really don't know. The only thing I remember about spring is that 'In the spring a young man's fancy lightly turns to—'"

"Hush!" said Miss Murgatroyd. Then: "I *know* what one does for spring. One decorates."

"But you've said that – I mean, you've said that you were going to buy a new hat."

"No, silly! I mean, decorate one's house. Paint it. Paper it."

"Whose shall we decorate first, then – yours or mine?"

"Mine. It's more proper. You see, Mother's living with me makes it proper. But she's out this afternoon, so it's all right."

"This is my own particular sitting room," said Miss Murgatroyd, when we'd reached it, "so if we can find anything to paper it with, we'll paper it."

We rummaged through the house and found some wallpaper in the basement, and while I was cutting off a strip, Miss Murgatroyd found some flour and water ready mixed in the larder.

"I've always heard that it's quite easy," she said. "You just get a brush and wet the back of the paper and hold it against the wall and it sticks."

We tried several times. Then I said:

"Why does it always go in gathers?"

And Miss Murgatroyd said breathlessly, "I don't know. For that matter, why does it never stick? Let's try once more."

So we tried once more and it stuck. It didn't look like wallpaper, unless there's a sort of wallpaper that's meant to be corrugated; but it stuck.

"Let's rest now," said Miss Murgatroyd. "It's more exhausting than you'd think, isn't it? I've always heard that it was so easy. It isn't depressing you, is it?"

"Not a bit," I said.

And it wasn't. Because, even though the wallpaper looked like nothing on earth, still I'd been trying for months to get Miss Murgatroyd alone like this. She's – but I won't try to describe her, because probably you wouldn't believe me. Anyway, she's very nice.

"Let's sit on the floor and talk," said Miss Murgatroyd. There weren't any chairs available, because wallpaper covered all of them. We sat on the floor just under our strip of wallpaper.

"What shall we talk about?" I said.

"Wallpaper," suggested Miss Murgatroyd.

"No," I said. "Let's talk about the spring."

"What can we say about the spring?"

"'In the spring'," I quoted again, "'a young man's fancy lightly turns to—'"

She let me finish that time.

At the critical moment our strip of wallpaper came down upon us, but neither of us noticed it till several minutes later.

Miss Murgatroyd's mother was annoyed about it, because it turned out that she'd got the wallpaper for the drawing room, and it was a special sale bargain that couldn't be repeated. There had been only just enough for the drawing room, and as our strip by this time wouldn't have been recognised by its own mother, there now wouldn't be enough.

It also transpired that the flour and water was a batter pudding that she had mixed ready for dinner that night, and though we gave her back what was left of it, it was so full of bits of paper that she said it wouldn't be any good at all.

In fact, she was rather huffy about the whole thing, but I don't really mind, because, as I hope she's going to be my mother-in-law, I think it best for us to get used to each other.

Part 4
Introducing Delia

Good Resolutions
(The Humorist 10/1/1925)

"It's New Year's Day," said Delia. "Let's make good resolutions."

"Very well," I said. "You begin."

"I think it would be better to make each other's. Other people know one better than oneself."

"'Oh, wad some power the giftie gie' us'," I quoted in my best Scotch.

"I've never learnt Italian," said Delia coldly, "so I don't understand."

"It's not Italian."

"Well, Hebrew, then, or whatever it is. You begin. Think of a good resolution for me."

"I needn't think far," I said. "I propose that you try to be less extravagant."

"I beg your pardon," said Delia, haughtily.

"I suggested that you try to be a little less extravagant," I said clearly.

"May I ask," said Delia freezingly, "when you consider me to have been extravagant?"

"You may," I said. "I consider that hat you bought yesterday a pure extravagance."

"I think you're a perfect beast! I believe you'd like me to go about looking like a rag bag."

"No, I wouldn't. I only say that one hat a month is too much."

"When we were first married," said Delia quaveringly, taking out her handkerchief, "you liked me to look nice."

"I do still, but you can look nice without buying a hat every time you go out."

"I slave myself to skin and bone for you," sobbed Delia. "H-housekeeping for you and entertaining p-people for you, and when I buy a new hat because all my old ones are literally falling to pieces, you bully me and make a scene. I wish I hadn't married you. I *hate* you – and it was a bargain that might never have happened again – reduced from forty-five shillings to thirty-nine, and when I try to save your money and economise for you like that, you're b-beastly to me – and I wish I hadn't married you!"

"I say!" I said, bewildered. "How did all this start?"

"It was about good resolutions," said Delia viciously, "and I think while we're on the subject you might resolve to be less selfish."

"*Me selfish?*" I said indignantly.

"Yes, *selfish!* You buy anything you want yourself – golf balls and cigarettes, but when I want a simple little thing like an inexpensive hat—"

"I may remark that both golf balls and cigarettes are used equally by you."

"I'll never *touch* another of your beastly golf balls or cigarettes. You're the most *selfish* person I've ever met. You don't care *how* much inconvenience you give other people. You were *hours* late for dinner yesterday, and—"

"May I remind you that your clocks were all fast and I was *not* late?"

"You were!"

"I was *not!* I tell you the clocks—"

"You *were*. You contradict me and bully me, and last night you deliberately spilt cigarette ash all over the carpet."

"You never mentioned it then."

"No. We weren't quarrelling then."

"Well, if you won't have an ash tray in the room, what can you expect?" I said furiously. "You don't know how to run a house – clocks all wrong – nothing one wants—"

"And you left the bathroom tap running—"

"I shall leave the bathroom taps running whenever I like," I shouted angrily. "It's my house."

"You're simply beastly!"

"You're simply intolerable!"

We went out of different doors and slammed them. Then we collided with each other at the foot of the stairs.

"I beg your pardon," I said politely. "Did I hurt you?"

"Not at all. Did you mean any of those beastly things you said just now?"

"Not one. Did you?"

"Not one. What started it?"

"Good resolutions. I say, I've got a topping idea. Let's make a good resolution not to quarrel."

Delia sighed.

"I do hate a dull life," she said. "I've got it – let's make a good resolution not to make any good resolutions!"

"Topping!" I said.

We went back to the sitting room arm-in-arm.

A Sign of Spring
(London Opinion 14/2/1925)

All husbands know that spring is the really dangerous time of year. It isn't only Cleaning and New Hats. It's Marmalade.

In the spring a young woman's fancy lightly turns to thoughts of Seville oranges. Now some women can make marmalade and some can't. Delia can't. At the end of each marmalade season she admits it.

"Anyway," she says, "now I know I can't make it, so I shan't try again."

But by the time the next spring comes round she's completely forgotten the fact. The sight of those little yellow balls piled up cunningly in a fruiterer's window brings the madness upon her again.

When we were first married I used to spend hours cutting up messy bits of orange peel for her. I don't now. I've learnt sense. If marriage does nothing else it teaches one sense.

Of course, when it's an out-and-out failure it's not so bad. We throw it away, go about pale and tense with tragedy in our eyes for a day or two, then settle down to ordinary life again. But sometimes it's just eatable, so we just have to eat it. Those are the worst times....

Last week I was out with Delia, and we passed a horrid little fruit shop with a great pile of the wretched little yellow things in the window and a notice: "SEVILLE ORANGES FOR MARMALADE". I hastily directed her attention to something across the road, but though she pretended to take an interest in what I was saying, I knew, by the gleam in her eye, that she had seen and noted the fatal announcement. So when, soon after we reached home, she said that she was going to slip out and post a letter, I knew what she was really going to do. She said nothing that night, but there was a look in her eyes of mingled secrecy and determination. The next morning, as I was shaving, I saw a man with a large basket of them stagger to the back door. When I got down to breakfast there was a hectic flush on Delia's face.

"Going to make marmalade?" I challenged her.

"Well, yes – I thought perhaps I might," she said brightly, as if the idea had just occurred to her. Women are horribly double-faced.

When I came home that evening a sinister smell pervaded the house. Delia looked pale and tragic. I did not mention marmalade. Neither did she. We sat down to dinner. The joint was all that could be desired. I read the evening paper. So far all was normal. Then two dishes were placed before Delia.

"Trifle or fruit salad?" she said.

"Fruit salad, please," I replied.

Then I happened to look at the dish. A curious smell came from it. In it was a golden brown liquid, and in the liquid floated some bits of apple and banana, some grapes, and many bits of orange peel.

"Hello!" I said. "Hold hard a minute. Did you say fruit salad?"

She met my eyes brazenly, though she had the grace to blush.

"Yes," she said. "I made it today."

"I thought you were going to make marmalade."

"I changed my mind and made fruit salad."

"Well, I'll change mine and have trifle."

I stayed out to dinner the next night and the next. The third day I crept warily home. The smell had disappeared. There was no trace of the "fruit salad". We had store's marmalade as usual for breakfast. The tense tragic look is gradually disappearing from Delia's face.

The danger is over till next year....

Possessing the Power
(London Opinion 21/3/1925)

Delia was frightfully thrilled when she heard that Mrs Druce was going to be our next door neighbour. She's never met Mrs Druce, but she knows somebody who knows somebody who knows somebody who said that Mrs Druce is a nib in the psychic world. Spooks talk to her and write to her and sit with her and eat with her quite as a matter of course. Personally, I'd find them a beastly nuisance, but Mrs Druce presumably doesn't.

Delia called on her last week and came back agog with excitement.

"Darling," she said, "she's going to lend me a crystal ball to see whether I possess the power. She's going to send it tomorrow and I'm going to try it. Isn't it thrilling? She sees wonderful things in it. Of course, she says that everyone doesn't possess the power, but I'll know tomorrow when I look at it. Won't it be lovely if I possess the power and can see everything that's going to happen to us ever and can see you even when I'm not with you?"

I wasn't quite so sure about that. I'm a good man and a model husband but I wasn't quite sure that I'd like to be watched all day by Delia in a wretched little glass ball.

But as well as being a good man I am a tactful one, so I only said enthusiastically, "Lovely!"

When I came home the next evening, she met me on the doorstep, looking dejected and forlorn.

"Darling," she said, "I can't do it. I've been trying all day. I've got an awful headache with it. I can only see stars and jumps of light in it."

I felt cheered. I didn't mind her looking in the crystal as long as she could only see stars and jumps of light.

"Perhaps they mean something," I said optimistically.

"But I wanted to see people," said Delia mournfully. "I'm not interested in seeing stars and jumps of light."

After dinner, however, she cheered up.

"Suppose you try," she said. "You might possess the power. Mrs Druce said that often quite ordinary people have it."

Wives do say things like that sometimes. The most charitable thing to think is that they don't mean anything by it.

She ran to fetch the crystal and put it on the table before me.

"You just *look* at it," she said. "I won't make a sound."

She sat and watched me eagerly. I looked at the silly bit of glass in which I couldn't see even a star. Then I had a brainwave. I have quite good brainwaves sometimes.

"I see," I said in a deep thrilling voice, "I see a woman – wait a minute – it's coming clearer – it's – yes, it's you, Delia – you're wearing a white dress – chiffon and fur on it – you're passing some sort of light – the chiffon catches – you're on fire—"

Delia gave a little scream.

"It's that dress I wanted you to buy me," she said excitedly, "white chiffon and fur. You said it was too expensive at first, but then you said you would. But I'll *never* have it now – *never*. You've probably saved my life seeing that. Oh, do go on!"

It was being more successful even than I

had hoped. I went on.

"I see a train," I said. "It's going to some seaside place – I see a lot of passengers inside – but only two of them plainly. One is – yes, it's you again, Delia, and the other— Ah, it's clearer now – I believe – yes, it's me – I mean I. The train dashes on – right into another train that's coming from the opposite direction—"

"A collision!" screamed Delia, her hands up to her face. "*My goodness!* How awful! No, I'm certainly not going away for Easter now, however much you want me to." (She'd forgotten that it was the other way round.) "I shall stay at home now what *ever* you say. Do go on."

I went on.

"I see," I said dreamily. "It's a large gathering in a big hall. There's a stage at one end. The people are watching the stage. In the third row from the front there are – yes, they're the same two people—"

"Us?" said Delia breathlessly.

"Yes, us. The performance, whatever it is, is at an end. The crowd surges out. The two people—"

"Us?" panted Delia.

"Yes – us. They're in the foyer – now going down the steps into the street. The man slips – falls—"

Delia screamed again.

"Oh, I'll never go to a theatre with you again – not for *ever* so long. No, I *won't* – I don't care how much you beg me to. What a *mercy* you saw all those things. Do go on."

But I know when to stop. I'd done a good evening's work. Anyway, I shouldn't have to buy her that ridiculously expensive white chiffon frock. I foresaw two weeks of beautifully peaceful evenings at home. I hate bolting my dinner and rushing up to town to theatres. I saw a peaceful Easter at home.

I had done a very good evening's work indeed, and as an artist, I know the value of restraint. I insisted on sending the ball back to Mrs Druce that night. I said that I didn't want to use it any more. I found it very exhausting and I didn't think it right to tamper with that sort of thing.

Delia quite agrees with me. She's disappointed, but very proud of having a husband who possesses the power.

Coming Down
(London Opinion 9/5/1925)

"If we get the first prize," I said, "let's have the ten thousand pounds, not the fifteen pounds a week for life."

"I'd rather have the fifteen pounds a week for life," said Delia.

"I don't agree with you," I said. "I'd rather have the ten thousand pounds, and as it's in my name, I shall have what I like."

"You're being very selfish over it," said Delia distantly.

"Well, it's my prize," I said firmly, "and I shall do what I like about it."

"And what shall we do with the ten thousand pounds?" asked Delia.

"Buy a car for one thing."

"What sort of a car?"

"A fairly small one."

"I *hate* small cars. I want a large one."

"Well, I don't want a large one. I want to drive it myself."

"I want a chauffeur. I hate the jerky way you drive."

"Well, I'm not going to have a chauffeur."

"You're being *most* disagreeable about the whole thing," said Delia angrily. "I shan't come out in your horrid old car."

"I don't care. I'd just as soon you didn't. You always talk to me at the critical moments and drop your handkerchief and bag and powder all over the place."

"What else are you going to do with it, may I ask?" said Delia, ominously calm.

"We'll have a grand summer holiday on it."

"Where?"

"Switzerland," I said.

"I'd rather go to Egypt."

"It's my money and we're going to Switzerland."

"*I'm* not," said Delia stormily. "I'll go to Egypt by myself."

"You can't," I said. "You've no money."

"You're *hateful!*" said Delia. "I shall get a separation from you and then you'll have to pay me ali— whatever you call it, and I'll go to Egypt."

"Switzerland's a lovely place," I said, tactfully and soothingly, "and the day the cheque arrives we'll celebrate."

"How?"

"A box at a jolly revue."

"I don't like revues."

"Then you needn't come."

She stamped with fury.

The morning after that, Delia looked up from the paper at breakfast and grew pale.

"The results are out," she gasped, "and we haven't got anything."

"What a *shame!*" I said indignantly. "The advertisements practically *promised* us one!"

"It's *wicked!* Making you waste all that money on tickets!"

Still furious, she turned to her letters.

"Hello!" she said. "This is from Margate, from Mrs Muggs. She wants to know whether we want the rooms again this year."

"Bully!" I said. "I should think we do. We had a grand time there last year, didn't we? We've never had such jolly rooms before."

"What about Switzerland?" said Delia.

"I'm a wretched sailor," I said. "The crossing would spoil the whole thing for me. What about Egypt?"

"Too unbearably hot," said Delia. "I should hate it. Who's your letter from?"

I opened it.

"It's from young Jones. He's selling his motorcycle and sidecar. He'll let me have it for sixty pounds. It's almost new."

Delia clapped her hands.

"How *ripping!* Do get it. It *would* be fun. We've always wanted one!"

"I will," I said excitedly. "I'll write at once. I say, we'll have a top-hole holiday with a motorcycle and Mrs Mugg's rooms."

"I'm so excited," said Delia. "Let's celebrate. Come home in good time and let's go to the pictures."

We did. In the ninepenny seats. And loved it.

The Reason Why
(London Opinion 16/5/1925)

Muffles and I are in disgrace. And all because of Lady Sheldon.

Muffles is a dog and I am a man and Lady Sheldon is a PERSON in capital letters.

Muffles is a very small dog, yet his very small breast contains a very large hatred of cats. If you say "Poor Pussy!" in an endearing tone of voice to anything furry, Muffles is immediately transformed into a small, black, fluffy tornado of rage. If you stroke the anything at the same time, Muffles' fury is enough to make strong rats tremble. We have great games with him with fur gloves and things like that.

Now Lady Sheldon is very stately and aristocratic and unbending. For six years she has been (in a large way) neighbour to us (in a small way). By which I mean that though our whole house would fit nicely into one of her fireplaces we can distinctly see the grapes in her hot-houses from our bathroom window.

Last week she called. Without being snobs we felt pleased and proud because, let me tell you, Lady Sheldon is very careful whom she calls on. In Lady Sheldon's eyes, six years is quite a short time in which to size a neighbour up. I don't know why she called. Delia thinks it was because of her new drawing room curtains. I am pretty sure it was because of my new suit (a beautiful shade of grey, and very becoming). Of course it may have just been the spring going to her head. Anyway, she called, and we foresaw a future of pleasant intimacy with Lady

Sheldon and her hot-house grapes. But, like all ointments, she turned out to have a fly. She wasn't easy to talk to. Delia at last introduced her to Muffles and told her of his amusing little ways.

"If I hold anything furry—" said Delia, looking round the drawing room for something furry.

Her Ladyship took an elegant confection of fur and chiffon from her majestic shoulders.

"Try this," she said graciously.

Delia tried it. It was a great success. Delia stroked the confection of fur and chiffon and said "Poor Pussy!" and Muffles leapt up and down in an ecstasy of canine rage.

Her ladyship unbent. She almost smiled.

"Most amusin'," she commented.

Then she evinced a kind interest in our back garden (we haven't a front one), and we went out to inspect our bulb and raspberry canes.

We stayed there about a quarter of an hour. Lady Sheldon looked at them patronisingly through her lorgnettes and spoke to them kindly and encouragingly. Then she said she felt chilly and would like her wrap which she had left in the drawing room and, like the perfect little gentleman I am, I went in to get it for her.

I went into the drawing room. There on the hearthrug sat Muffles – in a little sea of dismembered fur and chiffon. He looked as Wellington must have looked after the battle of Waterloo. He was fairly swollen with pride. He was at least twice his usual size. His head was thrown back, and he was trying to look as if he had a chest. He looked the most conceited thing on this earth. Bits of fur and chiffon adhered to his whiskers and stuck out of his mouth and covered his fur.

Now I don't pretend to be a brave man. When there's any sort of a fight on, or a bolting horse, or anything like that, I'm the man who runs to fetch the police. I knew, of course, that I ought to have gone straight to Lady Sheldon and explained to her humorously and apologetically and tactfully and with *savoir faire* what had happened, while she listened to me through her lorgnettes. But I didn't. For one thing, I haven't any *savoir faire*. For another, lorgnettes always unman me.

So I crept out of the front door and went for a walk.

I went for a very long walk.

When I came back Lady Sheldon had gone and all was over.

But Muffles and I are in disgrace.

The Organiser
(London Opinion 23/5/1925)

"The Sale of Work went off beautifully," said my sister. "The vicar's wife has a real gift for organisation."

I have always been curious about this mysterious gift for organising.

"What does she do exactly?" I asked.

"She just tells people what to do."

"I see," I said, "and what does she do herself?"

"I've just told you – she tells people what to do."

"And is that all?"

"Of course it is. Anyone can do the actual work. It's the thinking out that needs a special gift. She tells people what to do. She organises the whole thing. A real gift for organising is awfully rare."

I began to think that it wasn't quite as rare as my sister imagined. I began to suspect that I too possessed the mysterious gift. It only needed developing. And I meant to have a jolly good try at it.

Delia wasn't a bit interested in the Sale of Work when I reached home. It appeared that the daily girl hadn't turned up. You've got to live in a house that depends on a daily girl to realise the tragedy of that. They do it on principle about twice a week just to learn you. They come the next day as usual and explain that their mother had mumps or their father had distemper or they'd come over all queer just as they were starting out, and you have to pretend to swallow it and try to look as if you weren't convinced that they'd really gone on the cheap trip to Margate. The day our daily girl doesn't turn up, Delia takes it out on me.

"I'm simply worked off my feet," she said as soon as I entered the house. "I haven't even had time to go out to get anything for dinner, so I *must* go out now before the shops close, and you must see to things here while I'm away. There are the tea things to be washed up and the potatoes to be peeled and the table set for dinner. Do hurry. Dinner will be awfully late, anyway."

I thought this a good opportunity for the exercise of my newly-discovered gift. I sat down and had a nice comfortable smoke by the fire till she came back. She was away about an hour.

"Well," she said, quite pleasantly when she returned, "have you finished everything?"

"Practically," I said. "I mean, theoretically. I mean, I've thought it all out. You must peel the potatoes first and then wash up the tea things and then put on the potatoes and they'll boil while you're setting the table for dinner and then—"

"*What!*" screamed Delia. "Haven't you done a *thing?*"

"Yes," I said firmly. "I've thought it all out. I've organised it. I'm developing my gift. If you peel the potatoes first and then—"

She interrupted me. I won't tell you what she said or how long she took to say it. But I've given up all idea of developing my gift for the present. Perhaps the vicar's wife and I are differently constituted. Perhaps the vicar is easier to practise on than Delia. Anyway, I've come to the conclusion that developing a real gift for organisation is one of the things that can't be done at home.

Burying the Hatchet
(The Humorist 13/3/1926)

I was quite prepared to like the Hammersleys when they came to live next to us. I'm an amicable sort of person. I like to live and let live, play the pianola and let play the pianola, keep chickens and let keep chickens.

Delia's like that, too. We're both easy to get on with, and generally people more or less take to us. But the Hammersleys didn't. They sent a note round at the end of their first week to say they'd be much obliged if we'd refrain from playing the gramophone or the pianola after nine-thirty at night because they went to bed at nine-thirty.

They also said that my mowing the lawn and singing in the afternoon had ruined Mrs Hammersley's midday rest, and added that our cat had deliberately walked over their newly-dug front bed, and unless steps were taken to put a stop to all these nuisances they would put the matter in the hands of the family solicitor. Or words to that effect.

Well, you'll understand that friendly relations were difficult after that. We did our best. When we played the pianola after nine-thirty we put the soft pedal down, but we couldn't stop our visitors being noisy. Delia and I seem to attract noisy people. So the Hammersleys wrote to us, threatening legal proceedings every morning, and glared through us ferociously whenever they met us.

Spirited hostilities went on whenever opportunity offered. When Bridget, our maid, tied a washing line to a branch of a Hammersley tree (which she'd done ever since we came to the house), Mrs Hammersley came out with a knife and cut down the line.

Of course, we didn't take this lying down. We're of the bulldog breed. We deliberately kept a handkerchief of Mr Hammersley's that blew into our garden from their line, and when Mrs Hammersley sent us a bill for it, saying that our cat had eaten it, we deliberately didn't pay it.

When Delia saw the Hammersleys picking and eating apples from a branch of our apple tree that hangs over their fence, she went and picked some roses from a Hammersley rambler that hangs over our fence and put them in a vase in the dining room window where the Hammersleys would be sure to see them. The Hammersleys, nothing daunted, cut off the rose branch. So we, equally nothing daunted, sawed off our apple branch. We ruined a perfectly good saw over it and nearly took the top off my thumb.

Then came last Saturday.

Last Saturday, the Hammersleys were having a temperance meeting at their house. They had posters of it at all their windows and on their front door and on their back door and on their front gate and on their side gate and on all their trees and all along their fence. Their posters made such a blaze of colour that people caught sight of them miles away and came to see what it was all about. It goes without saying that the Hammersleys were teetotallers. They were everything like that. They were vegetarians and early risers and eurhythmicians and, as I said, their bedtime was nine-thirty.

I went into the road and gazed enraptured at their poster display. Mrs Hammersley came out into her garden and put on her pince-nez in order to glare at me more successfully. I went in to Delia. Delia had just finished making jam. It's a point of honour with Delia to make jam as each jam season comes round. It's like eating pancakes on Shrove Tuesday, and making good resolutions on the first of January. Neither of us eats jam, but she works it off gradually during the year on tramps and relations and neighbours. She was putting two pots into a basket and covering them with a stalwart piece of brown paper.

"They're having a temperance meeting, Delia," I said. "Come and listen to their nice red posters shouting down the road."

But Delia's mind was full of jam.

"I'm going to take these to Granny's tonight," she said. "You've not forgotten that we're going there to supper, have you?"

"No," I said. Then, "I say, let's go for a walk."

"No," said Delia, very firmly, doffing her apron and taking the basket to the hall table. "I'll put it there and then I shan't forget it. I'm going to a meeting at the vicarage. A friend of the vicar's is going to speak. He's a member of the League of Love and Kindness."

"Don't, Delia," I warned her solemnly. "Things like that always end in trouble. I've noticed it often. We won't go to any meeting. We'll go for a walk."

But she wouldn't. She put on her second-best hat (the one she bought at the Sales) and set out for the vicarage.

As soon as she'd gone her grandmother rang up.

"You've not forgotten that you're coming to supper tonight, have you?" she asked.

"Rather not!" I reassured her cheerfully.

"My dear boy," she went on, "I'm so distressed. I've just discovered that I've nothing for you to drink in the house and it's early closing day."

"Don't you worry," I said. "I'll bring it round myself."

So I got a bottle of Bass from the larder and looked round for some receptacle. Then I thought of the basket that Delia had put the jam into. I was sure that the old lady didn't want any jam.

I took out the pots of jam, put them away in the larder, and then put my bottle of Bass in the basket under the brown paper. Then I went for a nice long walk.

When I came back, Delia was in the hall. She looked self-righteous and uplifted.

"Oh, John!" she said. "I've buried the hatchet."

"You've what?" I said.

"Buried the hatchet. The vicar's friend spoke so beautifully about being generous and forgiving your enemies and living in love and peace with your neighbours, and I decided to forgive the Hammersleys and live in love and peace with them and, John, everything's going to be all right now. I know it is. I've sent them the basket of jam I'd got ready for Granny. I just tied one of my cards on to the handle and wrote 'With compliments' on and sent it in by Bridget."

"You didn't happen to look inside, did you?" I asked.

"Of course not, John. I'd got it all ready, you remember, before I went out. I think it was awfully generous of me to bury the hatchet, don't you? And it's quite exciting, isn't it?"

I explained to her gently that it might be generous and it might be (probably would be) exciting, but it wasn't burying the hatchet. I told her that it was all her fault. Things like that always happen to women who go to lectures on Love and Kindness instead of going for walks with their lawful husbands.

Our Easter Holiday
(The Humorist 3/4/1926)

"Where shall we go this Easter?" said Delia, and simultaneously we said, "*Not* Margate!"

We'd decided last Easter not to go to Margate again. We'd formed a habit of going to Margate simply because we were too lazy to try other places.

"Suggest some other places, then," I said.

"Well, there's Devonshire," said Delia.

"Ye-es," I agreed, "and there's Cornwall."

"Ye-es," agreed Delia, "and there's Scotland."

"Ye-es," I agreed, "and there's the Lakes."

It's quite astonishing how many places there are in the world besides Margate when you come to think of them.

"The Grants are going to Venice," said Delia.

"That seems such a waste of money," I said, "when one can go to the Thames Valley, if one cares for that sort of thing, for a quarter of the price. And if we do go abroad, I've always wanted to see America."

"You couldn't," said Delia solemnly. "They wouldn't have you. Your record isn't blameless enough. They're frightfully particular about who they have in America. You've been fined for exceeding the speed limit."

"It was only a Ford, Delia," I pleaded.

"That makes no difference," she said sternly. "They'd count it moral turpitude and put you on to Ellis Island."

"What for, Delia?"

"Oh, just to learn you. Well, we haven't

settled where we're going yet, have we?"

I sighed.

"Delia, why *do* people go away at Easter?"

"I don't know," said Delia. "I've often wondered. *I* only go away for your sake. I'd much rather stay at home."

I looked at her reproachfully.

"How can you say that, Delia? It's *I* who go away for *your* sake. *I'd* much rather stay at home."

"Let's stay at home, then," said Delia. "I've always wanted to stay at home for a holiday. The Joneses always go away, and it would be so nice to sit in the garden without the Jones' heads talking to us all the time."

The phrase "the Jones' heads" calls for explanation. The Jones are our next door neighbours. They are rather tall, and our hedge is rather low. We encourage our hedge. We tend it and cherish it and nourish it and foster it. We pour fertiliser of every kind upon it with a reckless hand. And it does its best. I'm sure it does its best. It's grown to the Jones' necks. It almost hides Mr Jones' collar stud. But it doesn't seem able to get any farther. Or rather, it seems to grow, but the Jones' heads seem to grow with it.

Sometimes we fancy that a leaf or two is soaring upwards to the Jones' chins, but it always turns out to be imagination. And the Jones' chief hobby is talking to us over it.

"Where are the Jones going?" I said.

"They always go to Torquay. It will be jolly to stay at home without them. I'll paint the seat."

"And I'll mow the lawn."

"And I'll sow the hardy annuals."

"And I'll mend the fence."

"And nobody to ask us what we're doing and why we're doing it and what do we think of the weather – a heavenly, Jonesless peace. And it's going to be really warm, so we'll have tea out every day."

I went to survey the promised land and at once the Jones' heads appeared over our gallant little hedge.

"You going to Torquay?" I said.

"No," said Mr Jones' head. "We thought it would be rather fun to stay at home for a change."

"We want to give the garden a good doing up," said Mrs Jones' head brightly.

"I'm going to give the seat another coat of paint," said Mr Jones' head.

"And I know it's going to be fine, so we can *live* in the garden," said Mrs Jones' head.

"You going away?" said Mr Jones' head.

"Yes," I said.

And we did. We went to Margate.

A Mean Trick

(The Humorist 17/4/1926)

We spent Easter one year with Uncle Horace. Uncle Horace has what is called "the defects of his qualities", only in Uncle Horace's case the defects far outweigh the qualities.

One of the "defects" is a leaning towards practical jokes of the more obvious kind. Members of the family who stay with Uncle Horace generally come home foaming at the mouth with rage. He's been known to stoop even as low as the apple-pie bed. Chairs with unsteady legs, and excess of mustard or pepper with eatables, are the very breath of life to him, while elaborately made-up parcels containing nothing at all are, as it were, his daily food.

And it isn't only practical jokes. There's another and yet darker side to Uncle Horace, and that is an amiable little habit of keeping one box of (inferior) cigars for his guests and another (carefully concealed from view) for himself. He also has what used to be known as a "sweet tooth", and when lady members of the family visit him he keeps one box of (inferior) chocolates to hand to them and another box of (superior) chocolates for himself. He does it very cleverly. He'll hand you the box of cigars, and you'll take one, and he'll say, "I won't have one *just* now," and he'll send you into the garden and follow you in a few seconds, smoking one of his own brand. Or he'll hand a box of chocolates to your wife and, when she's taken one, put the box back in the cupboard, and as he does so slip one from his own (superior) box into his mouth.

Oh, he's a wily old bird, is Uncle Horace, and a cute old bird, and a very, very mean old bird.

He did the cigar trick and the chocolate trick on Delia and me the first evening of our visit, and then sent us out to examine the greenhouses. I returned rather sooner than he expected me, and saw him through the window at his dastardly work. He'd got two gigantic Easter eggs and two tiny little stumps of lead pencil and oceans of paper and string, and he was wrapping up the tiny stumps of lead pencil in innumerable wrappings and chuckling to himself. Finally he packed one into each Easter egg, and I knew that we should find them on our plates the next morning. So I decided to act.

A quarter of an hour later Delia and I strolled into the room. There was no trace of the Easter eggs. Uncle Horace was sitting on a chair in the shadow of the curtain. Before he had time to speak, I said to Delia in a very loud voice:

"Uncle Horace isn't here, dear, so I can tell you something that I think I ought to tell you. I just caught sight of two enormous Easter eggs as I passed his window some minutes ago. The dear fellow is going to give us such a delightful surprise tomorrow morning. But we must pretend to know nothing about it, of course."

Uncle Horace lay low.

"I wonder what he's going to put in them?" said Delia with exaggerated innocence (women always over-act).

I tiptoed to the cupboard and opened the door.

"These, or course," I said. "This box of lovely chocolates for you and this box of Corona cigars for me. I saw them when the dear old fellow opened the cupboard tonight and, as they weren't the ones he handed to us, I knew at once that he was keeping them for a surprise present for us."

"The dear, generous man," said Delia brokenly.

"When we get home, Delia," I said solemnly, "we must send him a really handsome present."

Then we went out, leaving Uncle Horace still lying low.

Yes, we found the boxes in the eggs on our plates all right the next morning. And when we got home we sent Uncle Horace two beautiful lead pencils in a very large box.

I don't know when we shall be asked to stay with Uncle Horace again.

A Moving Tragedy
(London Opinion 8/5/1926)

We were just "moving in" and we felt like – well, you know what you *do* feel like when you're just moving in. We ached through every square inch of us, and only our Spartan self-control prevented our falling into each other's arms and sobbing out our misery and despair on each other's shoulders. Nothing seemed to fit in anywhere. Our furniture seemed all the wrong shape and things that we'd already measured beforehand seemed to have swollen or shrunk in the move and refused to fit into their right niches. We looked round at it all tragically, and finally I said:

"Well, we'd better start *doing* something, hadn't we?"

"I like that," said Delia, irritably, "as if I'd ever stopped doing something for one minute for days and days and *days*."

I need hardly explain that Delia's nerves were a trifle frayed.

"All right," I said, soothingly, "go and lie down and have a nice little rest."

"How can you *suggest* such a thing?" she said, still more irritably, "when you *know* what a lot there is to do."

It's awfully difficult to please a woman, especially in the middle of moving in. So I didn't say anything else for a bit, not, in fact, until she asked me if I were going to read the morning paper all day. Then I said no, of course I wasn't. There wasn't enough reading in it to last a whole day. I'd nearly finished it already. So she asked me very, very politely (if you've ever moved in you'll know the sort of politely I mean) if I'd mind hanging "A Surrey

Pinewood" on the landing upstairs. We'd arranged exactly where we were going to hang "A Surrey Pinewood", so I lugged it upstairs (it's a beastly heavy thing) and then lugged the steps up. Then, with great trouble (it took a long time and almost inhuman skill) I lugged "A Surrey Pinewood" inch by inch, step by step, up to the top. And just at that moment the front door bell rang.

LUGGAGE IN ADVANCE!

"I can't go," called Delia. "I'm *filthy*. You'll have to."

"I'm filthy, too," I called down.

"You can't be as filthy as I am."

"I am. I'm filthier," I pleaded.

"Well, I'm not going, so you'll have to."

That, of course, was what in diplomatic circles they call an ultimatum. So I lowered "A Surrey Pinewood" very, very cautiously to the ground and, weary and

exhausted, went down to answer the front door.

It was a dapper youth.

"Excuse me, sir," he said, with a courtly bow, "I've called on behalf of Mr Green, the milkman. We can guarantee regular delivery, fresh rich milk—"

I shut the door in his face and returned to "A Surrey Pine Wood". Once more, very, very laboriously, panting with the exertion, I hoisted it up the steps. Just as I'd got it poised on the top step again, the front door bell rang.

"You'll have to go again," called Delia.

"I won't," I called; "it's your turn."

"I can't," said Delia triumphantly, "I'm scrubbing the scullery floor."

"That's no excuse," I said. "If it comes to that, I'm embracing 'A Surrey Pine Wood' on top of the steps."

"Oh, do hurry up," said Delia.

So I hurried up, or rather down. Step by step I lowered "A Surrey Pine Wood" to the ground again and went downstairs to answer the front door.

It was the dapper youth again.

"I should like to be able to take a definite answer in the affirmative back to Mr Green," he said. "I can assure you that there is no adulteration whatever in our milk. It is—"

I shut the door in his face again and returned to "A Surrey Pine Wood". I think I have already remarked that it is a fearfully large and heavy thing. Artists who paint that size of thing ought to be hanged, and so ought all relations who give them as wedding presents. Well, just as I'd breasted the summit with it once more the front door bell rang again.

"I'm not going this time," I called out very firmly.

"Darling," said Delia, changing her tactics, "*Do*, there's an angel. My face is all black and cobwebby and my hands are all wet and soapy."

"So are all mine," I murmured, plaintively, but I knew it was useless. I wearily lowered "A Surrey Pine Wood" and myself to the ground once more and went down to the front door.

It was the dapper youth again.

"Mr Green extends a hearty invitation to you," he said, glibly, "to visit his dairy any time and see the conditions under which—"

I shut the door in his face and returned to "A Surrey Pine Wood". I'd hardly got the thing balanced on the first step when the front door bell rang again.

"He's back again, Delia," I said. "What shall I do?"

"Throw something at him out of the landing window," said Delia.

That was rather a good idea. The landing window is just over the front door.

I looked around me. My first impulse was to chuck "A Surrey Pine Wood" down at him, but after a brief internal struggle more humane feelings won the day. Besides, I might just possibly have missed him with "A Surrey Pine Wood". So I picked up a bucket of water that stood conveniently near the window and chucked that out. Then – too late – I looked out.

It was the vicar's wife come to pay her state call....

And you'll hardly believe it, but Delia – who suggested it – blames me for the whole thing.

Daughters of Deceit
(The Humorist 26/6/1926)

Delia said that it wasn't the sixteenth Sale of Work that had been held in the village this year. She said that it was only the sixth. But whether it was the sixth or the sixteenth (and it felt more like the sixteenth to me), she let me in, as usual, for taking the tickets at the entrance for the first hour.

And to add insult to injury, Delia wasn't going herself at all. She gave a headache as an excuse. It was the sort of headache that women invent so unblushingly when they want to get out of anything. She looked outrageously healthy and was eating chocolates at quite an abnormal speed.

"Tell them that I'm so sorry I can't come and help," she said as she munched. "And I want you to buy me a black and gold brocade bag that Dolly Franks has made. You'll find it on the fancy stall, and it's only nineteen shillings."

"I shall do nothing of the sort," I said coldly. "I shall take the entrance tickets simply because convention doesn't allow a man to go back on promises made for him by his wife, and then I shall buy a buttonhole from the prettiest flower-seller in the room, and then I shall buy you a small present costing not more than a shilling, and then I shall come straight home."

"All right, darling," said Delia with disarming meekness.

I took the entrance tickets for an hour, and all I will allow myself to say about that part of it is that it was a very long hour.

Then I looked round for the prettiest flower-seller.

There was no mistaking her. She was simply adorable. She met my eyes across the room, and hers faltered and she blushed just as they do in novels. Though I am not a conceited man, I could not help seeing that she found the sight of me disturbing.

I don't say that she was really much prettier than Delia. But then Delia doesn't find the sight of me disturbing any longer. When Delia's eyes meet mine across a crowded room she's only wondering whether I shaved before I came out or whether I remembered to order the fish. (That, of course, is what marriage does to all fair women and brave men. I'm not making any complaint.)

I approached the flower-seller and bought a buttonhole from her. She had blue eyes and a beautiful husky voice and smelt of violets. The buttonhole just suited her so, of course, I had to pin it on her dress. Then I gave her tea. It was an extraordinary thing, but that girl had exactly the same views as I have on simply everything. We discussed all life's problems – police traps and oysters and the Charleston, and it was almost miraculous how our views coincided. I've never met anything like it in my life before. We might have been made for each other. And though, as I said before, I am not a conceited man, I couldn't help seeing how much she admired me. I told her the story of my life and it was obvious that she looked upon me as a sort of hero.

At last I said, "Well, I must get a little something for my wife before I go home."

She looked at me sadly and reproachfully and then helped me choose Delia's present. It turned out that she was on the fancy stall as well as being a flower-seller. She was very sensible about Delia's present.

I said very firmly, "Just a *little* thing. My wife told me I wasn't to spend more than a shilling on it."

She found me three little scent sachets at fourpence each, and then she said:

"You'd like a bag to put them in, wouldn't you?"

I said "Yes" thinking how awfully blue her eyes were and how many men meet their soul's affinity too late....

Then she gave me a brown paper parcel very neatly made up and tied with string, and I handed her a pound note and waited for change. She took it and said calmly, "That's just right. The bag's nineteen shillings," and smiled at me adorably and I swallowed and smiled back and walked away.

You can't tell a girl with speedwell blue eyes, who looks on you as her soul's hero and whose views on life exactly coincide with yours, that you hadn't meant to spend as much as that and will she give you nineteen shillings change, please? That sort of thing simply isn't done. Of course, had it been the vicar's wife it would have been different.

I went for a long, lonely walk before I returned home. I didn't know whether to tell Delia about the girl with blue eyes or not. I didn't want to make Delia jealous. On the other hand – I decided not to tell her after all.

When I entered the hall, I was met by the scent of violets and a beautiful husky voice coming from the drawing room.

"It *was* the gold and black bag you wanted wasn't it, dear?" the voice was saying.

"Yes," said Delia's voice, "The one at nineteen shillings."

"That's the one," said the other voice.

"He's got it and paid for it, so it's all right."

"Thanks ever so much," said Delia's voice. "You are a dear to do it. Was it much trouble?"

"None at all," said the girl's voice. "I just flickered an eyelash at him and he ate out of my hand."

Delia gurgled.

"The darling! He would! He does *love* to feel young and fascinating!"

I went quietly out for a still longer walk and I thought about women all the time, and the conclusion I came to was that something ought to be done about them. From Adam downwards, we men have put up with them far too long.

After All
(London Opinion 24/7/1926)

It was the Browns who gave us the tickets, and we really meant to go, because, when all is said and done, stalls are stalls, and alone and unaided we never rise above the Upper Circle (or perhaps I should say below it) – but a heat wave caught us unawares that morning.

"It's far too hot to go to a matinée," said Delia, firmly.

"But what about the tickets?" I objected, mildly. "Do you think if we took them to Keith Prowse he'd exchange them for tickets to a swimming bath or excursion tickets to Margate?"

"Don't be silly," said Delia. "We'll give them to the Joneses, and we'll go on the river or play tennis or – anything but a theatre on a day like this."

So we gave the tickets to the Joneses and went on the river. We punted and panted as far as Staines, and came to the conclusion that somebody must, after all, have set the Thames on fire. Then we played tennis and suffered the (presumptive) agonies of the damned even when only looking for lost balls in the shade. We couldn't find a cool spot anywhere. We couldn't find a breath of air. It was the sort of day you long for in winter when you've forgotten what it's really like and the pipes are freezing.

And in the evening we met the Greenes. They were the first happy-looking people we'd seen that day.

"Wasn't this afternoon ghastly?" I said.

"How?" said Greene, cheerfully.

"Hot," I said, tersely.

"Was it?" said Greene, "we were quite

cool. The Joneses kindly gave us tickets
for a theatre, and it most delightfully cool
in there!"

A Difficulty
(The Humorist 7/8/1926)

We are quite often maid-less, and
when you're maid-less and out a
good deal at tennis – as we are – it means
that tradesmen come to your door with
things you've ordered, and, after knocking
and ringing and looking through the
letterbox and teasing the cat and pinching a
few roses or lettuces, leave your parcels
with the next-door people.

Now some neighbours are neighbourly
(in the generally accepted sense of the
word) about that sort of thing, and some
are neighbourly in quite another fashion.

The Joneses were really nice. They
seemed actually to enjoy taking in our
parcels. Mrs Jones had what is known as a
large heart and took a real interest in her
fellow creatures. When Delia appeared in
a hat that had been left at Mrs Jones' the
day before, Mrs Jones would say with a
coy smile, "There! I *guessed* it was a new
hat!" She'd guess nearly anything. Once
she couldn't sleep because she hadn't been
able to decide whether it was a rat-trap or a
knife-box, and she came in before breakfast
to ask us.

So you see the Joneses as neighbours had
their points, but all good things come to an
end and so did the Joneses – or rather, so
did the Jones' lease, and they moved out to
Chislehurst (as all good people do before
they die) and we knew them no more.

They were succeeded by the Marksons,
and the Marksons, we soon discovered,
were in quite a different category. We were
out the first afternoon after their "moving
in", and though we got back quite early
they didn't bring in our groceries till the

next day, and they didn't bring them in at all nicely even then. There was something so forbidding about their manner of bringing them in that the rice puddings tasted quite sour till that packet of rice was finished.

The next afternoon we were out again, and as nobody brought anything in when we returned we concluded that Delia's new coat (most faithfully promised) hadn't been sent. So we went to enquire, only to be told that they'd sent it in the afternoon of the day before. So we bearded the Marksons and they held out the parcel between finger and thumb at arm's length (and that, mind you, though it was of real Kasha and half-lined silk) and asked us in a way that we couldn't possibly have misunderstood, hard as we tried, kindly to make some other arrangements in future for the reception of our parcels in our absence.

That left us rather at a loss, because we'd ordered a really artistic blue and gold bowl that very morning and had to go out to tennis that afternoon. So we went and left the whole matter to Fate. We thought that perhaps in the meantime the Marksons might have come to their better selves. But they didn't. We returned home, but no bowl appeared. We rang up the shop, and they said that they'd sent it up that afternoon. Then Delia came in from the garden quivering with indignation.

"The cheek!" she stormed. "The nerve! The face! The impudence!"

Words failed her.

"Draw a deep breath," I advised her, "and start again."

"It's our vase," she said. "They've got it on the table in their drawing room just in the window. The *cheek* of them!"

"I suppose it's meant to larn us," I said thoughtfully.

"Well, I'm going to larn them," said Delia. "I'm going to walk straight in and get it. The window's open and I don't care *who* sees me."

This may sound incredible to you, but you don't know Delia. She did it. She walked through the front gate, across the lawn, in at the French window as bold as brass, took the bowl, brought it home and put it on *our* table at *our* window in drawing room. Then she said, *"There!"*

And immediately there came a ring at the front door.

We thought it was the Marksons, but it wasn't. It was the man from the china shop with another bowl. He said that he was sorry that it hadn't been sent up, after all.

And then, just as we were gazing at the two bowls and trying to recover our breath, in swept Mrs Markson. She went up to the table, took up her bowl, said very sweetly, "Mine, I think," and swept out with it. She didn't wait for an explanation, and on second thoughts it might have been rather difficult to give one.

But you will realise that this puts us in rather a delicate position. We had to scratch from a tennis tournament only yesterday because Delia had ordered a mackintosh in readiness for the many cyclones and anti-cyclones and wedges of high pressure so generously promised by the British Broadcasting Company for the tennis season, and we dared not leave the house till it had come.

We offer a (small) reward to anyone who sends the best solution of the difficulty.

The Clothes Horse
(The Passing Show 9/10/1926)

I don't remember when Delia first began on me about the clothes horse. But it came to be a sort of routine with us. At the end of every weekend Delia would say with acerbity: "Well, have you chopped up the clothes horse yet?"

And I would say with dignity, "Not yet."

And Delia would say with more acerbity: "Aren't you ever going to?"

And I'd say with more dignity:

"Give me time, dear, give me time."

As you'll have gathered from this peroration, Delia wanted me to chop up an old clothes horse for firewood and I didn't want to. Or rather, I wanted to do it in my own time. I didn't want to be bullied into it. If you're a husband you'll understand.

One must preserve one's dignity somehow. One must impress upon one's wife that one does things because one wants to and not because she tells one to. Otherwise the very foundation of married life would be undermined. The psychological moment to do a thing is when she's just beginning to give up hope and to wonder how on earth she's going to get it done. Then you step in gracefully and do it with the ease and deftness of the Superior Male while she looks on, lost in admiration and gratitude. If she's in the right mood, that is. Of course, a lot depends on her mood.... But doubtless you know all this already. So to return to the clothes horse.

I began to get rather tired of the words "clothes horse". They're uninspiring words at the best of times. And Delia's voice was just reaching the right inflexion of hopelessness and weariness when she uttered them, so I began to think the time had come to act.

I decided to do it when Delia was out to tea. It's always so much more effective to present your wife with a *fait accompli* rather than to let her watch you labouring and perspiring your way through every stage of it.... So I came home early from the office and went into the kitchen. There was the clothes horse leaning against the wall. I took it out into the back garden and I set to work on it with the axe as though I were a pioneer in a virgin forest, and in a few minutes there was nothing left of that clothes horse but little sticks of firewood.

I tied them up in neat bundles, stacked them up in the back garden and went into the hall glowing with heat and virtue. Delia was just coming in. I looked at her in the way you look at anyone you've just performed a Herculean task for and I began kindly:

"Well, Delia—"

I was just going to tell her how I'd been slaving for her while she'd been out enjoying herself but she interrupted me.

"Hello, dear," she said pleasantly. "How are you? Well, I had to do it myself after all."

"Do what yourself?" I said.

"Chop up the old clothes horse, of course. I did it this morning and put the firewood away in the wash-house. It was no trouble at all. I can't think why you made such a fuss about it. I had to get the old one out of the way because the new one had come. Do come and look at the new one. It's such a beauty. It's in the kitchen...."

But I murmured something about having forgotten something in the village, seized my hat and hurried out.

Not that it made any difference.

I was out for nearly an hour, but it takes women such a long time to get over things....

Touring with Delia
(London Opinion 16/10/1926)

Delia sits beside me in the front. My duty is to drive and hers to look out for signposts and tell me which road to take.

"Which way?" I ask, as a signpost approaches.

"To the right," says Delia, primly.

I take the right in my best style.

"Sorry," sings out Delia, cheerfully. "I mean the left."

I back in an eloquent silence and turn to the left. We skim along to the next signpost.

"To the left," says Delia.

I turn to the left. We go on for some miles.

October 16, 1926

LONDON OPINION 2D

With Rod and Lyin'

"I'm sure this is wrong," I say at last. "We ought to have gone to the right."

"Didn't I say the right?" says Delia.

"No, you said the left."

"Did I? I meant the right…. What did you say?"

"Nothing."

I go on for a mile or so until I can turn, then return to the signpost and turn to the right and we proceed to the next signpost.

"Turn to the right," says Delia.

Grimly I turn to the left.

"You're going in quite the wrong direction," says Delia after some time.

"Well, as you said the right, I naturally thought you meant the left," I explain.

"No, I meant the right. *Our* road really goes straight on, but I did so want to see that ducky little cottage on the road to the right and could just see its thatched roof through the trees. But this road doesn't lead anywhere. Shall we go back?"

This is a typical half-hour of our motoring – Delia's and mine. And Delia blames me because we don't do more than fifty miles a day.

Appropriate
(London Opinion 30/10/1926)

"We're going to do a play," said Delia.

"Who?" I groaned, because I knew that whoever it was, I should have to go to it.

"Our Dramatic Society," said Delia.

"I didn't know you had one," I said mildly.

"No, we hadn't until yesterday, but we made one yesterday because we thought it would be rather nice to do a play."

"And what play are you going to do?"

"We haven't decided yet. It's only to be very short – about twenty minutes. We discussed it for two hours last night and we couldn't agree…. You see, when someone suggested a scene from *Romeo and Juliet*, Mrs Groome said that she'd taken part in a charade as Juliet at school so she was obviously the one to do Juliet, and Mrs Blake said to us all afterwards that if Mrs Groome was Juliet she'd resign from the committee, and as she's going to pay for the scenery we had to give up *Romeo and Juliet*."

"Who's your committee?" I said, with interest.

"Well, darling," she said, "it's not *quite* decided yet. We had a two hours' meeting about *that* this morning. There are all sorts of complications…. You see, Mrs Brown wants to be President and Mrs Franks has told people privately that if Mrs Brown's the president she won't produce the play at all, and she's awfully good at producing plays – she's learnt elocution, you see, so nobody's *really* elected yet…."

"I see," I murmured dreamily.

"Darling," she said. You've got such a

nice far-away look in your eyes. Are you thinking how much you love me?"

"No, dearest, I was imagining a business run on your lines."

"We'd manage *any* business far better than you do," she said, with spirit.

I was eloquently silent.

The next day was cook's evening out, but when I arrived home I found a pale and exhausted Delia and, though I sniffed tentatively, no pleasant (or otherwise) smell of cooking.

"I'm afraid there's only sardine or tinned tongue – whichever you prefer," said Delia, "because I haven't had a *minute* to cook anything. We've been having a committee meeting of the Dramatic Society *all* the afternoon and evening."

"Fresh complications?" I suggested.

"Darling, you're *awfully* perceptive. Yes, you see, Mrs Franklin met Mrs Brown this morning and saw that she had an awful cold – she really *has* – and then wrote her a nice little note – quite polite – saying that if she didn't feel better she mustn't come to the meeting because we could get on perfectly well without her, and Mrs Brown took offence and has resigned, and isn't speaking to any of us, and it's such a pity, because she's got some lovely Queen Anne chairs that would do beautifully for a Shakespearian scene."

"Why?" I said, wildly. "Why would Queen Anne chairs do beautifully for a Shakespearean scene?"

"Because they're old, darling," she explained, kindly, "and Shakespeare's old…. And then there's another complication because Miss Blocks has a suit of Shakespearean clothes and so she insists on being the hero and she's over forty and looks it, but she says they're made of real velvet and wouldn't fit any of us but her."

"So you're really no nearer?"

"N-no," she admitted, "but we talked quite a lot and some of them have been awfully nasty to each other, but Mrs Lewel provided a glorious tea. Mrs Franks said that she did it so as to get a good part, but I don't *think* that's true."

The next day I came home to find Delia pale but triumphant.

"Darling," she said, "we've settled on the scene at last. The only thing left to do now is to select the cast and the committee."

"And what scene are you going to do?" I said.

"We're going to do a scene from *Much Ado About Nothing*."

What's in a Name!

(London Opinion 6/11/1926)

"I want to go to a – to a – what *do* you call it? Oh, I know – a phrenologist."

I was rather surprised to hear that. Delia, as a rule, professes only contempt for that sort of thing.

"Are you sure you do?" I said.

"Of course I'm sure," said Delia. "Do give me credit for knowing my own mind. They've never given me any trouble all my life till now, but just this week they've been quite painful."

"What have?" I said.

"Oh, you *are* silly!" said Delia. "Didn't you hear me say that I must go to a phrenologist?"

November 6, 1926

LONDON OPINION 2D

BATH ROOM

The Bath "Tap"

"Yes, dear," I said, soothingly.

No doubt at all that she was feeling under the weather.

But I believe in humouring one's wife, so with a great deal of trouble I found a reputable phrenologist and made an appointment for her.

"Well," I said when she returned, "how did you get on?"

She looked rather cross.

"He didn't do me a bit of good," she said. "He just talked about my character and felt my head."

"Well, what did you expect him to do? They always do that."

"Do they?" said Delia. "It seems to me quite the wrong way to set to work. I suppose the idea is that the brain's the centre of everything, and the treatment sort of reaches them from the brain. But it seems to me very round-about."

I looked at her rather anxiously.

"I shouldn't mind if it had made them feel any better," she went on, "but they feel *just* as they did before I went, and he charged me quite a lot of money. I think it was such *cheek* of him to discuss my character with me."

Just then Mrs Brown came in.

"I've been spending the morning at the chiropodist's," she said, cheerfully. "I want to keep in good form for the tennis. One gets so chilblainy in the winter."

Delia stared at her open-mouthed, a light dawning in her eyes.

"Chiropodist!" she said, slowly. "Of course – why, *that* was the word I was trying to think of."

John and Delia

(The Humorist 13/11/1926)

"John, darling," said Delia, handing me a catalogue, "isn't that simply a finger of Providence?"

"What?" I said, gazing blankly at a page of willowy figures striking attitudes and looking as if they were trying to play skipping rope with their chains of beads.

"That," said Delia, pointing out one particular figure.

"Why?" I said. "It's the shape of a finger, I grant; but it's meant to represent a human being. And why of Providence?"

"Don't you *see*?" said Delia, impatiently.

I looked more closely. Beneath all the willowy figures were inscribed female names: "Kathleen", "Susie", "Gladys", "Naomi". And beneath the one to which Delia was pointing was the name "Delia". A light dawned on my spirit, and a great caution came over me.

"Yes," I said, handing her back the catalogue. "Pretty, isn't it? I saw Mrs Loman today."

But Delia refused to be drawn by Mrs Loman. She didn't even ask what she was wearing. She returned to "Delia".

"I think it would be such a pretty compliment if you bought it for me, darling," she said.

"I don't," I said, promptly. "I think it would be an insult. I shouldn't dream of doing it. It would look as if I weren't satisfied with you as you are. And I am. I love you in the dresses you've got. I shouldn't love you half as much in 'Delia'."

"I'd simply love to have it."

"You may buy it, dearest," I said, generously, "out of your dress allowance."

"I haven't any left."

"That's a pity," I said, and added: "The Marsdens seem to be having a party on this afternoon."

But she refused to be drawn even by the Marsdens.

"Don't you remember, darling," she said, "I particularly said when we arranged about my dress allowance that I didn't want you to feel that you couldn't buy me a few little things when you felt like it."

"Exactly," I said, "but I don't feel like it."

She returned to a wistful study of "Delia".

"It seems like flying in the face of Providence," she sighed, "to meet a dress called by your own name and not buy it. It would probably bring us all sorts of good luck. Like wearing your birthday stone. We may have *very* bad luck if we let it go."

"I don't think you need worry," I reassured her, kindly. "I don't think that there's anything in those bad luck ideas. You know, you once told me that you broke a looking-glass the day before you met me."

"Yes, and—" began Delia; then, in view of the fact that she wanted "Delia", decided not to continue her train of argument. I took the book and studied "Delia" more carefully.

"I don't like her, Delia," I said. "She looks a minx. She's making horrible eyes, and her arms are too long and her anatomy's a scandal. The poor girl's absolutely deformed. Look at the size of her feet. She must have had them bound in China. And she hasn't got any nose, and her mouth's the size of one eye. She ought to have been painlessly put out of her misery years ago."

"It's the *dress*, you old idiot! Look, it's

awfully pretty. It's got the new waistline, and such pretty sleeves, and it's only four guineas."

"No," I said, firmly, "I could never see you in it without thinking of this poor deformed creature who first wore it, with her tortured feet and nose-less face and distorted anatomy. The poor woman must be in agony. Look, her arms are the same length as her legs."

"Oh, do stop talking about her! It's the *dress*." She tried another line of argument. "It looks so nice and warm. I do think that now coal's so expensive it's the duty of all of us to buy as many warm clothes as possible in order to economise coal. I think that that's what every patriotic citizen ought to do. At any sacrifice."

"Delia," I said, "you've got the type of mind that would take you far in politics."

"Well, are you going to buy it for me, or not?"

"Meet me for lunch tomorrow," I said, "and we'll go out in search of 'Delia'."

We entered the department. An assistant came up to us and Delia produced the book of words.

"That's the one I want," she said, pointing to it. "'Delia'."

"I'm so sorry," said the assistant, "we sold the last one of that this morning."

"I'm sorry, too," I said, simply and sincerely. "I was looking forward to meeting the poor girl. On the other hand, perhaps it's as well she is no more. As I said to my wife, she must have suffered a good deal."

She looked at me in a scared sort of way and transferred her whole attention to Delia.

"We have any of the others on that page, madam—" she began.

I intervened.

"No. It was 'Delia' we wanted. The others won't do," I said, raising my voice slightly to drown Delia's protests. "It was a case of the finger of Providence – one's birthday stone – bad luck and that sort of thing. Good afternoon."

Very determinedly I walked out of the department, leaving Delia and the assistant gaping after me.

The next department, through which I had to pass to reach the lift, was a man's outfitting department. On a stand near the door was a pullover, a really gorgeous pullover, the sort of pullover I've always longed to have. I'd noticed it on my way in.

"What's that?" I said to an assistant, pointing to it.

"A pullover, sir," said the man.

"Yes, but what's its name?" I asked.

"It's name, sir?" said the man, politely.

"Yes," I said. "Hasn't it got a name?"

"No, sir," said the man. "It's a pullover."

"There's no reason why it shouldn't have a name, is there?" I asked.

The man looked round as if to reassure himself that help was near, in case I suddenly got violent. He also backed several yards away from me.

"No, sir," he said.

"Well, let's call it John, shall we?" I said, pleasantly.

"If you like, sir," said the man, growing rather white about the gills.

"How much is it?" I went on.

"Four guineas, sir."

At that minute Delia appeared, having reluctantly torn herself from "Kathleen" and "Susie" and "Gladys" and "Naomi".

"Delia," I said, "look at this pullover. It's called 'John'. I think it would be simply flying in the face of Providence for me not to buy it, don't you?"

And I bought it before she could recover her breath.

Delia isn't speaking to me yet. But John is very warm and comfy and all that could be desired.

The Finding of Muffles
(The Humorist 20/11/1926)

"I've lost Muffles," said Delia, tragically.

"Where?" I asked, trying to look a little less unmoved than I really was.

"I don't know. I went out shopping with him, and I came back without him. That's all I know. I've no idea where I lost him."

I continued to receive the news stoically. I am as fond of Muffles as a man generally is of a small dog. And I was glad that Delia's mind would be taken off my tie.

Delia had been knitting me a tie for Christmas. She's knitting it of a sort of rainbow silk which shades artistically from green into pink and from pink into mauve and from mauve back again into green. You may not have seen any silk like that. If you haven't, you have much to be thankful for.

Delia often remarks that it will be very pretty when it's finished. She works at it whenever she has a moment to spare. I always try not to look at it, but it had a horrible fascination for me. I've told her quite frankly that I don't like it, but she says that it's time men were broken of their silly habit of pretending that they don't like pretty colours, and she continues to knit it. So I welcomed the losing of Muffles as a counter-irritant.

"Well, that will do to start on," I said. "Now let's try to track the beast down."

"Don't be unfeeling," said Delia.

"I'm not," I said. "I'm deeply stirred. Where did you go first?"

"I went to the fir department in Parrods."

"Ah," I said, "then I'm afraid that little Muffles will now be a neat little choker or a chic little collar and cuffs. But I suppose there's just a chance that you didn't leave him there. Where did you go next?"

"To call on Angela."

"Tut, tut!" I said. "And Angela has an Alsatian. The papers are full of the savagery of Alsatians. Muffles will make one neat mouthful. However, I suppose you may not have left him there. Where did you go next?"

"To the butcher's," said Delia.

"*Delia!*" I said. "Go down to the butcher's at once and insist on being shown his sausages. Say 'Muffles!' to them, and if any of them wag you'll know the worst."

And then suddenly I saw Muffles. He was playing quite happily in the garden, and he was playing with my green and pink and mauve tie. He'd just got it off the needles. I stood so that my broad, manly back blocked the window.

"Where did you go next, Delia?" I said.

"I came home then. I can't have lost him in the street, because I was carrying him."

"Did you go in a taxi at all?"

"Oh, goodness! Yes, I did."

"Delia, I hope the next fare didn't sit on him."

"Oh, *don't!*" moaned Delia, putting her hand up to her eyes as if to blot out the horrible vision thus called up.

I glanced over my shoulder. Muffles was getting on very nicely with the tie.

"Calm yourself, Delia," I said. "Let's go into the hall now and ring up all the places you've been to this afternoon. If he isn't in any of them we will do something drastic – write to *The Times*, or send his description to the BBC to broadcast, or set a bloodhound on his track or something."

So we rang up all the places where Delia had been that afternoon and, needless to say, Muffles was not in any of them. The butcher was rather touchy when I mentioned the sausages, Angela said that her Alsatian was looking a bit off colour and she *hoped* he hadn't eaten anything that disagreed with him, and the police said they'd let us know at once if there was any news.

Then we returned to the drawing room again. I glanced out of the window. Muffles had made a pretty complete job of it by this time.

"I really don't feel that I can settle down to your tie tonight," said Delia. "My thoughts are so full of poor Muffles. But I suppose I ought to—" She began to hunt round the drawing room. "Oh, dear, I've lost *that* now!"

"Delia," I said, "are you *sure* you took Muffles with you?"

She paused and considered this point of view for the first time.

· "Well, not exactly *sure*, perhaps. At least – well, I know I generally do – I mean, I don't remember not doing—"

"Look, Delia," I said, pointing out of the window.

Delia looked. There sat Muffles in the middle of the lawn panting, wrapped round and round with strands of chewed and ravelled green and pink and mauve silk. Delia gazed and gazed and gazed. Such emotions as relief, joy, horror, fury, succeeded each other on her face. They were followed by suspicion. She turned to me.

"How long have you—" she began.

But I didn't wait to hear the rest. I set off for a nice long walk.

124

Bob's Box
(The Humorist 25/12/1926)

It was our turn to have Aunt Matilda at Christmas. Aunt Matilda spends most of the year in chaste and select resorts, such as Bath and Tunbridge Wells, and only descends on her family at Christmas time. But it is a real descent, and her host and hostess of the year generally end by being cut out of her will.

This is not as tragic as it sounds, because when she crosses the next one out she always puts back all the others, so it's only a matter of waiting till next Christmas, and I don't think that anyway she's got much to leave.

But, of course, as you will see, it lends a certain piquancy to the situation. She had stayed with Bob last year, and Bob's wife had offended her by giving some mince to Tootums for lunch after Aunt Matilda had quite definitely said that twice-cooked meat didn't agree with him. Tootums is a toy dog of the rat species who is Aunt Matilda's inseparable companion.

I went round to see Bob the week before Aunt Matilda arrived. I found him in the shed engaged in torturing by means of diabolical instruments honest pieces of wood which had never done him any harm. Bob is one of those people who is inflicted with the hobby mania.

It is a sad sight to see the poor fellow – otherwise an intelligent and companionable man – spending hours and hours making little holes in pieces of wood; but his family have done all they could, and have finally given up his case as hopeless.

He raised his head from his deadly work and greeted me.

"I hear that you're going to have Aunt Matilda this Christmas," he said, cheerfully. "So I suppose you'll be crossed off and I'll be put back."

"Nonsense!" I said. "I bet you anything you like that we carry it off all right. She only wants a little humouring, and Delia and I are quite capable of humouring the old dame."

"There's Tootums, you know—"

"Well, we shall take example from your fall. Tootums shall not so much as smell mince, even in a pie."

"How much will you bet that you aren't crossed off?"

"A fiver," I said, largely.

"Done!" said Bob, returning to his little wooden holes.

Aunt Matilda arrived. She was very pleasant and easy to get on with. She was delighted with her room and her bed and her view and everything else. Delia, too, put up quite a good show with the objectionable Tootums, even imperilling her immortal soul by calling him "sweet".

Christmas things were pouring in by this time. Bob's present to us had arrived the night before. It was an elaborate fretwork box, about six inches square with a door in one side. We didn't know what it was meant to be, but then no one ever does know what Bob's presents are meant to be. And it doesn't much matter. They generally might be anything. I mean, if you get an ornamental box from him and plant bulbs in it, you're quite likely to find out afterwards that he meant it for keeping collar-studs in.

We'd bought Aunt Matilda a writing-case for Christmas, but of course she was to know nothing about it till Christmas morning. Then – to our horror – on Christmas Eve she looked at us coyly and said:

"Tootums and I are so much looking forward to your Christmas present – Tootums especially."

And then – too late – I remembered. I'd met her for a day in Bath or Tunbridge Wells or Bournemouth or one of her select resorts in the summer, and she'd confided to me how much she'd like to have some sort of box or basket to hold darling Tootums on journeys when she had to stay with relations. I'd said that I would consider it a great honour to be allowed to give her one for her Christmas present, and then had never once thought of it again – till now. When she'd gone to bed, Delia and I stared at each other blankly.

"What shall we do?" I said. "We're absolutely dished. We can't give her the writing-case now, and it's too late to buy anything."

But Delia is of the stuff of which Britons are made. She never knows when she's beaten.

"Bob's box," she said. "We'll give it to her. She can put a little shawl in and it will be quite cosy. There is a sort of door there already. It's just the thing. And we haven't shown it to her, so that's all right."

So the next morning, directly after breakfast, we presented her with Bob's box as Tootums' travelling case, and she was delighted.

"Tweetie tweetie ickle house for darling Tootums in puff-puffs," she explained to the animal. "Come upstairs and find a nice warm shawl and see how darling Tootums likes his tweetie tweetie ickle house for puff-puffs."

So she went upstairs with the animal and the box, and I turned my attention to the post, which had just arrived. There was a letter from Bob:

"Dear Old Boy" it ran, – *"Hope you got the rat-trap all right. I didn't send any explanations with it, but it's quite simple. You put a piece of cheese or something in the further part. The creature enters by the door, which then closes automatically. The fretwork, of course, is just to make the thing more ornamental. The holes are not large enough for the creature to escape. As soon as the creature reaches the middle of the cage a heavy weight is automatically released from the roof and stuns the creature completely and—"*

I started up wildly, but it was too late. From upstairs came the mingled yells of agony from Tootums and Aunt Matilda. Evidently the weight had just been automatically released....

That night Aunt Matilda made a completely new will.

And the bitterest part of the whole thing is that I owe Bob a fiver.

The Daily Guide

(London Opinion 1/1/1927)

"I've got my Daily Guide," said Delia at breakfast.

"Have you?" I said, non-commitally, because I wasn't sure whether it was a New Thought book or a set of racing tips for the week. With Delia it might have been either.

"It's a horoscope," said Delia. "I sent the date of my birth and ten-and-sixpence, and they've given me advice for every day of the year."

"I'd have given it to you for less than that," I murmured.

"But it's made from the stars," said Delia in a hushed voice of awe. "He just looks at the stars and then he knows everything that's going to happen to everyone all through the year."

"I'll run over and see him myself," I said, "nearer the Derby."

It was the next week that I came home one evening and found a new standard lamp in the drawing room, new cushions on the sofa, and a new dress on Delia.

"Hallo!" I said. "Have you come into a legacy?"

"No, darling," she said. "I haven't paid for them yet. I mean, the bills are coming in to you. But it's quite all right."

"Is it?" I said. "How do you make that out?"

"Well, I *had* to buy something. My Daily Guide said, 'Your undertakings are under favourable auspices today. Venture freely in financial matters'. So I ventured freely, that's all."

"Delia," I said, sadly, "you're one of those women we read of in books who aren't fit for a good man's love."

"But, you see, I *had* to," said Delia. "One can't escape one's fate."

I realised then what a potent weapon a Daily Guide is in the hands of an unscrupulous woman.

LONDON OPINION

January 1, 1927.

2D.

DANGER

A Cold "Snap"

But I'm not the man to take that sort of thing lying down. I didn't imbibe the sentiment that Britons never, never, never would be slaves with my mother's milk for nothing. So I found that Daily Guide in Delia's bureau one afternoon when she was out paying calls (it had told her on that day not to ignore her friends, which I said referred to me, but Delia insisted referred to Mrs Robinson), and I had a good look at it.

For the next day it said, "Beware of theft", so I asked Jones to dinner. Delia

127

didn't seem pleased when I told her. She said that she was tired and that she'd got nothing in the house fit to eat, and that she particularly wanted a quiet evening, and that she'd nothing to wear, and that Jones was a dreadful bore, and that she'd thought of letting Jane have the evening off, and that she wanted to go to bed early, and that he'd only ask us back and she was sick of listening to Jones and me discussing business....

Those were just a few of the objections. She didn't mention the real one, however, but I knew what it was. She wanted to spend the whole day bewaring of theft; in other words, to collect all her valuables and sit over them guarding them, from early morn to dewy eve, and she knew that she couldn't if Jones came to dinner.

He came, however, and we played cards after dinner in the drawing room, except for about ten minutes, when I remembered suddenly that I'd got to ring someone up, and left Jones to discuss the electricity bill with Delia (he labours under the delusion that he understands it). At least, not discuss exactly, because Jones does all the talking.

He was still talking when I returned, and Delia was still sitting with her eyes fixed on the window. I knew that she was watching for some furtive cat-burglar's hand to appear at the latch. Jones didn't go till after twelve. The minute he'd gone Delia ran upstairs to count her jewellery. Then she ran down to the morning room. And in the morning room she found her bureau open and her silver inkstand and silver candlesticks and silver calendar gone, and – her Daily Guide gone!

She was distraught.

"There!" she said. "Why *did* you have that Mr Jones to dinner? All my silver gone! *And* my Daily Guide!"

"Never mind, Delia," I consoled her. "That man in the stars saw that your things had to be stolen, so they *had* to be stolen. You'd have felt that you'd wasted your money if they hadn't been, wouldn't you? One can't escape one's fate."

"Well," said Delia, "it *is* rather wonderful when you come to think of it. Confess that you're convinced, anyway."

So I confessed that I was convinced.

She decided that she wouldn't buy another Daily Guide because if she had to buy another every time is said "beware of theft" (and it said it quite a lot of times) it would come too expensive.

The silver things were returned anonymously the next week. But not the Daily Guide. Delia says that it will serve him out because he'll probably try to use it and the advice won't apply to him at all (unless he happens to have been born on the same day, which isn't likely), and he'll be doing all the things on the wrong days. But the whole thing has impressed her tremendously. You'll often hear her talking about it. She says:

"And, my dear, it really was *wonderful*, because the *very* day it said 'beware of theft'...."

And you'll notice if I'm there I don't say anything.

The Name
(The Humorist 23/4/1927)

Delia and I have built a new house. It stands with a dozen or so others in a large field which has been sold in building plots. Their only drawback is that they are rather exposed to the public view, because it happened to be a field which hadn't any trees. And, of course, there is that new look. When you see them standing in a row, all very red and white with red slanting roofs, the years slip back and you can almost hear someone telling you to put them away in the box now, because it's nearly bedtime.

It's much easier to build a house than Delia and I thought it was going to be. You simply go to a man and tell him the sort of house you want, and that it mustn't cost more than a thousand pounds. Then he smiles and tells you that that sort of house costs four thousand, and so you say you'll go home and think it over.

So you go home and think it over and the next morning you go back to him and ask him what sort of a house you can have for not more than a thousand pounds, and he tells you, and you say you'll have that sort then, and so he builds it for you.

You see, so far it's amazingly simple. You go over and watch it every weekend, and every weekend it grows a little more like the houses you used to build on the nursery hearthrug on wet afternoons, till one day you find it's all finished, and a man comes and fetches your furniture for you, and the local butchers and milkmen begin to call on you to tell you how much better they are than each other, and so you find you're "in".

Of course, I knew there must be some catch in it somewhere. It was all so simple that there must be a catch in it somewhere. And last week I found what the catch was. We'd been in the house for a whole day when Delia suddenly screamed:

"Goodness! A name! We've not got a name for it!"

A cousin of Delia's happened to be there, and he at once took command of the situation. He's one of those people who are never happy unless they are taking command of situations. He's what refined people call "a born organiser", and vulgar people "a nosey parker". I tried to get in first. I murmured: "Let's call it 'Box No.1, Simple Models', but he ignored me and said:

"The great thing in making a choice of this sort is to be methodical. One must, of course, avoid the pretentious, such as 'Balmoral', and equally the affected such as 'Weald Cot'. I think the best thing is to consider the thing under general classifications."

I said, "Exactly," because he evidently wanted someone to say something. It seemed to encourage him. He proceeded.

"One way of naming one's house is to name it after some bird that haunts it, such as 'The Rookery'."

"'The Sparrowery' in our case, I said, brightly. "Or must it be a bird? Why not 'The Mousery'? Delia saw two in the pantry this morning."

"Or again," he went on, ignoring me, "another custom is to name it after some feature of the garden such as 'The Larches' or 'The Elms'."

I glanced out of the window. Edwardes, our newly-engaged jobbing gardener, was just beginning to wrestle with the chaos.

"'The Tin Cans'," I suggested, helpfully.

"I think it should be a tree," said Delia's cousin, pained.

"We haven't exactly got a tree," I admitted, "but I'm hoping to have some rhubarb in before long. Why not call it 'The Rhubarbs'? I've always wanted to live in a house called 'The Rhubarbs'."

"Or," went on Delia's cousin, throwing me a cold glance, "they are sometimes called after the view they command, such as 'Belview' or 'Meadow View' or 'River View'."

I glanced again through the window. In the distance among the trees smoked the chimneys of a local institution.

"'Workhouse View'," I suggested.

Again he ignored me.

"Or sometimes," he said, "the occupants call the house by the name of the place where they spent their honeymoon, such as 'Cliftonville' or 'Hove'."

Delia's cousin is one of those very refined people who never speak of Margate or Brighton – only of Cliftonville and Hove.

"It's unfortunate that we happened to spend ours in the Scilly Isles," I said, thoughtfully, "but perhaps we could shorten it somehow – 'The Scillies', or just 'The Isles'."

"I don't think we ought to decide anything in a harry," said Delia's cousin, solemnly. "I'll think it over and let you know my decision in the morning."

"And I'll let you know mine," I said, because, hang it all, it was my house. It was my Building Society that was paying for it, not his.

He arrived quite early the next morning.

"I've decided on the name. 'Euphrosyne'," he said. "It's uncommon and poetic and cultured."

"Let's go and measure the gate first," I murmured.

Delia's cousin is always quite impervious to sarcasm. He followed me round to the gate. And there we found Edwardes nailing a brass plate on to it. The brass plate bore the legend "The Beeches".

"Noticed you hadn't got a name for it, sir," he said cheerfully, "so picked this up cheap for you. House they were pulling down up the road."

I recovered myself with an effort.

"But Edwardes," I said, "there – there aren't any beeches."

"That's all right, sir," he said soothingly. "I've planted a beech nut in the middle of the garden this very morning."

So we're called "The Beeches". I feel there's something distinctive in being called "The Beeches" when the garden consists solely of old paint tins. People stop to look at it. I feel that only a superman, a man with a Napoleonic faith in his star, would dare to do it. It occurred to me suddenly last night, though, that Edwards ought to have planted two beech nuts instead of one, as the title is in the plural, but as I don't suppose they would ever come up it doesn't matter.

And, anyway, it's better than 'Euphrosyne'.

A Question of Licence
(The Humorist 30/4/1927)

"It's a plain-clothes policeman," said Delia, in a horror-struck whisper. "He's come about the licence."

Now both Delia and I have very bad memories, and we'd suddenly discovered when we were out in the car that morning that we were still sporting last quarter's car licence, which should have been renewed a fortnight ago and hadn't been. We'd not been using the car lately and we'd simply never thought about renewing the licence.

Of course, as soon as we discovered it we tore home and wrote off to the licence people. But, as Delia gloomily remarked, "Someone's *sure* to have seen us. They'll be sending to arrest us after lunch."

"They won't arrest us, darling," I reassured her. "They'll only summons us."

"That's just as bad," groaned Delia. "I've never been in a police court in my life before. I shall simply die of shame."

So when she came to me white with horror after lunch I knew that the worst had happened.

"Where is he?" I hissed.

"In the morning room. Oh, isn't it *terrible*, John?"

"Nonsense!" I said. "Leave him to me. I'll deal with him."

"Don't do anything *rash*," she pleaded. "I mean – we'll be together anyway – even in prison."

I went into the morning room. A stern-looking man turned from the window.

"Good morning, sir," he said. "It has come to my notice that—"

"Sit down, won't you?" I said, propitiatingly. "A tiring day, isn't it? Hot for this time of year. Allow me."

I opened the cupboard door where I keep the best whisky, and a bitter, bitter struggle took place in my heart. That best bottle of whisky had been sent to me from Scotland last Christmas by Uncle Sandy, who knows what good whisky is, and there was only one glassful left – one glassful which I was treasuring for some noble occasion.

Still, for Delia's sake, I conquered the stirrings of my lower nature and poured out the glassful for him. He put a little soda water into it, then drained it.

"Good whisky," I said with a wistful note in my voice. "What?"

"Rather," he said feelingly. "Well, sir, it has come to my notice that—"

Again I interrupted.

"You were looking at the garden when I came in," I said. "Are you interested in gardens?"

"Yes, I am," he said. "You've got some extraordinarily fine azaleas there."

"Haven't I," I agreed cordially. "Let me give you some cuttings." Then, after another inward struggle, I said, "I've got some fine forced mushrooms, too. Do you like mushrooms?"

It appeared that he did like mushrooms. It went to my heart to give him those few choice treasured mushrooms but – for Delia's sake – I did it.

"Very kind of you indeed, sir," he said, as we went back to the house. But it didn't stop him. Oh, no. The minute we got back to the morning room he began again.

"What I really came about – it has come to my notice that—"

I am not a man to give in without a struggle. I interrupted him by pressing a ten-shilling note into his hand.

"A little contribution towards your expenses," I murmured. "I'm sorry you've had the trouble of coming out to me here. Everything very difficult nowadays, isn't it?"

I've always heard that the police are incorruptible but, of course, one never knows.

"Oh, no, sir," he said. "I couldn't possibly take that."

"Oh, yes," I said. "I insist."

He pocketed it.

"Thank you, sir," he said. "Very good of you, sir. Well, as I say, what I really came to see you about is that it has come to my notice that—"

"Excuse me a minute," I said, and went quickly from the room.

Delia was waiting for me, white and tense with anxiety, in the drawing room.

"Well?" she said.

I sat down and mopped my brow.

"It's no use, Delia," I said brokenly. "I can't stop him. He's like one of those juggernauts we read of in books. I keep placing offerings in his path and he just rolls on and on. By the way, I suppose you're *sure* he's a plain-clothes policeman come about the licence?"

"He must be," said Delia simply, "because he's in plain clothes, and it's just after we've been out without a licence."

I returned to him.

"Yes?" I said bluntly. "What was it you came to see me about?"

"Well, sir," he said, "it has come to my notice that you have just purchased a new mowing machine. Here is my card. I undertake the oiling and sharpening of lawnmowers at regular intervals, undertaking to keep them in perfect condition without the owner's having any responsibility in the matter at all. If you will—"

But at this point I'd recovered from my stupor.

He must have thought me a very hasty-tempered and unreasonable and changeable man, but as I never heard anything from his lawyer I presume that that glass of Uncle Sandy's whisky and those azalea cuttings and those mushrooms and the ten-shilling note compensated, in his eyes, for having been thrown down my front steps.

The Vase

(The Humorist 21/5/1927)

"You mustn't practise in the garden," said Delia. "You'll only break a window or something."

Now when you're only just beginning golf it is very tempting to practise in the garden. A man feels so much less of a fool in his own garden than on a public green. But I only said coldly:

"My dear Delia," I have other things to do than practise golf in the garden."

And I went into the study and looked very busy there till I saw her pass the window and go out of the front gate.

Then I went and got my clubs and practised golf in the garden.

I approached the house very cautiously to see exactly what the damage was. Fortunately the drawing room window had been left open, so the ball had been able to enter the drawing room without breaking it. But inside the drawing room? I hardly dared to hope. No, there it was, lying on the hearthrug among the fragments of a vase which had been one of our wedding presents.

Now Delia is frightfully sentimental about wedding presents and, being a woman, would be sure to say "I told you so". I came to a quick decision. I pocketed the golf ball, picked up the pieces of that silly little vase, wrapped them in paper, and drove into town to match it.

And I did match it, too, but – well, I'd no idea that Uncle Frederick had given so much for it. I think that the habit of giving expensive wedding presents is a very inconsiderate one, and ought to be stopped. It comes unduly hard on one when one practises golf in the garden.

Fortune, however, was apparently on my side.

I got the new vase safely on the mantelpiece and the pieces of the old one safely buried in the garden before Delia returned.

The new vase was exactly like the old one, and I was convinced that no one could have noticed any difference, but all the evening Delia sat and stared at that vase in a petrified kind of way. Moreover, she was rather pale and – for Delia – quiet. At last I took the bull by the horns.

"Why ever do you keep looking at that vase?" I said.

Delia gulped; then spoke with a gasp:

"I'll tell you," she said. "It's the most *extraordinary* thing that's ever happened to me in my life. I'd never have believed it if anyone else had told me. I broke that vase this afternoon." She made a dramatic pause, in which I began to speak, then hastily checked myself.

She went on: "I was tearing the date off the calendar just over the mantelpiece, and I knocked the vase clean off the mantelpiece on to the hearthrug, and it broke into smithereens. I was so late for Mrs Smith's that I hadn't time even to stop to pick the pieces up. So I just simply left it where it was.

"And while I was at Mrs Smith's people were talking about Eastern people and their sort of magic powers, and somebody who'd been to the East said that some of them could make material things do what they wanted, and I said, 'I wish I could. I broke a vase just before I came out. I wish I could find it unbroken again when I get home.'

"And John," added Delia, faintly, "now

comes the *strange* part of it. I *did*. Look, there's the vase quite unbroken again, though I left it in pieces on the hearthrug! I must possess those strange magic powers, like Hindus and people like that. It – it rather frightens me."

Well, of course I reassured her and told her the whole story, and – and, would you believe me, she was mean enough to refuse to pay even half the new vase. And instead of being relieved to find that she did not possess strange and terrible magic powers, she seemed quite offended about it.

The whole episode has disgusted me so much that I've almost decided to give up golf altogether.

Two to Tea
(The Humorist 28/5/1927)

I met Mrs Brown at the corner of the road.

"I'm so depressed!" she said.

"Why?" I asked, kindly.

"I've promised to go to tea with Mrs Jones, and I don't want to a bit. What does one do in such a case?"

Now, I pride myself on being the most gallant and hospitable man in our garden city. So I said, "One rings up Mrs Jones and one says that one is not well enough to go to her, and one comes to tea with us instead."

"That does sound rather nice," she said, wistfully. "Wouldn't Delia mind?"

"Delia would love it," I said quite truthfully, because Delia is the sort of woman who loves having people to tea. She feels a day is wasted if no one comes to tea. "You'll simply save Delia's life."

"Well, of course, if you put it like *that*," said Mrs Brown. "The thought of having tea with Mrs Jones has been hanging over me like a leaden weight all day – she's such a terrific bore – but I'd simply *love* to have tea with you and Delia. I know it's wicked, but you've tempted me and I'll fall."

We'd just reached her gate.

She said, "Just a minute," and ran into her house. A moment later she ran out.

"I've done it," she said. "I've rung her up. She was out, but I left a message. I said that I wasn't well enough to go to tea with her – and now for a nice cosy time with you and Delia."

Delia wasn't in when we got back, so I settled Mrs Brown in the best armchair in the drawing room, and was just beginning to entertain her in my best style when I heard the front door open and Delia come into the hall talking to someone.

"Hullo, darling!" she called from the hall.

"Hullo!" I replied. "I've got a nice surprise for you."

"So have I for you," called Delia. "I've brought Mrs Jones to tea. Isn't it nice? I met her when I was coming up from the village, and I said that I'd no one to have tea with – except you, darling, and you don't count – and she said that she was expecting a most terrific bore to tea, or she'd come.

"So I said, 'Put off the terrific bore.' She said she would, and she went home to do it, but fortunately she found that the terrific bore had put her off, so it was all right. And I've brought her along and here we are."

She flung open the door and appeared on the threshold with Mrs Jones.

No, I won't go on. There are some situations that defy the power of description and are best left to the imagination.

Mrs Brown isn't speaking to Mrs Jones or us, and Mr Jones isn't speaking to Mr Brown or us, and Delia says that it's all my fault, and I say that it's all Delia's. But I quite agree with her when she says that it's enough to make one want to go into a monastery.

Our Country Walk
(The Humorist 4/6/1927)

"I suppose we shall go out in the car for the day as usual?" I said to Delia after I had greeted her affectionately on Whit Monday morning. I don't greet Delia affectionately on ordinary mornings, because the 8.35 doesn't leave time for it.

I'd noticed a very earnest look on her face when I entered the room, but I wasn't prepared for the deep earnestness of the tone in which she replied.

"No. *Not* in the car."

I was surprised. All the years I have known her we'd gone out in the car on Bank Holidays.

"Why ever not?" I said.

"I've been reading an article in the newspaper," said Delia yet more seriously.

I groaned inwardly. Delia has an unfortunate habit of taking newspaper articles seriously, and of course nothing complicates life so much as taking newspaper articles seriously.

"What did it say?" I asked apprehensively.

"It said," replied Delia even more earnestly than ever, "that we are ruining ourselves and our country by going about in cars. It said that it was a sign of the degeneracy of the times and that we ought to make a stand against it. It said that we ought to get back to simplicity and *walk*. It said that we ought to go out and discover the by-ways of our country and tramp over the hills and across the fields and past the dear little farms. It all sounded so beautiful, and when I read it I made up my mind that that was how we'd spend the next Bank Holiday."

I blinked and swallowed, but knew by experience that it's no use arguing with Delia when she's been reading newspaper articles and is feeling earnest. So I said:

"Right you are. Let's set off at once. How soon can you be ready?"

"Ten minutes," said Delia. "It's so lovely to think that in our tiny little humble way we're helping to nip the tide of decadence in the bud, isn't it?"

"You mix your metaphors," I protested mildly, "but yes, isn't it?"

"Am I suitably dressed?" said Delia when I met her at the front door ten minutes later. She was frightfully suitably dressed. She wore very large shoes and an old hat and carried a walking-stick. And she still looked earnest.

"You are," I said. "You'll cow the cattle for miles around."

"Cattle?" said Delia anxiously. "Do you think there'll be many cattle about?"

I told her that I didn't think there would. Not really savage ones, anyway.

"Isn't it glorious?" said Delia as we swung up the hillside. "I can't think why we've never done this before, can you? It's so wonderful, isn't it?"

"Isn't it?" I agreed.

We swung on some more. At last Delia stopped and rested on her stick.

"I'm only stopping to admire the view," she explained, panting. "I'm enjoying it awfully. It's all so wonderful, isn't it?"

"Isn't it?" I agreed again.

We walked on again. Gradually Delia stopped talking about the scenery. It took too much breath.

But after about half a mile, past the top of the hill, she said again: "It's all so wonderful, isn't it?"

It seemed rather more of a question than

when she'd said it before. It sounded wistful and as if she wanted someone to answer it. So I said: "Yes, isn't it? I think I'll sell the car."

"Oh, I wouldn't do that," said Delia, with deep feeling. "They – they have their uses – cars. I – I don't believe in going to extremes in anything. How many miles have we walked?"

"Nearly two," I said.

"Nonsense!" said Delia sharply. "We've walked twenty at least. I *know* we have. I can *feel* we have. I should think that it's nearly one o'clock, isn't it?"

"No," I said. "It's not eleven yet."

We walked in silence again for half a mile. Then Delia said: "Think of all the cars surging down the Brighton road now. Aren't you glad you're not with them?"

"Are you?" I said.

"I wish you wouldn't keep *arguing!*" said Delia wearily. Then, after another long silence: "There doesn't seem to be anyone *about* in the country, does there? And I'd no idea the roads were so rough."

"But isn't it wonderful," I said, "to think that in our tiny little humble way we're helping to nip the tide of decadence in the bud?"

"Oh, do stop saying that!" said Delia irritably.

After another quarter of a mile, she said in a far-away voice: "There's something so jolly and friendly in rolling down a nice big smooth main road with a lot of other cars, I always think, don't you?"

"No, Delia," I said. "I think it's a far, far better thing to get back to simplicity and discover the by-ways of our country and tramp over the hills and past the dear little farms and—"

"I do wish you'd stop talking so idiotically," snapped Delia.

We came to a farm. The air was rent by the fierce barking of its faithful watchdog. Delia suddenly clung to me hysterically.

"I won't go past that hateful dog," she said. "I can hear by its bark that it's an Alsatian or something bloodthirsty like that, and there's a cow in the field just beyond, and I *know* it's a bull, and these great big shoes are hurting my feet, and I'm lonely and tired and hungry, and I think the country's horrible and—"

A man came out of the farm.

"Have you any sort of conveyance?" I asked.

"Only a wagonette," he said.

"A wagonette will do quite nicely," I said.

So Delia and I drove home in the wagonette, and Delia changed her shoes and hat, and we got out the car and drove down to Brighton.

The Lift
(The Humorist 11/6/1927)

"There's an automatic lift here," said Delia, as soon as we reached our bedrooms in the hotel.

"Beastly things," I said. "I hate them."

"Why?" inquired Delia.

"Because they never work," I snapped. "They're always out of order."

"They aren't," said Delia, "and they do. You're frightened of them, that's what it is. You're a coward. You don't know how to work them."

"I do," I said, indignantly, "and I'm not." I was feeling just as one does feel after a long journey. "You just press a button and they come – or rather they don't come, because they're always out of order, and you have to walk downstairs."

Delia was in a pugnacious mood. She, too, of course, had just had a long journey.

"None I've known have ever been out of order," she said.

"All I've known have," I retorted. "Look here," I went on, "I'll make you a sporting offer. I'll go out to the lift now and press the little button, and I'll bet you ten shillings the thing doesn't come."

"Done!" said Delia, promptly.

I went to the end of the passage where the lift was, pressed the little button, and waited. Nothing happened. My spirits rose. I always enjoy being in the right. I pressed the little button again. Again nothing happened. Delia came along the corridor to me.

"I've won my ten bob," I called out, triumphantly. "The thing's out of order. I've pressed the button twice and it hasn't come!"

With a gurgle Delia opened the gate and stepped into the lift.

"No, darling," she said, "because it happens to be here already. Ten bob, please."

Ancient v Modern
(The Humorist 2/7/1927)

Aunt Jennie is, as far as I know, the only person in England who has never been for a drive in a motor-car.

She has a very sedate victoria drawn by a very sedate horse driven by a very sedate coachman. In the family we call it "The Hearse". At intervals we try to convert her to a motor-car, but she always has some excuse.

However, last week I tried again.

"A carriage is so *slow*, Aunt Jennie," I said. "I bet you anything you like that once you've been out in a car you'll never look at the hearse – I mean, the victoria, again. With a car you just get in, and before you know where you are, you're over the edge of the horizon."

"It does sound rather attractive," said Aunt Jennie, who is quite a sport in her own way.

"Let me come and take you out on Monday," I said.

Aunt Jennie considered.

"Very well," she said at last, "I suppose I ought to move with the times."

I drove up in fine style on Monday afternoon, and just went in for a little chat with her first. When we'd discussed the weather and the state of the garden and the high price of coal and the slackness of the vicar, I said:

"Now, let's have the drive. You just get in, and before you know where you are you'll be in the next village."

We went out. I leapt into my seat, and pressed the self-starter. The self-starter refused to self-start.

"Oh, I know," I said. "The thing's not been charging. Fuse gone or something. It won't take a minute."

I got out and swung the starting-handle. It started. I got in again. It stopped. I got out again.

"A bit cold," I explained, and swung again. It started beautifully. Aunt Jennie got in beside me and we slid off.

"Now, this *is* something like, isn't it?" I said. "Better than the old hearse, what? Before we know where we are we'll be in—"

It stopped again.

"By Jove!" I said. "I forgot to turn on the petrol."

I got down and turned on the petrol and started the engine again. Then I got in again.

"*Now!*" I said, enthusiastically, as we slid off again. "Before you can count ten we shall be in—"

It stopped again. I got out and examined it.

"Probably an airlock in the petrol pipe," I explained, or it might be a bit of grit in the carburettor. Won't take a minute, anyway."

Aunt Jennie turned and held up her hand. And at once, out of the stable, came the hearse – sedate victoria, sedate horse, sedate coachman.

Aunt Jennie turned and looked at me demurely.

"I'd heard that they generally do this," she twinkled, "so I told John to be ready so that we could really get a drive before the sun goes down."

So I left the car where it was – we hadn't got as far as the gate – and went for a nice sedate drive with Aunt Jennie in the victoria before the sun went down.

And so Aunt Jennie is still the only person in England who has never been for a drive in a motor-car.

The Name

(The Humorist 23/7/1927)

"John wants you to be godfather and me to be godmother," said Delia, looking up from the letter which announced the arrival of my first nephew.

"All right," I said obligingly. "What do we know about it?"

"We buy it a silver mug and choose its name."

"Good," I said. "We'll choose something uncommon. We'll call it Habakkuk. I've always wanted to know someone called Habakkuk."

"We'll do nothing of the sort," said Delia firmly.

"Delia," I said solemnly, "a godfather takes precedence of any mere godmother. The Church tells wives to be subjects to their husbands in all things. It's going to be called Habakkuk."

"No clergyman would christen a child with such an outrageous name."

"He would. He'd have to. He'll say 'Name this child', and I shall say 'Habakkuk', and he'll *have* to call it Habakkuk. You aren't allowed to forbid the banns in the baptism service and, besides, it's a perfectly good name. It comes in the bible. No clergyman could refuse it. Archibald or Clarence, or whatever name *you* want to call it, isn't in the bible at all. What name do you want to call it, anyway?"

"Michael," said Delia dreamily. "I think that Michael's such a nice name."

"I don't," I said. "It's a rotten name. It simply doesn't compare with Habakkuk. Michael! Why, every hero of every soppy story I've ever read has been called Michael. Have you ever read a soppy story whose hero has been called Habakkuk? No! Why? Because Habakkuk isn't a soppy name. It's a strong name. It's a he-man's name."

"It's an outrageous name," said Delia angrily.

"Hush, Delia," I said reproachfully. "He wouldn't like to hear you talking like that."

"Who wouldn't?"

"Habakkuk. John's son."

"Do you mean Michael?" said Delia.

"No. I mean Habakkuk."

"I'm its godmother," said Delia, "and I *insist* on Michael."

"I'm its godfather," I said, "and I *insist* on Habakkuk."

Delia took up her novel and refused to answer me when I spoke to her.

So I took up my newspaper and refused to speak to her.

Then suddenly she took up John's letter and read it again.

"Hullo!" she said. "Here's a postscript. I hadn't noticed it. He's to be called 'George'," she read.

A Little Fortune-Telling

(London Opinion 27/8/1927)

"Do come and have your fortune told by cards," said Delia. "George's sister does it. Everyone says she's wonderful."

So she took me to George's sister, who spread out the cards on the table and said in a deep voice:

"There's a fair woman in your life."

Delia raised her eyebrows meaningly. Delia is dark.

George's sister went on to tell me a lot more interesting things about legacies and sudden journeys, and I quite forgot about the fair woman till we got outside, when Delia burst out passionately:

"It's Miss Menzies. I *know* it's Miss Menzies."

"What's Miss Menzies?" I said, mystified.

"The fair woman," she said. "I've noticed you've not been *half* as nice to me lately."

"*Delia!*" I said in outraged innocence, but she went on tearfully:

"I've *suspected* that there must be someone and now I *know*. It *must* be true if it's in your cards.

"I see it all clearly now. You were talking to her at the church fête. She put a flower into your buttonhole. I *saw* her."

"I paid one-and-six for it," I murmured. "I had to. It was for the new organ."

"And you played tennis with her in the tournament."

"I had to," I murmured again. "My name was drawn with hers."

"Of course you've got excuses," said Delia. "You probably made them up behind my back."

"Delia," I said, very solemnly, "I swear to you—"

But Delia burst out again passionately:

"Why is she still unmarried – a pretty girl like that – if it isn't that she is in love with you?"

I couldn't think of any other means of diverting her attention from my imaginary love affair, so I said:

"Delia, you never had your fortune told. Come back to George's sister and have it done now."

So we went back to George's sister, and George's sister spread out the cards for her and said:

"There's a dark man in your fate."

I ground my teeth. I am fair.

George's sister then told her a lot of rot about legacies and sums of money and sudden journeys, and at last we got away.

"It's Mr Hammett," I said sternly as soon as we got out of the house.

"What's Mr Hammett?" said Delia.

"The dark man," I said bitterly. "I might have known. Here I go off to work day after day, slaving myself to a skeleton" – Delia threw a glance at my well-filled figure – "and all the time you're carrying on with Mr Hammett behind my back."

"I'm not," said Delia furiously. "How dare you say such a thing. I don't even like the man."

I gave a snarling laugh.

"Oh, no," I said. "You didn't have him to tea last week, did you?"

"His mother was there, too," said Delia, "and tea's nothing."

"Tea!" I snorted. "Oh, no! Tea's nothing. But tell me. Why is it the man's still unmarried – a nice-looking man like that – if not because he's in love with you?

Why—"

We collided with Mrs Greene, our next-door neighbour.

"Have you heard the happy news?" said Mrs Greene.

"No," I said. "There isn't any happy news to hear."

"Yes there is," said Mrs Greene brightly. "Miss Menzies has just got engaged to Mr Hammett."

And she passed on.

"Delia," I said simply; "I have misjudged you. Forgive me."

"And I didn't really mean anything I said about Miss Menzies," said Delia humbly.

"I can't kiss you in the middle of the High Street," I said, "but let's do something to celebrate."

So we did.

We went to the pictures.

In the one-and-sixpenny seats.

And we saw a beautiful film about a husband and wife who were jealous of each other, but it all came right in the end.

The Explanation
(The Humorist 10/12/1927)

"She's given notice," said Delia, looking white and stricken. "She's going."

"*What!*" I said, aghast.

After weary years of searching we had found the perfect cook. We had lured her to our home, and we were straining every nerve to keep her there. We'd had wireless installed in the kitchen. We had scrapped all its old furniture and got the entire kitchen suite of the £500 furnished house of a really superior furniture shop. We put an art carpet down for her. We gave her the best dining room armchair. We bought her novels about sheiks and strong silent men. We'd done all we could think of, and now after only one week came the bombshell. She was going.

"B-but why?" I stammered.

"She says you've insulted her," said Delia. "And we shall *never* get anyone else who'll make omelettes like that again!"

"I've *never* insulted her," I said, indignantly. "How *could* I insult anyone who makes Yorkshire pudding as she does?"

"Then *do* go and tell her you didn't mean it. She's packed her trunk. She's going tonight. She's frightfully angry. When I think of her soufflés—"

"And her pastry—"

We blended our tears for a few minutes. Then Delia said again:

"*Do* go and apologise to her."

"How can I apologise for something I've never done?" I said, testily.

"Then go and tell her you've never done it. When I think of her omelettes—"

"And her Yorkshire pudding!" I moaned. Delia stamped her foot.

"*Do* go and apologise to her," she said, "instead of standing there bleating."

"I wasn't bleating, Delia," I said with dignity. "I was moaning." Then I took my courage in both hands and went over the top. I walked into the hall, stood for a few seconds outside the kitchen door to gather my strength, and then entered. Stern and frowning, Cook faced me across the table.

"I'm afraid there's been some misunderstanding, Cook," I said, brokenly. "Your mistress tells me that – that I have unintentionally offended you."

"Hunintentionally is as hunintentionally does, sir," said Cook, grimly. "Words wrote is words wrote."

"I – I've never written anything about you, Cook," I said, pleadingly. "I – I appreciate your Yorkshire pudding more than I can possibly say."

"It's a pity you didn't think of that before, sir," said Cook, more grimly than ever.

"Before what?" I said.

"Before you wrote what you wrote, sir."

"What *did* I write?" I demanded, wildly.

"*You* ought to know that best, sir," said Cook, icily. "And now I'd be glad if you'd kindly order me a cab."

"Cook—" I began in passionate pleading, but she had gone upstairs to put her things on.

I returned, a broken man, to Delia.

"I can't stop her," I said. "She's going. She says I wrote something about her. I never did. I've never written anything about her in my life."

"We shall *never* get anyone to make omelettes like hers," said Delia. "And her mayonnaise—"

"Don't," I moaned. "Don't remind me of it."

Again we blended our tears for a few minutes. Then the cab came to the door, and Cook came downstairs in her best hat and coat.

"Cook," pleaded Delia, "is it any use to beg you to overlook whatever has annoyed you and to promise that it won't occur again?"

"None at all, ma'am," said Cook, very decidedly, and got into the cab.

Then she leaned out of the window and said to me:

"If you didn't like what I give you for lunch, sir, it would have been more gentlemanly to speak to me about it instead of writing to the papers."

Then she drove off.

"*Did* you write to the papers about what she give – gave – you for lunch?" gasped Delia.

I tore my hair.

"*No!*" I said. "NO! The woman's mad. She's been dreaming. I've only written one letter to the paper in my life, and that was last week about the new open-air swimming bath."

Now, I don't know why I'd written to the local paper about that, but I had. I'd spent nearly a whole day in the new open-air swimming baths the week before, and I suppose that some of the water had got on my brain, because when I came home I felt suddenly moved to write an account of it to the local paper in the form of a letter, and I'd written it and posted it before I returned to my normal self. Not that I really regretted it. It looked extraordinarily well in print.

"That's the only one I've ever written, Delia," I went on, "and I didn't mention Cook in it at all."

We returned sorrowfully to the kitchen.

There upon the dresser was a copy of the local paper in which my letter had appeared.

"Here it is," said Delia, mournfully. "How *could* it have annoyed her?"

She turned to my letter and read it again. Then she gave a little scream.

"This must be it," she said. "Look. The top of the 'h' isn't printed properly. It looks just like an 'n'."

I snatched the paper from her. In my letter I had written:

"I went home and after a hasty lunch returned to the swimming bath."

Delia was right. The top of the "h" in "hasty" wasn't printed properly. It looked like an "n".

That's the first letter I've ever written to a newspaper, and it will be the last.

Uncle Frederick's Christmas Present
(London Opinion 17/12/1927)

We always begin to get our Christmas presents ready the week before Christmas. We bring them down and spread them over the dining room table. Delia takes one side for her side of the family and I take the other for mine.

I am much more punctilious than Delia. Delia just puts scraps of paper with "*With much love. In great haste, Delia*" scribbled on to them in her parcels. Delia hates writing letters, so she always puts "in haste" to give the impression that if only she'd had time she'd write the sort of letter that Madame de Sévigné or Lady Mary Wortley Montague used to write, but that she never has a second to spare. So she finished all hers while I was still writing to Uncle Frederick. I always take the most trouble over Uncle Frederick's letter, because Uncle Frederick sends cheques for Christmas presents and always waits to see what we send him before he makes out his cheque.

Uncle Frederick has a fiendish temper and needs very careful handling. It isn't that he wants us to give him expensive presents. He only wants it done the right way. So I always try very hard to do it the right way. I send him something useful (like most rich people, he loves presents that will save him having to spend a shilling or two on himself), and write him a nice long letter showing that I've taken a good deal of trouble over choosing his present and implying that he is never for one moment out of my thoughts.

This year I bought him a shaving mirror, because the last time I was at his house I noticed that his shaving mirror was looking rather wonky. Then I wrote the nice little letter. In it I said that I'd taken a lot of thought over his present and added: "*I shall think of you looking at this every morning and seeing your dear old face in it.*"

Affectionate, you see, and lightly humorous. I thought that he ought to be really pleased about it.

We decided not to wrap up the parcels till I'd got back from the office. We left them neatly arranged down the two sides of the table, mine with their beautifully-written letters upon them, and Delia's with her little "in haste" scrawls.

When I get back from the office Delia met me on the doorstep looking proud and pleased.

"I've done it all, darling," she said. "There's nothing for you to do at all. I've packed them all up and addressed them and taken them down to the post office, and they just caught the late afternoon post. Aren't I noble?"

"Awfully," I agreed. "I hope you packed mine just as I left them."

"Almost," she said. "I did just change one thing. I took your Uncle Frederick's shaving mirror for Danny" (Danny is Delia's brother) "because I *know* that Danny wants one and you aren't *sure* that your Uncle Frederick wants one. He probably *likes* his wonky one. It's probably fraught with memories of his youth and has twined itself round his heart."

"I'm sure it hasn't," I said, indignantly. "A shaving mirror couldn't twine itself round anyone's heart. And what about poor Uncle Frederick?"

"Oh, I sent him a nice etching instead. He'll love it. And it cost more than the shaving mirror."

"But I'd *written* about the mirror," I objected.

"Oh, well, I expect the letter would do for any present. You didn't actually mention a shaving mirror, did you?"

"N-no, but—"

"Then it would do for any present."

I thought over the letter in silence.

"It wouldn't, Delia," I said; "and anyway, what was the subject of the etching?"

"Oh, he'll love it. Anyone would. It was of the *sweetest* little donkey."

Cat and Mouse

(The Humorist 31/3/1928)

"Darling, *do* you know of any way of getting rid of mice?" said Delia.

"Have we got mice?" I asked.

"We've got a mouse," said Delia, "and it's a very big eater for its size."

"What about a trap?" I said.

"I've tried a trap," said Delia, sadly. "It knows all about traps. It simply laughs at them. I've heard it."

"A cat, then?"

"But we haven't got a cat."

"Why not get one?"

"How do you get one? I mean, what sort of shop do you go to for a cat? Would they have one at the Stores?"

"Possibly," I said.

So she rang up the Stores. They had one at the Stores. It was thirty-five shillings. Delia consulted me, anxiously.

"It wouldn't go with the house, would it?" she said. "I mean, a thirty-five shilling cat's out of all proportion to a £300 completely furnished. It would turn up its whiskers at everything. It would know that the cushions weren't real down, and it would sneer at the hair carpet. It would shudder at the Borris-Dowley, and it would probably guess that the whole thing had come in a plain van. And I'm sure it wouldn't want to catch our mouse. It's quite an ordinary, cheap sort of mouse. I've seen it. An expensive cat like that would probably be used to a very superior brand of mouse. How does one get a common sort of cat? The sort that goes with hair carpets and vegetable down, and a mass-production car?"

I considered for a minute.

"I think they come as strays," I said, thoughtfully, "and you speak kindly to them and they stay on."

"I see," said Delia. "Well, I'll just wait and hope."

So she waited and hoped for a week, while the mouse made nightly raids on the larder, and no strays strayed our way.

At the end of the week she began to get rather irritable.

"Haven't you found out how you get cats *yet?*" she said. "The mouse ate an enormous piece of cheese last night."

"No," I said, taking up a defensive attitude. "Cats are not my department. I pay the income tax and lock up at night and look for your glasses and clean the car. I really can't be expected to see about cats as well."

"All right," said Delia, with spirit. "I'll ask the milkman about it."

Whenever Delia wants to make me feel really inadequate she says that. So she asked the milkman about it, and the milkman, as usual, was equal to the occasion.

"The only thing to do, ma'am, is to ask heveryone you know if they 'appen to know of someone with one to dispose of. Sooner or later you're sure to come across someone that does know someone with one to dispose of. I come across a good many people on my round with cats to dispose of. I'll try'n get you one, ma'am."

It always piques me when Delia consults the milkman, so I decided to surprise and impress her by producing a cat myself.

I could ask everyone I met if they knew of anyone with one to dispose of as well as the milkman could. I did, but without any results. No one knew of anyone with one to dispose of. At length I gave up all hope and stopped asking.

And then, just as I was passing Mrs Jones's house, she rushed out and placed something black and furry in my arms.

"I heard you wanted one," she said, breathlessly, "and I'm so glad to be able to send it to a kind home. We really have enough."

And she disappeared into the night. She didn't seem to want to give its kind home a chance of refusing it. The journey was a difficult one. It hadn't a nice disposition. I wasn't surprised that Mrs Jones wanted another kind home for it. But I comforted myself with the reflection that Delia would be pleased.

I found Delia sitting in the dining room gazing with concern at two cats that shared the hearthrug.

"People are *so* kind," she said, faintly. "Mrs Smith and Mrs Robinson have *both* sent cats in, but I really didn't want two."

I put mine down.

"Here's a third," I said.

Delia screamed.

The front-door bell rang. I went to answer it. The milkman stood there with a basket.

"I've brought something that'll please the lady," he said with a complacent grin.

"Take it in to her," I said. "I'm just going out for a walk."

I went out for quite a long walk. When I came back Delia met me in the hall. She looked pale and tragic.

"Well?" I said. "What about the mouse?"

"There isn't one," said Delia. "They've caught it."

"Who? The four cats?"

"The six cats," said Delia, wildly. "Mrs Frank and Mrs James each sent one after you'd gone. Just handed the baskets in and went away. They said they'd heard I wanted one. They've just had supper. The cats, I mean. They seemed awfully hungry, even after the mouse. They've drunk all the milk. I don't know what we shall do for breakfast tomorrow. I'd ever so much rather have the mouse. It didn't eat half so much.... Darling, *do* you know any way of getting rid of cats?"

The Clicking of Clarence

(London Opinion 12/5/1928)

"Isn't it," said Delia, "perfectly adorable?"

It was a black cat who had walked into our house and taken complete possession. It had sampled all the chairs, found that it liked mine best, had a nice nap in it, and was now sitting in front of the fire washing its face. In the intervals of doing all this it had made up to Delia shamelessly, purring at her and rubbing against her and jumping on to her knee.

"It's simply wonderful, isn't it?" went on Delia. "I mean – I mean it seems a sort of omen of good luck. Just walking in and making itself completely at home. I'm certainly going to keep it."

"Do you know, Delia," I said, looking at it thoughtfully, "it looks to me awfully like Mrs Davie's cat from down the road."

"Of course it isn't," said Delia indignantly; "and I don't care if it is. Surely a cat's got as much right as anyone else to leave its home if it doesn't like it and find another more congenial one. I think it's most touching the way Clarence – I'm going to call him Clarence – has singled us out. He must have noticed us and thought we looked nice people. I'm *certainly* going to keep him. Yes, I am, darling," in a tone of nauseating affection to Clarence. "I wouldn't send you back to that nasty old Mrs Davie for the world."

"Of course if you call that honest," I said, coldly, "if you call that behaving like a good citizen—"

"Yes, I do," said Delia aggressively, to me, and then in a tone that I can only describe as maudlin, to Clarence: "Yes, sweetie, I *do*. It's the duty of all good citizens to keep down rats."

"If you think that thing's going to turn out a ratter—" I said, contemptuously.

I felt a bit peeved by the way she was behaving with that cat. I've got to do more than just walk into the house and sit on all the best chairs for her to use that tone of voice on me.

"Of *course* he's going to turn out a ratter; aren't you, darling?" she went on.

Clarence turned his great face to her with a soppy sort of purr, then gave me the shadow of a wink.

"*There!*" said Delia, as if the case were now proved beyond a doubt. "*There! I said* that he was!"

She gave him a large saucer of milk for his tea, and he wouldn't touch it. He wouldn't touch it till she'd warmed it and added sugar. She took the whole of tea-time finding out how he liked it. I, of course, not being Clarence, had to take what she gave me. She hadn't even time to pour me out a second cup of tea because she was so busy finding out how Clarence liked his milk. I began actively to dislike Clarence. There was something smug about him. And there was a sardonic leer in his eye whenever he turned it on me.

After tea, Delia, who'd been dancing till three the night before, slid into a doze. I seized Clarence by the scruff of his neck and carried him into the garden where the shed is. I keep the chicken food in the shed, and I know that a rat of strong communist persuasions, whom I have christened Trotsky, visits it regularly. I put Clarence in.

"You can jolly well stay there till you've caught Trotsky," I said to him sternly.

He purred at me impudently.

I closed the door and watched him through the window.

And I completely revised my opinion of Clarence. I'd simply never have believed it of him. He went straight to Trotsky's private entrance and crouched there, every whisker a-quiver.

In a few minutes Trotsky appeared. Clarence was on him like a greyhound on a mechanical hare whose works have gone wrong. There must be something about warm milk with sugar in. I'm going to try it before the next golf match.

Anyway, in less time than it takes to tell, Trotsky had joined his forefathers, and Clarence was standing in an attitude of negligent pride over his mortal remains. I opened the door. Out came Clarence, lugging his precious burden. He lugged it into the house and to the drawing room. I crept round to the window to watch. I wasn't going to be accused of having any part in it. Delia was still dozing by the fire.

Clarence dragged his burden across the room, jumped with it on to the arm of Delia's chair and dropped it into her lap.

Delia, without opening her eyes, put out a sleepy caressing hand.

I crept away.

Half an hour later I returned. There was no sign of either Clarence or Trotsky, and Delia was looking rather pale.

"Where's Clarence?" I said, innocently.

"I rang up Mrs Davie," said Delia, "and she sent for him. I thought it wasn't quite honest to keep him, after all."

"But what about good citizens and keeping down rats?" I reminded her.

"Oh," she said, carelessly, avoiding my eyes, "I think you were right; I – I don't think he'd have turned out a ratter."

After the Thriller
(The Passing Show, 17/3/1928)

We'd just come in from seeing one of those glorious mixtures of mystery and murder which the modern theatre stages so effectively.

Our heroine had been doped and dragged to a den in the underworld and our hero had passed scatheless through almost (if not quite) incredible dangers to rescue her. A bewildering number of people had shot each other or themselves. At regular intervals mysterious hands had crept round curtains to switch off lights and the resultant darkness had been full of bloodcurdling screams.

We still had that thrilled feeling as we settled down by the fire with our hot milk.

"It was very good, wasn't it?" I said.

But Delia wasn't taking any notice of me. She was sitting up listening intently.

"Do you hear someone on the roof?" she whispered.

I listened.

"No," I said. "It's the rain. It always makes a noise like that, you know."

"I suppose it does," said Delia with a sigh.

There was a short silence. Then Delia pointed dramatically to the curtains.

"I could have sworn I saw them move," she hissed. "See if anyone's behind them."

I went to look. No one was behind them. Delia sighed again.

After another short silence she said:

"Have you any enemies? I don't mean the man who bags your seat on the 8.35 or anyone like that. I mean a real, ruthless enemy. The sort who dogs your steps all your life waiting for a chance of revenge?"

"I don't think so," I said.

Again Delia sighed.

Then she said, "Have you ever had a rich uncle who died in mysterious circumstances and whose will has never been found?"

"No," I said. "Uncle James died of liver trouble and he left a will leaving everything he had to the Mission to Deep Sea Fishermen. There was never anything at all mysterious about Uncles James' liver and they found the will all right. What they didn't find was anything for the Deep Sea Fishermen, because shortly before Uncle James died he had put it all on a horse that was deeper than any sea fisherman."

But it was quite obvious that Delia wasn't interested in Uncle James, so I stopped talking about him.

"Did it strike you," she said slowly, "that we were being followed as we came home this evening?"

"No," I said.

"A man," went on Delia in a deep, mysterious voice, "followed us all the length of the street. I heard his footsteps behind us all the way."

"That was old Robinson," I said. "He wasn't following us. He was going home. He lives next door, you know."

"He might," said Delia, still more mysterious, "have been someone *pretending* to be Mr Robinson."

"He might," I agreed, "but he wasn't. He was smoking one of the cigars that Robinson's wife gives him for Christmas. No other man's system could stand them. Robinson's is inoculated to them."

Delia sat forward in her chair.

"Listen!" she said. "I heard a scream."

I'd heard it too. I know it quite well by sight. In the daytime it wears an innocent look and a white chest and sits washing its face on the opposite doorstep. I explained to Delia.

"Perhaps you're right," she said with a sigh.

But a minute later she started again.

"What was that?" she rapped out.

"What?"

"That strange gurgling noise. It sounds like someone gagged trying to scream for help."

"It's the water in the hot pipe," I explained; "it always does that."

After another short silence, Delia said:

"You're sure there's no one on the roof?"

"Quite."

"Or behind the curtain?"

"No one."

"And you haven't any desperate enemies who've sworn to be revenged on you?"

"No."

"Nor an uncle who died in mysterious circumstances and whose heir you should be?"

"No."

"And we weren't followed?"

"No."

"And those noises were cats and the pipe?"

"Yes."

Delia sighed yet another sigh deeper and more tragic than all the others.

"Real life's frightfully dull, isn't it?" she said. "I suppose, then, that there's nothing for it but just to go to bed?"

Spill Fever

(The Humorist 22/9/1928)

Occasionally, Delia has an outbreak of spill fever. She'll go on normally for months at a time using matches and tapers in an ordinary civilised way and then quite suddenly with no warning at all she'll have an outbreak of spill fever. She'll lay hands upon every bit of paper she can find in the house and make spills of it. She'll fill every available receptacle in every room in the house with spills. She'll put boxes and boxes of spills in all the cupboards. If you try to find the copy of the monthly local timetable to look up a train, it won't be there, because she'll have made it into spills. If you try to find the current stores catalogue to find out how much port is this month, it won't be there, because she'll have made it into spills. When the spill fever's on her she'd make her mother's marriage certificate into spills if she could lay hands on it.

Now we come to the story.

She told me yesterday in good time that she was going out in the evening to a strictly feminine whist drive to which I hadn't been invited, so I purposely didn't read the paper earlier in the day. I miss Delia when she goes out in the evening and I like to have the paper to make up. I didn't really worry about Delia's going out because, as I said, I had the paper and the wireless to occupy my time.

She had already gone out when I reached home, and the first thing I did was to switch on the wireless. It made the sort of noise that generally means a symphony concert, so I began to look for the paper to find out if it really was one. I scoured the whole house for that paper and couldn't find it. It was nowhere. And then I noticed the sinister fact that every receptacle in every room was full of spills. Delia had been having an attack of spill fever.

Frenziedly I flung myself upon the nearest vase, took out a spill and unrolled it. It contained part of the evening's wireless programme. I took out another. It was part of the week's murder. I took out another. It was a bit of financial news. She'd made the whole of the morning paper into spills. And I'd not read a word of it. My blood was up. I'm a man of great determination. I'd meant to spend the evening reading that paper and I was going to spend the evening reading that paper. I tore out to the nearest shop and bought dozens and dozens of those little rolls of transparent sticky paper. Then I started on the spills. I unrolled every single one of them, flattened it out and fitted it where it ought to come. You'll say that it was an impossible task – but you don't know me. I'm a man of indomitable perseverance and determination. I once got 2s 6d back from the Income Tax people. I'm rather good at jigsaw puzzles. In the influenza season I do them more quickly than anyone else in our row. I know I do, because I always finish mine and send it in to Smith long before Brown has finished his and sent it into me. But to return to the spills. At least they weren't spills now. They were all fastened together by strips and strips and strips and strips of transparent sticky. They didn't exactly look like a newspaper. On the other hand, they didn't look like spills any more.

All this, of course, took me some time and I'd only just got finished and was settling down to read it when Delia came in. (By the way, I'd found out what the wireless was doing. It wasn't a symphony concert. It was zoo noises from Regent's Park.)

Delia's eyes opened with horror as they fell upon my newspaper.

"What on earth is that thing?" she said.

"It's the newspaper, Delia," I said pleasantly. "I'm reading it."

"Good heavens!" gasped Delia. "But – I made the newspaper into spills."

"I know you did, Delia," I said. "You shouldn't have done. I hadn't read it. So I've made it back into a newspaper."

"You've – you've—"

Words failed her. She stared at me in helpless horror. Then she went to bed.

But the incident had broken her nerve.

She went out the next morning and bought a dozen large boxes of tapers.

So we're safe now for several months.

Our Christmas Change
(*The Humorist 8/12/1928*)

"Let's not go away for Christmas this year," said Delia. "Let's have a nice quiet Christmas at home."

We're always deciding to have nice quiet Christmases at home, but somehow it never comes off. We always end by going to stay with Aunt Jane or Uncle Charles or cousin Martha, or whoever happens to be giving the Christmas family party that year, simply because we haven't the moral courage to refuse. We belong to a clannish family. But this year we decided to put our feet down.

"I've longed for a quiet Christmas for years," said Delia, pathetically.

"So have I," I admitted. "But I don't see how we can decently get out of it."

"I do," said Delia. "Leave it all to me.

I'll manage it. I'll use finesse. Men, of course, haven't any finesse."

"What sort of finesse shall you use?" I asked with interest.

"I shan't say, of course, that we don't want to come, because if I did they'd all come over to persuade us. I shall pretend that we're longing to come, but that insuperable obstacles prevent us."

"What insuperable obstacles?" I asked.

"That," said Delia thoughtfully, "will need careful planning."

"Say that we can't afford the fare."

"They wouldn't believe us, but they'd still send it us."

"Say that we've been in contact with mumps, or the plague, or something."

"No, because in that case how should we explain your going to work as usual? But I think that it should be something connected with health…. Darling, haven't you felt a bit tired lately?"

"No," I said. "I haven't. Not a bit."

"You've looked tired."

"Have I?" I said.

"Terribly," said Delia, gazing at me with womanly sympathy and concern. "I'm sure that any doctor would tell you that you ought to take a complete rest over Christmas."

"Do you really?" I said, beginning to take a great interest in myself, because there's nothing that makes a man feel so interesting as to be told that he looks tired.

"I think," said Delia slowly, "that in your state of nervous exhaustion it would be fatal for you to go away for Christmas."

"My state of what?" I asked.

"Nervous exhaustion. You need complete quiet and rest."

"They won't believe it," I said. "I've never been ill in my life. They know I haven't."

"People who've never been ill," said Delia, more darkly than ever, "are always worse when they *do* break down. It's a case of the strung bow, you know. You don't bend, but you break. Your spirit's too big for your body. You go on living on your nerves till – till—"

"Till I've eaten them all up," I suggested.

"Yes, that's it. More or less. Well, as I said, it's fatal to play about with a sacred thing like health. I'll write at once to Aunt Jane and tell her that you're terribly run down and done up and all that sort of thing, and that the doctor says that it's absolutely imperative for you to stay at home and take a complete holiday at Christmas."

"But, Delia," I objected, "it isn't true. The doctor hasn't said so."

He would if he knew all the facts," said Delia. "So why waste money getting an opinion from him when you *know* what it will be? To me it's exactly as if the doctor *had* said it, and I'm going to write to Aunt Jane tonight and tell her."

I looked at Delia with admiration. There's a ruthlessness and unscrupulousness about women that I've always secretly admired.

So she wrote to Aunt Jane. It was rather a good letter. It breathed noble resignation at the prospect of missing Aunt Jane's Christmas party, and wifely devotion to an ailing husband. It stressed the fact that, though this Christmas rest was absolutely necessary, there was no need for alarm, and that after this rest my health would probably improve considerably.

Aunt Jane wrote back a nice, understanding letter in which she praised Delia's wifely devotion, and realised what a nervous strain my work must be, and said that though they'd miss us very much they'd try to make the best of things without us.

After that we breathed freely and began to plan our quiet Christmas. We got in a stock of light novels – really light novels with a murder on every page – and we decided that we didn't mind what we had to eat as long as it wasn't turkey or plum pudding. We were looking forward almost with rapture to spending Christmas in a house where no holly or paper festoons could fall into the soup.

Our neighbours frankly envied us. The Joneses were going to stay with Mrs Jones's mother, and the Browns were going to stay with Mr Brown's father, and the Robinsons were going to stay with an uncle of Mrs Robinson's, and the Smiths were going to stay with an aunt of Mr Smith's, and the Greens were going to stay with a distant cousin.

"I've often thought," each said to us, wistfully, "that it would be rather nice to stay home for Christmas."

"My husband," said Delia, "is rather run down, and is taking a quiet holiday by doctor's orders."

And they looked at her in the way that people do look at a woman when they don't believe her, but are too polite to say so.

When I came home from business the night before Christmas Eve I found that Delia had already begun preparations for our quiet Christmas.

"I've rung up the butcher," she said, "and told him to send anything he likes for Christmas dinner as long as it isn't turkey; and I've told the Bruce children that they may take all the holly in the garden – and if you wish me a happy Christmas I'll murder you."

"I won't," I said fervently. "I won't wish *anyone* a happy Christmas."

Then we settled down happily with our thrillers. After a few seconds, however, there came a knock at the door. Delia went to it. Mrs Jones stood there clasping a plant pot to her bosom.

"I *wonder*," she said, in that peculiar voice that women use when they're going to ask a favour, "I *wonder* if you'd be an angel and keep this for me over the Christmas holidays, as you're not going away? It only wants watering twice a day. Thank you *so* much."

When she had gone we put the plant pot on the table and looked at it doubtfully.

"I *hate* watering plants," said Delia; but just then there was another knock at the door. I went to it this time. It was Mrs Brown, with a large cat that she thrust unceremoniously into my arms.

"We hear that you aren't going away for Christmas," she said. "We'd be *so* grateful if you'd look after Toby for us. He frets so if he's left alone. A little milk's all he needs."

Then she disappeared into the night.

I put Toby on the table by the plant pot, which he promptly knocked over on to the floor.

"I've always disliked that cat of the Browns," said Delia, pathetically, picking up what was left of the plant pot.

Just then came another knock at the door. I went. It was Mrs Robinson, with a dog on a lead.

"I hear you aren't going away for Christmas," she said. "I'd be *so* grateful if you'd have Pat till we come back. Just for the Christmas holiday, you know. We can't take him with us because my uncle doesn't like dogs, and we've no one to leave him with. He's no trouble at all. He'll eat any old scraps – just a bit of meat and potatoes and gravy. He's a *very* lovable fellow. Thank you *so* much."

And she disappeared into the night, leaving me with a dog's lead in my hand, and a dog at the end of it. He followed me into the sitting room and leapt exuberantly to the pursuit of Toby. He chased Toby for ten chaotic minutes before we managed to catch him and shut him up in the dining room. Then we began to collect the wreckage. But before we'd finished there was another knock at the door, and there stood the young Greens, with a cage containing two guinea pigs.

"Mummie said," chirped the young Greens, "that she was sure you wouldn't mind looking after them as you're not going away for Christmas. They aren't any trouble at all. They only want feeding. We've brought their food."

I tried to protest, but already the young Greens were disappearing into the night, leaving me with the cage of guinea pigs in one hand and a paper bag in the other. Meanwhile, Toby had scratched Delia again, and Pat was raising Cain in the dining room. But we'd no time to do anything about it because the little Smiths had arrived with two rabbits in a hutch.

They said that they'd heard we were looking after the Greens' guinea pigs, so would we mind looking after Wilfred and Wilfreda as well? They added that Wilfred and Wilfreda were no trouble at all, and disappeared into the night.

I raised my hand to my brow.

"I suppose this is all," I said, in a faint voice.

"No, it isn't," said Delia, wildly. "The little Joneses have a goldfish, and the young Browns have a grass snake and a couple of white rats."

"Delia," I said, "would it be possible to get to your Aunt Jane's tonight?"

Wrapping her handkerchief round Pat's last scratch on her hand, she took up a railway timetable.

"Yes," she said, "if we hurry we can catch the 9.30."

"Let's hurry, then," I said.

So we hurried. We packed our bags and then phoned for a taxi. We piled into it Pat, Toby, the guinea pigs, the rabbits and the plant. Then we set off. We called at the Joneses' first; put the plant pot on the doorstep, rang the bell, and disappeared into the night before anyone came. We did the same at the Browns', the Robinsons', the Greens', and the Smiths'. We stopped at the post office and Delia sent a wire: "John much better. Doctor advises change of surroundings. Arriving 10.30."

Then we drove to the station and just caught the train.

Part 5
Miss Thomson et al

Getting the Number
(The Humorist, 5/2/1927)

"I'm going to be on the telephone," I said to Miss Thomson, proudly.

"When?" said Miss Thomson, registering due excitement.

"Any day now. I've got my book of words and all the apparatus. I'm only waiting for the British workman to appear."

"He's a coy, elusive creature," sighed Miss Thomson. "I remember that when ours was put up we'd quite forgotten that we'd decided to have one by the time he appeared. It was a shock. We thought he'd come to mend the wireless, and it was quite a long time before he could make us understand. Then we found that someone had sent both the book of words and the apparatus to a jumble sale by mistake in the interval, so we had to start all over again."

"I don't believe a word of it," I said sternly. "I believe you're making it all up."

"Well," said Miss Thomson unblushingly, "one must say something, and I always find a conversation conducted entirely upon the principles of truth and accuracy so uninspiring. Who are you going to give your maiden call to?"

"My what?"

"Your maiden call."

"Oh! Why not you?"

"Just what I was going to suggest," said Miss Thomson, calmly. "I collect maiden calls. They're so much more interesting than stamps or cigarette cards. Do you know, you'll be the twentieth person to have rung me up first of all on a new telephone. You must give me your autograph and a passport photograph of yourself for my maiden call album."

"Why a passport photograph?"

"Because they're so much more amusing than ordinary photographs."

I sighed.

"There's something very callous about you," I said, "I've often noticed it. What's your number?"

She told me.

"It's quite easy to remember," she said. "It's the date of the Battle of Waterloo."

"Good!" I said. "I like something to hold on to. It ought to be in by the end of the week."

"I admire optimism," said Miss Thomson, "but let's say a fortnight."

As a matter of fact, it was a month. But at last it really was in, and I sat before it proudly thinking how new and neat and beautiful it looked, before I took off the receiver to give Miss Thomson my maiden call.

"Number, please," said the exchange.

I hesitated. A cold horror stole over me.

"Er – what was the date of the Battle of Waterloo?" I said.

Exchange happened to be a man. I suppose the girl had gone out to her tea. I can't help feeling that she'd have been more sympathetic about it. He was so disagreeable that I almost decided to send the whole thing back to the Postmaster-General the very next morning and demand my money back. I hung up the receiver and turned to my bookshelves.

I have a book called 'Every Man's Lawyer', and another called a 'Guide to the Lake District', and another called 'Lives of the Martyrs' (my only school prize), and another on Butterflies and Moths, a short handy text-book, and several novels by Jacobs and Wodehouse. I skimmed them all through but couldn't find a single reference to the Battle of Waterloo.

I am, however, not lightly baffled, and I had decided that Miss Thomson and no one else should have my maiden call. I went out, meaning to take the bus down to the Free Library, but it happened to be market day and all the buses were full. So I doggedly tramped the three miles to the Free Library. And – would you believe it? – there was only one book dealing with the Waterloo period and some blighter had got it out. The head librarian was away and the assistant librarian seemed never to have heard of the battle of Waterloo. He suggested a railway timetable, but didn't take an real interest in the problem.

The only thing to do was to go home again. I got a bus this time and asked the bus conductor if he knew it. He said he hadn't no time to be thinking of riddles, and dates didn't interest him any more because he'd finished with women altogether.

So I went home and rang up Exchange again and asked if they had found out the date of the Battle of Waterloo. I hoped that the girl was back from her tea, but she wasn't, and the man was even more disagreeable than he had been before.

I began to feel really disheartened. Then I remembered a schoolmaster acquaintance of mine. A schoolmaster would be sure to

know the date of the Battle of Waterloo. He lived at the other end of the town. I had to walk all the way again because it was still market day. I was spent and exhausted when I reached him. But he couldn't help me. He was on the science side, he said, and didn't know anything about history. He admitted that he must have learnt history when he was a boy, but he said he'd forgotten it all. I searched through his science books in the hopes of finding a chance reference to the Battle of Waterloo – without success. I thought that perhaps Archimedes or Galileo might possibly have had views on it, but apparently they hadn't. I went out, hailed a taxi, and drove to Miss Thomson's. I was shown into her drawing room – a pitiful spectacle of exhaustion and despair.

"What was the date of the Battle of Waterloo?" I gasped.

"1815," she said. "It's our telephone number."

"I've been hunting around for it all the afternoon," I said.

She gurgled.

"Why didn't you look me up in your telephone book?" she said.

I gulped.

"I – I never thought of that," I said.

A Brief Respite
(The Humorist, 9/10/1926)

"Are you going up to town?" I said, meeting Miss Thomson on the station.

"Yes," she said, "are you?"

"Yes. Here's a perfectly good carriage looking at you with such a wistful look in its window."

She entered with a deep sigh.

"I notice that you don't register violent joy at the thought of travelling up to town in my company," I said.

"Oh, I don't mind *you*," she answered with another deep sigh – this time one of resignation. "It's – that!" She waved her hand at the gloomy bleakness of the day outside. "It's the awful thought that summer is really over. Do you know what I'm going up to town for?"

"No."

"To buy a winter hat. Isn't it dreadful? It's the death knell of summer. It seems only yesterday that I was going up to buy my first straw hat of the season. There's a thrill in that that one simply can't describe."

"I know," I said moodily. "That's where you score over us. Yet I remember the time – and it seems only yesterday – when *we* used to wear straw hats, too. I remember the thrill of bringing out one's straw hat on the first day of summer. One cleaned it with salts of lemon. It always lasted two years. Why don't we wear straw hats any more? It was a glorious fashion! Who put a stop to it? And why did we so meekly give it up? Why shouldn't we have some such simple little ceremony any more to mark the passing of winter?"

"At least," said Miss Thomson gloomily, "you haven't to undergo the agony of putting it away and realising that the winter is upon us once more. I *hate* the end of the summer. It calls to one's mind leafless trees and hot-water bottles, and—"

"Schedule D," I supplied with a groan.

"What's that?" said Miss Thomson.

"Happy innocent!" I said. "Schedule D is a discipline sent by Providence to remind us of the curse of Adam."

"Something to do with apples, wasn't it?" said Miss Thomson vaguely. "It's going to pour in a minute."

"Yes," I agreed, "it's one of those wretched little cyclones. You know, we haven't had any really decent weather since broadcasting came in. This nightly harping on depressions and wedges of high pressure and cyclones encourages the little beggars. They hear themselves talked about regularly to the whole of the British Isles every evening at seven and nine-thirty, and they get swelled heads. They go swaggering about all over the place. It makes the weather awful. That's why the summer's come to an end so long before it ought to have done…. Do you know what I'm going up to town for?"

"No."

"To order a winter overcoat. I was nearly frozen yesterday. But let's go and celebrate the passing of summer first. Let's go and eat baked meats somewhere."

"Why baked meats?"

"They eat them at funerals. At least, they did in Hamlet's time."

There was a long silence. Neither of us dared to mention it, but the sun was certainly coming out.

"After all," said Miss Thomson with a new note of cheerfulness in her voice, "after all, we did win the Ashes, didn't we?"

"Yes," I agreed, "and there's Mr Alan Cobham—"

"Yes, there's nothing really to get depressed about," said Miss Thomson brightly.

Impossible to ignore it now. The sun was pouring through the carriage window.

"Welcome, little anticyclone," I murmured, fondly. "We've been premature," I said to Miss Thomson. "Summer isn't nearly over yet."

"No, it isn't. We'll cut out the baked meats."

"Yes. We'll go and have an ice instead. And it would be very churlish to buy winter hats and order winter overcoats on a glorious afternoon like this."

"What shall we do instead?"

"We'll go on the river," I said.

Culture and Cunning
(London Opinion, 15/01/1927)

"Did you have a nice Christmas?" I asked Miss Thomson, meeting her in the street about a week after Christmas.

"Y-yes," said Miss Thomson, doubtfully. "On the whole, I think I did. It was rather full of relatives. The sort, you know, who only come at Christmas, and spend the time hinting that you've changed very much for the worse since they saw you last."

"I know," I sighed. "We have them too. Aunts, chiefly."

"Yes," said Miss Thomson. "We call it Auntitis. They tell you the sort of thing they used to do when they were young, and it always sounds like a page from *Ministering Children* – only one suspects them of concealing a good deal."

"Didn't you do anything but that?" I said, compassionately.

"Oh, yes – we had games. And we danced sometimes. But the Charleston has a bad effect upon Auntitis. It increases the symptom and makes it almost virulent. Even the fox-trot brings on a bad attack, and one gets so tired of valses – but we had someone with us who could do character reading, which was rather fun."

"Did he read yours?" I said, distantly.

"It was a she," said Miss Thomson, demurely. "She did."

I unbent.

"That's better," I said. "I mean, I expect that if it had been a man he'd have talked an awful lot of tosh to you."

"Like the tosh you talked that time when you read my hand?" she asked, innocently.

"No," I said, with dignity. "That wasn't tosh."

"You mean," she said coldly, "that he'd have taken the opposite view of my character?"

"N-no," I said. "I expect that he'd have taken pretty much the same view, but what would be tosh said by him is sound sense when said by me."

"I see," she said. "Have you had your character read?"

"No," I said. "But I ought to have because I possess quite an exceptional character. There's something outstanding about me." I suspected her of glancing at my ears, so hastened on. "What I mean to say is that I've had unique experiences. Once I took a correspondence course in business methods, and was not offered the post of manager after it. What else did you do?"

"We played silly games. We played 'I love my love'. I had to love mine with a C, and I couldn't think of anything to love my love with a C for. In the end," she shot me a demure glance, "I had to love him with a C because he was conceited. It was the only thing I could think of."

"You should have said 'cultured'," I said.

"But I don't know anyone cultured," objected Miss Thomson.

"You know me," I said. "I'm cultured. Ask the encyclopaedia people. They know I'm cultured. That's why they want me to have an encyclopaedia. They've told me in so many words that mine is a cultured home, and that's why they want it to have an encyclopaedia in it. They believe in my culture so much that they'd go to any trouble to set their final seal of approval on it. They simply can't bear to think that anyone should get a wrong impression of me and think I'm not cultured because I haven't got an encyclopaedia in my home, so they write to me about it by registered post. They'd send me the whole cart-load today if I asked them to, simply because they think I'm so cultured."

"Don't they want you to pay for them?" said Miss Thomson, impressed.

"They don't stress that part of it at all," I said. "It's me and the appearance of my cultured home they care about. They want me to become, if possible, even more cultured than I am already. They've got pictures of me sitting with my family around me, each with a volume of—"

"You haven't got a family."

"I have. I've got a sister. I'm taking her out to a dance-tea this afternoon."

Miss Thomson looked wistful.

"Are you?" she said, and sighed.

I looked at her and plunged headlong.

"Would you have come with me if I'd asked you?" I said.

She sighed again.

"You haven't asked me," she said. You've asked your sister."

"No," I said. "I've just remembered. She rang me up this morning to tell me that she's in bed with a cold, so if you won't come with me I can't go."

"Well, as you put it like that—" said Miss Thomson.

We had just reached her house. I opened her garden gate.

"I'll call for you," I said, "in an hour's time."

Then I went home and rang up my sister and told her that I was in bed with a cold, and couldn't take her out to the dance-tea.

Cunning – that's it – not conceited or cultured, but cunning. I must remember to tell Miss Thomson when I call for her why she loves her love with a C.

The Title

(The Humorist, 25/09/1926)

I saw Miss Thomson just in time, and drew the car up to the kerb.

"Come for a drive?" I said cheerfully.

"I can't," said Miss Thomson; "I'm going out to tea."

"Where are you going?"

"To Margery's."

Margery is my cousin once removed.

"You know what Margery is," I warned her. "She'll have a ghastly game where you have to write down the names of five British statesmen beginning with Z or something of the sort. You've been there before. You'd be far better occupied going for a drive with me."

"No," said Miss Thomson firmly. "I'm going to tea with Margery."

"All right," I said; "I'll come too. Jump in."

Margery didn't seem really pleased to see me. She said, "Oh, you've come, have you? I never asked you," in the tone of voice in which one might tell the fishmonger that he needn't leave anything today because the last hadn't been at all fresh.

"I know you didn't," I agreed, unabashed, "but I've come. I know my duty as a cousin once removed even if you don't."

Margery, of course, had arranged a competition. All the guests had to go out in twos and then come back and act the title of a book, and the others had to guess it. I may say that it took all my ingenuity to secure Miss Thomson as my partner, but by the exercise of great perseverance and a certain amount of ruthlessness I achieved it.

"It must be a well-known book," said Margery as we went out, "and don't spend too long thinking of it."

We went into the morning room to think.

"Well, what shall we do?" said Miss Thomson.

I looked at Miss Thomson. She has the most glorious golden hair that I've ever seen.

"What about 'Gentlemen Prefer Blondes'?" I said.

"Don't be silly," said Miss Thomson; "we couldn't act that."

"I think I could," I said, thoughtfully. "I think that if you left the acting entirely to me I could give a very fair interpretation of the title."

"Don't be absurd," she said, blushing. "Let's get a list of classics. There'll be one at the end of that book, I think. Read some out and let's see which are actable."

I found the list and read out a few.

"What about 'The Canterbury Pilgrims'? It's only about forty miles to Canterbury. We could go there and then come back and then let them guess. No? 'Gipsies in Spain' then. We could dress up as gipsies, and you could be eating an onion and I could be eating a Barcelona nut to show that we're in Spain. No? What do you suggest then?"

She looked over my shoulder.

"What about 'The Woman in White'? I've got a white dress on, so I wouldn't have to dress up at all, and—"

"And what about me?" I interrupted, indignantly. "I wouldn't have credited you with such selfishness. I refuse to be left out of it. I tell you what, it's much easier to think out of doors. There's more room for the brain to expand. Come along."

We went out into the garden, where my

car was.

"Jolly little thing, isn't it?" I said, proudly.

"Yes," said Miss Thomson, "but what title shall we act?"

"Oh, anything," I said, gazing with loving pride at my four-wheel-brakes triangle (I haven't got four wheel brakes. I painted the triangle myself because it looks better). "'Hard Times', and I'll go in with my last Income Tax demand. Or 'The story of a Short Life', and I'll find the remains of that wasp I've just killed in the hall and take them in. It's rather tiring standing, isn't it? What about taking a seat?"

We got into the car.

"I'll just see if it's going all right," I murmured.

It was. We glided down the drive.

"'Far from the Madding Crowd'," I murmured.

Miss Thomson leant back against her seat with a deep sigh.

"Isn't it jolly?" she said.

We had a glorious drive. We stopped for tea at a charming little inn, and then, and not till then, Miss Thomson began to look worried.

"What's the matter?" I said. "Is Margery beginning to lie heavy on your conscience?"

She nodded.

"I'll ring her up," I said.

I did, and got through to her almost at once.

"Hullo," I said cheerfully. "Have you guessed?"

Margery talked for quite a long time. Evidently they'd waited for us for half an hour, and were still looking for us. Some of them were in favour of dragging the pond, and others of notifying the police.

"Well, we've been acting it all the time," I explained. "We can't help it if you're in the wrong place. Can't you guess what it is? We've won the prize then, I suppose."

And I hastily rang off.

"What *are* we acting?" said Miss Thomson. "It would be as well to know."

"Oh. 'Far from the Madding Crowd' if you like, or 'Voyages of Adventure', or 'Pilgrim's Progress'. Anything. It doesn't really matter. May I call you Helen?"

"Yes."

I took a deep breath.

"Helen, will you——"

"Certainly no."

I rang up Margery again.

"Margery, I'll tell you the name of what we're acting, if you can't guess. It's 'Love's Labours Lost'."

"You – you rather jump to conclusions," murmured Helen. I hung up the receiver.

"Helen," I said earnestly, "do you hate and despise me?"

"No."

"Can you almost endure me?"

"Y-yes."

"Do you almost like me?"

"Y-yes."

I rang up Margery again.

"Margery, I told you the name of the book wrong. It's 'Eric, or Little by Little'."

I didn't wait for Margery's reply. I returned to Helen.

*   *   *   *   *

These dots represent ten minutes, during which—— No, on second thoughts I'll simply say that these dots represent ten minutes.

At the end of ten minutes I rang up

Margery again.

"Margery," I said, "the last title I told you was wrong. The real title is 'The Betrothed', but 'All's Well That Ends Well' would also get full marks!"

Margery's quite a sport at heart. She's going to come to the wedding. She's rather grieved that you can't get up competitions at wedding receptions, but she's going to make the best of it.

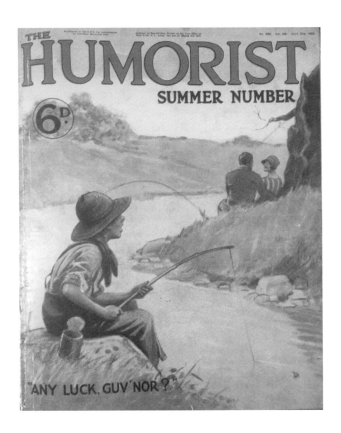

In the 'Bus

(The Humorist, 5/4/1924)

On one side of me sat a son of toil who had evidently imbibed, at no very distant period, a moderate amount of liquid refreshment. On the other side of me sat a woman more conspicuous for physical size (in a horizontal direction) than for refinement of form or feature. She nursed on her capacious lap a large child, a large basket, and a large string bag.

"Wot've they done, I arsks yer?" said the son of toil. "I arsks yer, wot've they done?"

"Riz sugar, that's wot they've done," said the large woman, with a sarcastic sniff.

"Eggsackly!" said the man, "riz sugar. 'Ow are we better orf than before they come in? I arsks yer, wot've they done? Bin in a monf, they 'ave, an' wot've they done? I arsks yer."

"'Cept riz sugar," said the woman.

"Eggsackly. 'Cept riz sugar. Wot've they done, I—"

It seemed the sort of conversation that might go on for ever, but an inspector caused a diversion by entering and demanding to see our tickets. The son of toil produced his from his knee tie. I produced mine from my coat sleeve. The inspector moved on to the large woman.

"Wot aye, Percy?" she said. "Oh, me ticket! Wyte a mo'."

She slowly turned out two pockets in her coat and two in her skirt. No ticket appeared.

"Well," she said confidingly, "ain't it strynge the wye these here things seems ter myke orf loike jus' when yer wants 'em?"

"'Urry up, ma!" said the inspector, impatiently.

"You moind 'oo yer starts a-callin' ma of, young feller," she said indignantly. "'Ere, myte," she suddenly thrust a dusty forest of feathers and artificial flowers against my nose, "I 'aven't put me ticket in me 'at, 'ave I?"

I withdrew my face as far as I could from the horror.

"I don't see it," I said.

"'Ave you gotter ticket, or 'aven't you?" said the inspector.

"If yer'd use yer oiyes, young feller," she said, "yer'd see I was *lookin'* fer me ticket as 'ard as I can. 'F yer'd sent a postcard ter sye as yer was comin' I'd 'ave 'ad it ready wrapped up in tisshu paper."

She was burrowing in her basket and bag as she spoke. A large tin of sardines fell on to the toe of a prim old gentleman opposite.

"Thank yer, dearie," she said, graciously, as the old gentleman handed it back to her.

Then, without warning, she suddenly placed her bag on the floor, her basket on the knee of her other neighbour and the large child on my knee.

"Jus' half a mo'," she said, apologetically, and began again to burrow in her pockets.

The fat child and I regarded each other dispassionately.

"If you can't perduce a ticket," said the inspector, firmly, "I must ask you to pay again. I can't stay 'ere all day."

She glared at him pugnaciously.

"I've pyed for one ticket, young feller," she said, "an' I'm pyin' fer no more. Arsk 'im," and she pointed suddenly at the conductor, who hastily turned away and pretended to be examining the horizon.

"Arsk any of 'em if I pyed fer me ticket. I'm a honest woman, I am. I don' travel in no conveyance wot I can't pye fer me ticket. 'Ave you got a woife an' choild yersel', 'cause if yer 'ave—"

"I'm here," said the inspector, pompously, "in an offishul capacity, an' if yer don't either perduce a ticket or pay fer one—"

The prim old gentleman opposite bent forward.

"If you would kindly allow me to pay for your ticket, madam," he said, handing a coin to the inspector, who handed it to the conductor.

The large lady beamed at him.

"Thanks, dearie," she said. "That's ever so noice of yer!" She beamed round upon us all. "Ain't it *noice* of 'im?"

Blushing to the ears, the old gentleman rang the bell and descended from the 'bus.

The large woman gathered together on her knee again the bag, the basket and the baby.

Still gazing dispassionately at me, the baby began suddenly to dribble bits of 'bus ticket out of the side of its mouth.

The large woman seized upon the fragments excitedly.

"'Ere, young feller," she called to the conductor. "'Ere's me ticket!"

The conductor pretended not to hear. She turned indignantly to me.

"You was a-'oldin' of the kid," she said. "'Aven't yer got oiyes in yer 'ead? Didn' yer see it was a-chewin' up of me ticket?"

"I'm afraid I didn't," I said.

She snorted scornfully, and transferred her attention to the conductor.

"I'm wytin' fer me penny back," she said, sternly. "Two pennies 'as bin pyed fer one lydy, an' I demands one of 'em back. Profiteers, that's wot you are – you an' yer busses – a-grindin' dahn the fyces of the pore, tykin' two fares fer one lydy. Well, 'ere's me ticket," she held out the chewed

fragments, "an' I demands a penny back. I—"

The 'bus drew up.

"Marquis o' Granby," said the conductor.

"*You're* a gintleman, Percy," said the large woman to me aggressively. "Carn't yer stick up fer a lydy wot's bein' done the dirty on – you an' yer spats?"

"I'm sorry," I said, rising. "I get out here."

"Yer would!" she commented bitterly. "A-shirkin' of yer responsibilities – jus' loike a man."

I went down the 'bus. My progress roused the man of toil from slumber.

"They've bin in dyes an' dyes, weeks an' weeks, monfs an' monfs," he muttered sleepily, "an' wot've they done – 'cept riz sugar? I arsks yer."

"'Ere's me ticket an' I demands me penny," said the large lady monotonously, "I—"

I jumped off the 'bus.

It lurched on through the fog out of sight and hearing.

A Strike in Fairyland
(Punch 20/11/1920)

The fairies were holding a meeting. "They grumble when we send the rain," said a Rain-fairy, "and they grumble when we don't."

"And we get no thanks," sighed a Flower-fairy. "The time we spend getting the flowers ready and washing their faces and folding them up every night!"

"As for the stars," said a Star-fairy "we might just as well leave them unlit for all the gratitude we get, and it's such a rush to get all over the sky in time. They don't even believe in us. We wouldn't mind *anything* if they believed in us."

"No," agreed a Rainbow-fairy, "that's true. I take such a lot of trouble to get just the right colours, and it has to be done so quickly. But I wouldn't mind if they believed in us."

"I wonder what *they'd* do," said the Queen, "if no one believed in them?"

"They'd go on strike," said the Brown Owl (he was head of the Ministry of Wisdom). "They always go on strike if they don't like anything."

"Then we'll go on strike," said the Queen with great determination.

They all cheered, except the Flower-fairies.

"But the flowers," they said, "they'll get so dusty with no one to wash them, and so tired with no one to fold them up at nights."

"I hadn't thought of that," said the Queen. "When *they* go on strike, how do things get done?"

The Brown Owl considered for a moment and everyone waited in silence.

"Of course there are sometimes blacklegs," he began.

"I don't know what blacklegs are," said the Queen cheerfully, "but we'll appoint some." And she did.

"Is that all?" said the Queen.

"Someone ought to have a sympathetic strike with us," said the Brown Owl. "*They* always do that."

So a fairy was sent off to the Court of the Birds to request a sympathetic strike.

"Is *that* all?" said the Queen.

"You ought to *talk* more," said the Brown Owl. "*They* talk ever so much."

"Yes, but they can't help it, can they?" said the Queen kindly.

And so the strike began that evening.

None of the birds sang except one little blackleg Robin, who sang so hard in his efforts to make up for the rest that he was as hoarse as a crow the next morning. The blackleg fairies had a hard time too. They hadn't a minute to gossip with the flowers, as they usually did when they flew round with their acorn-cups of dew and thistledown sponges and washed their faces and folded up their petals and kissed them good night.

"But what's the matter?" said the flowers sleepily.

"We're on strike," said one of the other fairies importantly, "not for ourselves, but for posterity."

The Brown Owl had heard *them* say that.

Meanwhile the rest of the fairies sat silent and rather mournful, awaiting developments.

Then a Thought-fairy flew in. Thought-fairies can see into your heart and know just what you think. They get terrible shocks sometimes.

"I've been all over the world," she said breathlessly, "and it's much better than you

166

think. *All* little girls believe in us and—"
She paused dramatically.

"Yes?" they said eagerly.

"All fathers of little girls believe in us."

The Queen shook her head.

"They only pretend," she said.

"No, that's just it," said the Thought-fairy. "They *pretend* to pretend. They never tell anyone, but they really believe."

"Then we'll end the strike," said the Queen.

Here the Brown Owl bustled in, carrying a little notebook.

"I've found out lots more," he said excitedly. "We must have an executive and delegates and a ballot and a union and a Sankey Commission report and a scale of the cost of living and a datum line and—"

"But the strike's over," said the Queen. "It was a misunderstanding."

"Of course," he said huffily. "All strikes are that, but it's correct to carry them on as long as possible."

"And the blacklegs are to have a special reward."

"That's illogical," said the Brown Owl.

He was right, of course, but things *are* illogical in Fairyland. That's the nicest part of it.

High Commerce
(London Opinion 23/2/1924)

I saw him coming up the walk, and went myself to the front door to meet him.

"You've been here before, sir," I said sternly; "you came here last year. It's a mistake to come twice to the same house. We know you, you see, and we don't want any more of it. We don't want any more of your Patent Glacé Linoleum Surface."

"Did it not retain the surface?" he asked with interest.

"It did," I groaned. "You said that one application would give it a permanent glacé smoothness—"

"Did it not?" he said politely.

"It did," I said grimly, "and we can't get it off. The baby falls on it every day. I fall on it every other day, and my wife falls on it three times a week. I've sprained my ankle on it, and my wife's cut her head open on it, and the baby's permanently ruined its temper on it. We put down sand and ashes, but they only make it more uncomfortable to fall on to. You talked me into it. You could talk anyone into anything, but you can't talk me into the same thing twice," I said triumphantly. "I can talk about the Patent Glacé Linoleum Surface, too, now."

He took out his notebook and began to write in it.

"I will book an order for you, sir," he said calmly. "I am not now travelling for the Patent Glacé Linoleum Surface. I am travelling for the Patent Non-skid Linoleum Treatment. One application will render the surface completely harmless.

Almost a gritty effect. Very comforting after the other. Guaranteed to succeed. Money returned if not satisfied. Can be applied by a child."

"Look here!" I said weakly, "how many people did you sell the other stuff to?"

"Four thousand and eighty-two," he said glibly.

"How many do you expect to sell this to?"

"Four thousand and eighty-two."

"There's no common sense in it," I burst out; "an ordinary cheap polish in the beginning would have had the same effect."

"Exactly," he said proudly, "but you did not buy an ordinary cheap polish."

Then a light overspread his face. He looked like Joan of Arc or somebody or other inspired by an ideal they'd have gone to the stake for.

"It is not a question of mere common sense," he said scornfully. "It is a question of the spirit of High Commerce. Patent Non-skid Linoleum Treatment—"

"All right," I said feebly. "Send the stuff along soon."

The Collector
(London Opinion 8/3/1924)

I have a collection of Georgian silver and old china and various other *bibelots* that is almost worthy of a capital C (thus... Collection).

I have a cousin who, I have now decided, is over-officious.

That is the setting of the story. Now begins the plot.

The cousin wrote to say that he had a friend, a Mr Jones, a collector with the same tastes as myself, who was passing through the town on a certain day and would like to meet me. I wrote to say that I should be very glad to receive Mr Jones and show him my collection on the certain day.

The certain day arrived.

So did Mr Jones.

I saw him coming up the walk and went to open the door myself.

"Mr Jones?" I said.

"Er – yes," said Mr Jones.

"I hear you are a collector," I went on pleasantly.

"Er – yes," said Mr Jones again.

Somehow I was disappointed in Mr Jones. He didn't look a bit like a collector. However, I showed him my Georgian silver and my Spode and my slipware and my Dwight and my miniatures and my etchings. He looked at them in silence. He didn't seem impressed. His expression implied that he didn't think much of it all, anyway. It annoyed me. I began to swank. One does in such circumstances. I pointed out the rareness of some of my things. He still looked merely bored. My blood rose. I made up my mind that by hook or by crook, I would impress the man before he left the house.

"You'd be surprised if you knew how much I spend on this collection," I said. "I never let a chance pass. I go from one end of the country to the other to auctions. And I have my ordinary business to attend to as well. My ordinary business brings me in er – roughly – er – £2000 a year." (This was an exaggeration, but, as I said, I was determined to impress the man somehow, and if he wouldn't rise to a collection, I'd try him with something else.) "I spend quite half on this collection."

I had succeeded.

He brightened. He showed signs of life. He even began to write in a note-book.

At that moment I saw a man pass the window. He looked every inch a collector. I heard him being admitted. The housemaid entered.

"Mr Jones, sir," she said. "I've shown him into the dining room."

I turned to my companion, gaping.

"You said you were Mr Jones," I said.

"I am," he said.

"You said you were a collector."

"I am," he said, simply. "I'm the income tax collector."

Fire Eater
(London Opinion, 12/4/1924)

There were four of us in the railway carriage, a large, ferocious-looking man in a corner, a small woman asleep opposite him, a clergyman reading a book, and myself reading a paper.

"We've got the thin end of the wedge in, we 'ave," said the large man pugnaciously. "Call it Labour or Soshullism or what, we're *hin*, we are, an' you won't *hout* us so easy, let *me* tell *you*."

The small woman went on sleeping. The clergyman went on reading his book. I went on reading my newspaper, feeling rather uneasy.

"Yuss," went on the large man, "an' you'd better look hout, some of you. We're hout to stop at nuffin'. Revolushun, that's what's comin', an' some of us 'ave bin ready an' waitin' for it this many a year."

Nobody looked up or answered. I began to feel still more uncomfortable. After all, it's the straw that shows which way the wind's blowing. I began to think over my investments. I might realise them and try to find something fairly safe abroad, if there *was anything* safe abroad. No use putting it off till it was too late. The large man glared with bloodshot eyes round the carriage. I cowered before him.

"Yuss, it's yer money we want all right an' we'll get it, too. But let *me* tell *you*, that that's not orl. No, it's berlood we want, too, streets runnin' with berlood; you an' me'll live to see it, wipe out the bloomin' hidle rich, we say, an' start afresh."

The small woman went on sleeping. The clergyman went on reading his book. I went on reading my newspaper. I was thinking over safe little villages in Switzerland, or perhaps Portugal, whither I might retire with my little bit of realised capital. No good waiting till the deluge.

"Yuss," went on the big man, "we're not afraid of nuffin', we're not, an' there isn't nuffin' that'll shut our mouths. We're givin' you fair warnin'. There isn't no one nor nuffin' that'll scare us or—"

The small woman woke up.

"You've gone an' roused me with your talkin' again, George," she said shrilly. "Can't you be quiet an' let folks who want to, sleep?"

He seemed to shrink.

"Sorry, Maria," he said pacifically.

"I should think so," she said sternly. "Well, read a bit if you must do somethin', an' for 'Evvings sake don't go an' make a row turnin' over the leaves."

"No, Maria," he said meekly.

He took the paper she passed him and began to read it as she had folded it, without daring to open it out. The article at which it was folded was "Women's Dress in Paris This Spring".

Silence reigned. The small woman went to sleep again. The clergyman went on reading.

I decided to let my investments and myself stay where they were for the present.

Seven Days
(London Opinion, 19/4/1924)

It was the first morning of the strike. He arrived at the office rather late, but rosy and glowing and cheerful.

"Magnificent exercise – walking!" he said. "Nothing like it! We need a transport strike occasionally to teach us to enjoy the simple pleasures of life. It's shameful to see – in normal times, I mean – strong men crowding into stuffy tubes and 'buses and motors instead of enjoying a brisk walk through the fresh morning air. It tones up the muscles. It clears the brain. It saves pounds on doctors' bills for the liver. It keeps down the weight. It brightens the temper. It – well, anyway, it's great! It's a new lease of life to have rediscovered the joy of walking. I've taken a vow to walk to the office every day rain or fine, strike or no strike, for the rest of my life till I retire and I wager I'll out-live you all."

He went on like that all the morning.

He walked the next morning and we had it all over again. But I noticed that his eloquence was exhausted a little sooner.

He arrived rather later the third morning and I thought he looked a little less cheerful.

"Walked?" I said.

"Yes," he said shortly. "Splendid exercise – simply splendid. Many letters?"

He arrived still later the next morning. He looked almost bad-tempered.

"Walked?" I said cheerfully.

"Yes!" he snapped.

On the fifth morning I distinctly saw him descend from a motor-lorry at the corner of the road.

"Walked?" I said when he entered.

He pretended not to hear.

"Walked?" I said again, louder.

"Good Heavens!" he said irritably. "How you do chatter."

On the sixth morning he rang up to say that he could not come as the man who had promised to give him a lift had had a smash.

On the seventh morning he arrived rosy, glowing, cheerful.

"I've garaged it just across the road," he said. "a perfectly ripping little two-seater. Well, I don't consider it an extravagance. One must do something to meet these emergencies. And I got it quite cheap – it saves the awful fag of walking and the uncertainty of lifts from other fellows, you know. I say, I'll give one of you fellows a lift home tonight if you're going my way."

"That's all very well," I said, "but what about toning up the muscles, and clearing the brain, and keeping down the weight, and brightening the temper – the joy of walking, you know, and that vow you took."

He adjusted his glasses and looked at me very coldly.

"I haven't the slightest idea what you mean," he said.

I was going his way but I had a kind of feeling that he wouldn't offer me a lift.

He didn't.

The Plot That Failed
(London Opinion, 17/5/1924)

People in fiction who have rich aunts are always trying by moral suasion to make them (the aunts) leave them (the people) – this is a more difficult sentence than I realised when I first embarked upon it – heirs to vast fortunes. Now, I am not like that, and Aunt Matilda is not like that. I have as little hope of being mentioned in Aunt Matilda's will as she has intention of mentioning me. (That is quite a good sentence. Read it again.) But Aunt Matilda always pays us a visit in the spring, and then she sends me a cheque for my birthday a little later. The value of the cheque varies in proportion as Aunt Matilda has or has not enjoyed her visit. We always spend it on our summer holidays. Once it took us as far as Scotland. That was the time she'd liked the sermon the vicar preached. It was more or less to the effect that we ought to try to put up with other people's faults even if we have none ourselves.

It was my wife who first gave me the suggestion.

"Let's go to Switzerland for our summer holidays this year," she said.

"Yes – let's," I agreed pleasantly, "and let's buy a Rolls Royce and dine at the Ritz and take a country house and—"

"Don't be silly," said Isabel. "I'm serious. I mean, let's be extra nice to Aunt Matilda."

"My dear," I explained soothingly, "one only has one's natural degree of niceness, and one can't go beyond it. We're nice to her up to the very limits of our natural niceness every time she comes. It's not our fault if our natural niceness has limitations and only takes us as far as Scotland. We live in a finite world."

"Oh, be quiet!" said Isabel. "I mean, let's *do* something – something extra."

Then I had the great idea.

I knew that Aunt Matilda hated mice. I once heard her scream so as to be mistaken for a factory siren a mile away because she thought she heard a mouse in the wainscotting.

I caught a mouse. I kept him in a large box and fed him on cheese for the few days before her visit. He was a nice mouse, and we grew fond of each other. I called him Horace. I don't know what he called me.

The night before Aunt Matilda arrived, I disclosed my plan to Isabel.

"As soon as she's gone to her room I shall slip Horace under her door. Then when she screams, I shall dash in and bravely capture Horace.... No, I couldn't bear to kill him. I shall have some cheese concealed in my hand and I shall just capture him. That ought to run to Switzerland, don't you think?"

Aunt Matilda arrived. Isabel showed her to her room. I slipped Horace beneath the door.

The scream that followed winded me for a moment but, recovering quickly, I burst into the room.

Aunt Matilda stood in a corner, her back to the wall.

"Save me!" she screamed. "Kill it! Save me! It's got me in a corner."

I ran to her and looked around for Horace. But Horace had played me false. I found afterwards that Horace had sneaked under the chest of drawers without even letting Aunt Matilda see him, and was curling his whiskers and grinning at me. As I was gazing round for Horace, something touched my nose, and looking up, I saw between Aunt Matilda and myself, suspended by a long thread from the ceiling, a large fat grey spider pawing the air.

"Kill it!" she screamed again. "Save me!"

Now I am, in ordinary circumstances, a brave man. I served with distinction in the Great War. I once contradicted a staff officer. I am not, generally speaking, a coward.

It is only spiders that make me feel like that.

But spiders do....

With a yell of terror I fled from the room.

Aunt Matilda left half an hour later.

She left after some very eloquent and well-worded comments on my cowardice and brutality and selfishness and discourtesy and lack of chivalry. I forget the rest. There was quite a lot.

We're going to spend our summer holidays at Margate this year. It's a nice bracing place and so conveniently near London....

The Gift

(London Opinion, 31/5/1924)

We were both waiting for the bus. He wore corduroys and a dejected expression.

"You can 'ave Wembley!" he said to me suddenly and ferociously.

"Thanks so much," I murmured, "but really I shouldn't know what to do with it."

"*Burn* it," he said, with equal suddenness and ferocity. "*Burn* it or chop it up, or give it to this 'ere Lybour Government fer a 'oliday 'ome. I've done with it."

"Really?" I said politely, looking down the road to see if my bus was coming. It wasn't.

"Wot's it corst?" he went on. "Thahsands and thahsands, an' wot do *I* git aht of it? Tell me that!"

"A little pleasure, surely," I said.

"*Pleasure?*" he ejaculated, and spat with bitterness and contempt.

"Have you been there?" I said.

"Bin there?" he said. "Bin there? Yuss, I 'ave."

"Didn't you enjoy it?" I said.

He turned to me and drew a deep breath.

"I bin there yesterdye. I won' sye nuffin' abaht goin' there 'cause I bin in a pal's cart wiv 'is moke an' it din' corst me nuffin'. Well, I gets there an' I 'angs rahnd waitin' fer a charnst till a hold female sez, 'Will you carry me bag for me, man?' so *I* carries it rahnd and hexplains the sights. Whenever she sez ter me 'Wot's that, man?' I sez 'A nytive village, mam,' 'cept once when I sees the folks goin' dahn undergrahnd, and then I sez 'That's Tootie's tomb, mam, that is,' an' she sez, 'That's a huntruth, man. I know that's not

hopened. That's a coal mine.' 'Well, mam,' I sez sarcastic, 'I suppose you knows,' an' rahnd an' rahnd we goes, me a-tirin' meself aht a-luggin' 'er bag an' syin' 'Nytive village' till she'd 'ad enough, an' then she sez ter me 'Thank you, man,' an' guess wot she give me!"

"A shilling."

"Freppencyp'ny," he said. "That's yer Wembley!" with infinite scorn. "Corstin' us thahsands an' thahsands an' wot do we get aht of it? Freppencyp'ny. Wearin' meself ter death readin' abaht it in the pypers an' 'earin' folks talkin' abaht it an' luggin' 'er bag an' tellin' 'er abaht nytive villages, an' wot do I git in return? Freppencyp'ny. That's justice, that is! Wembley justice!"

A bus came along, not the one I wanted. My acquaintance, however, lurched up on to the step. The conductor rang the bell. My acquaintance spat into the road and looked back at me as the bus moved off.

"You can *'ave* Wembley!" he said again.

So now Wembley belongs to me.

But I shall continue to allow people to look round it as before.

Mrs Hawkins on the Drama
(The Humorist, 14/6/1924)

Mrs Hawkins was clearing away my breakfast things.

"Do you often go to the cinema, Mrs Hawkins?" I said.

Mrs Hawkins appreciates a friendly interest in her doings. She carefully balanced my empty cup on the empty milk jug on the tray; then rested one hand upon an enormous hip.

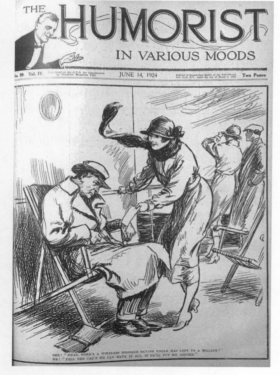

THE HUMORIST
IN VARIOUS MOODS

JUNE 14, 1924   Two Pence

"Yes, I does, Miss. Cheap an' comfortable plyces on the 'ole – an' 'igh clarse, too – velvet seats an' flowers an' music an' whatnot. An' some luvly fillums an' all. I like the drarmas of 'igh life meself, folks be'avin' so beautiful, an' hopenin' doors fer each other an' such like. I orfen tykes Alf ter see 'em. 'E's a good 'usband, Alf is, but 'e 'asn't got no 'igh clarse manners. Now Bert, me first, 'e wasn't much of a 'usband but 'e 'ad beautiful manners. 'E'd blow 'is tea so dainty like, an' 'e'd put a 'ole pot o' grease on 'is 'air on Sundays. Always the gent, Bert was."

"I didn't know you'd been married more than once, Mrs Hawkins," I said.

"Alf is me third, Miss. The others hall died – nachural deaths – an' beautiful funerals they 'ad. Bert's was a fair treat. I looks me best in widows' weeds, though I sez it as shouldn't. I bin married to Alf two year now. The Lord meant us to 'ave 'usbands the same as 'e meant us to 'ave other troubles an' sorrers.

"As I sye, Alf's a good 'usband but 'e aint got no soul. I took 'im to the pickshers last week an' there was a luvly one of a young girl what died of a broken 'eart. 'Ain't it beautiful, Alf?' I sez, the tears runnin' dahn me fyce, an' 'e sez, 'I'd rather 'ave Felix the Cat'. 'E 'asn't got no soul, not like what I 'ave, an' p'raps it's as well." She heaved a sentimental sigh from her capacious bosom. "They're 'appier without 'em."

"Do you ever go to the theatre, Mrs Hawkins?" I said.

"Now, it's funny you should sye that this mornin', Miss, fer we went there larst night, me an' Alf, an' a fair wash-aht it were, too. On the 'ole, Miss, I generally prefers the theatre to the pickshers. I prefers the sound of the yuman voice to the sound of the lydy nex' door suckin' peppermints."

"What theatre did you go to, Mrs Hawkins?"

I find the spell of Mrs Hawkins' conversation difficult to resist.

"It were Mrs Brown, what I does for on Thursdays, what gave me the tickets. It were called The Merchant of some foreign place or other – some ole chap goin' on somethin' awful, such a set aht 'cause 'e wanted a pound o' somebody else's flesh – balmy, 'e were, I should sye, poor ole chap. An' a nice 'andsome young feller the other one were, the one what 'e wanted the pound o' flesh off, but it were all proper melancholy an' the ole bird what 'ad caused all the to-do moanin' and groanin' all hover the plyce.

"Nothin' cheerful, not a single rousin' chorus nor a dance nor nuffin', an' a saucy young piece come in mykin' speeches an' carryin' on an' syin' the ole chap 'ad ter be a Christian fer a punishment, though what punishment there were in that beats me, fer we're all supposed ter be Christians, I thought, though I hexcludes Mrs 'Iggins what lives nex' door an' what I'll tyke me dyin' oath took me stockin's orf me line larst week, sye what she will, though that's neither 'ere nor there, an' I give 'er a piece of me mind what she won't forget in an 'urry.

"'Owever, abaht the plye – as I sez to Alf as we come aht, 'In reel loife they'd hall be in Colney 'Atch'. An' such a hawdience – oh, Lor! Long fyces an' stryght 'air 'an spectacles, not a soul ter 'ave a joke wif."

"Did you tell Mrs Brown what you thought of it?"

"I did, Miss, an' she sez it were me wit wot were lackin' in happreciation, an' it were a beautiful plye. Well, as I said to 'er, I'd rather be lackin' in happreciation, than be like them folks, a-moanin' an' a-groanin' an' carryin' on an' wantin' pounds of hother people's flesh. It were made up by a chap o' the name o' Shakespeare. Well, 'e didn't know nuffin' abaht reel life, that's hall I can sye. I've lived fer forty years in a busy plyce like Poplar, an' I've never yet 'eard of anyone wantin' a pound of anyone else's flesh – outside of a lunatic asylum – not even in the Sunday papers an' there's not much abaht yuman nycher they don't get 'old of in the Sunday papers."

"I see what you mean," I sighed.

"Now, the 'All at Poplar, that's the plyce fer yer money, an' now the hentertainment tax is orf—"

I handed her two shillings.

"Treat yourself to a seat there tonight, Mrs Hawkins," I said.

"Now, that's kind o' you, Miss," beamed Mrs Hawkins. "Me'n Alf'll go. I feels as if I needed somethin' to cheer me up after larst night."

"Tell me about it tomorrow," I said.

"Yes, Miss, an' it'll be a very diff'rent tyle to this."

In any case, I feel it will be a tale worth hearing.

(Laughter.)

(London Opinion, 14/6/1924)

The restaurant was crowded and he apologised profusely as he took the other seat at my table. I noticed his expression of strain and intensity, and also that he looked tired. I entered into conversation with him. Yes – he led a strenuous life, a very strenuous life, indeed.

"I have to attend the courts regularly," he said.

"The legal profession?" I said tentatively.

"Er – yes. The legal profession. But my branch of the legal profession is more wearing than any other branch of the legal profession," he said with a sigh.

"Really?" I said.

"Yes. Nerves at a stretch all the time."

"Are you a barrister?" I said.

He didn't look like a barrister.

"N–not exactly," he said. "But I have to attend the courts regularly."

My curiosity was aroused.

"Do you mind my asking what exactly is your work?" I said.

"Not at all," he replied. "I'm proud of my— profession. You read of my work every morning in every paper, though I always remain strictly anonymous."

"Really?" I said, interested.

"Yes. Whenever you read the word 'Laughter' after a remark of the judge, think of me. It's wearing work, too, I can tell you."

I looked my bewilderment.

"But what work is it?" I said.

"It's highly specialised work," he said. "It's taken years of training and close observation. I'm the man who can tell when the judge has made a joke – and I start the laughter. The others follow. I know the exact expression of each judge's face when he thinks he's said something funny, and I start the laughter. I tell you it's strenuous work, but it's necessary work. Someone has to do it. Of course, I can't go with every judge every day, but I help 'em turn and turn about. Whenever you read of a trial without a single joke – flat kind of show – no 'laughter' – you may know I wasn't there."

"But," I said, "do you mean to say that they don't make jokes when you're not there?"

"They try to," he said compassionately, "but without me to start the laughter they aren't recognised as jokes. You see, the legal temperament isn't sportive. It's soon discouraged in the sportive line. When I start laughter at the first attempt, it encourages them and they try again and sometimes things get quite lively. When I've started laughter several times I've known them to make a joke you'd have recognised as a joke in the papers without the word 'Laughter' after it. Not often, of course. But sometimes. Even then it's a perpetual strain for me. Continually watching the expression, you know, for fear I miss one and they lose heart and things get flat again. If you knew," he said desperately, "the trouble it is to keep things going in Law Courts – why, sometimes even when I start the laughter it's not followed up, though one laugh in the court counts as 'Laughter' in the papers. Did you know that?"

"Do you mind my asking," I said, "whether – I mean – what remuneration do you get?"

"Remuneration?" he said. "No remuneration. I'm not personally known to the judges, though I think some of them know me by sight. I think some of them have a strong feeling of gratitude towards me. No, it's merely the life I have chosen – my way of serving mankind. I'm probably the most hard-working and unrecognised philanthropist in London. Well, I must be going. I've no time to waste."

"I'm afraid you find it a strain," I said.

"To nerves and throat," he admitted, "terrible – terrible. But I must carry on as long as I have strength. Good day!"

I watched him bustling off hurriedly in the direction of the Law Courts.

The Treat
(The Humorist, 21/6/1924)

He was eight years old and my housekeeper's nephew, and he came to spend a week with her. I never met him in the house, but whenever I went into any of the rooms at the back of the house I saw him swinging solemnly to and fro on the gate of the back garden. Vaguely it began to depress me. His visit drew to a close. I thought of his having come from Shropshire to spend a holiday so near the great metropolis of England and spending it thus. On the morning of the last day of his visit I broached the subject to my housekeeper. I offered to take him up to London for the day and show him its sights. My housekeeper is a woman of few words and no emotion whatever. She said, "Very good, sir. Thank you."

I took Ernest to the zoo and to Madame Tussaud's. I gave him a good lunch and then took him to Westminster Abbey. I expended much eloquence and energy on the day. Ernest received it all in silence, and without any change of expression. Then I took him to have tea. Towards the end of tea I remarked a slight brightening of his expression. I wondered on which of all the pleasures of the day his thoughts were lingering.

"What are you thinking of, Ernest?" I asked, kindly.

He looked at me. In his expression were mingled endurance, hopefulness, and anxiety.

"I'm wond'ring," he said, "whether there'll be a bit of time left for swingin' on the gate when we get home."

The Method

(The Humorist, 30/8/1924)

It was on one of those few occasions when I went for a walk before breakfast that I met him. He was in a wood, just arising from slumber. His boots consisted of worn and broken uppers tied round the soles of his feet with string. His rags were hardly decently held together by patches.

"Good morning," I said.

"Goo' mornin'," he replied, placidly performing his morning toilet. This seemed to consist of passing both hands lightly over his face and hair. Then he stretched, whistled "Horsey, Keep Your Tail Up", and began to walk along with me.

"On the tramp?" I said.

"Huh," he affirmed.

"Jolly sort of life!" I said.

"Grand!" he said.

"Do you want work?" I said, thinking that he might cut the grass in the front garden.

For answer he turned to me and closed one eye.

I rather liked him.

"What are you going to do for breakfast?" I said.

"Oh, don't you *worry!*" he said. "I'll git me *breckfust* orl right."

"Beg?"

"Not *eggsackly* beg," he said. "I've gotter method, I 'ave."

I was curious. We walked together to the village. We discussed Ascot and the Derby and Goodwood, at all of which events I found that my friend had been present.

"Mind yer, I don't *bet!*" he said. "I don't approve of bettin'. I just takes 'em on me tramp an' there's orften a charnse o' pickin' somethin' up, like."

Again he honoured me with a friendly wink.

We were at the first house in the village. It happened to be mine.

"Well," he said, "I'll start 'ere."

I hovered round expectantly. I was curious to see his "method".

He stood at the gate for a minute and assumed an expression of wistfulness and pathos. It was a wonderful expression. It must have taken years of practice. Then he took a can from his pocket. Then he coughed a hollow cough. The hollow cough was a masterpiece. Then, still coughing, he walked up to the back door.

Brown, our housemaid, answered it.

My friend held out his little can.

"Can you let me 'ave a bit o' 'ot water for me tea, Miss?" he said, in a hoarse whisper. "I'm trampin' ter the fruit pickin' in Kent fer a bit o' work."

He put a hand to his chest and, with an expression of great pain, coughed again. Brown's grim expression relaxed. She disappeared and soon my wife appeared.

"The kettle's just boiling," she said kindly. "Where's your tea?"

"Ain't got no tea," he said, with a fresh spasm of coughing.

She disappeared.

"Sugar and milk?" she called from the kitchen.

"Yes, if you please, mum," said my friend, faintly.

Soon she reappeared with a can of hot tea and a pair of boots.

"God bless you, mum," said my friend, gazing at her pathetically.

I could see that it was all she could do not to kiss him.

He came down to me proudly bearing a

can of tea and water and sugar and milk (all paid for by the sweat of my brow) and my gardening boots. I looked at them sadly. I was fond of them.

"Going to put them on now?" I said.

He looked at them with admiration and shook his head.

"Naw!" he said. "Can't abide the feel of boots on my feet. Drive me wild, they do. 'Sides, oo'd give me any more boots if I was wearin' these?" He glanced down fondly at his own derelict footwear. "So, I wouldn't part with these 'ere boots, not if you was to give me the British Hempire in exchange. Why, they're worth a bob a day ter me." He glanced appraisingly at mine. "I'll get two bob for this pair from somebody. Quite decent boots, isn't they?"

I looked at them fondly and regretfully.

"They is," I replied.

He stopped at the next gate and handed me his can and boots.

"'Old these, mate," he whispered confidingly, and, assuming his pathetic look and hacking cough, he went up the path. I stood in the shelter of the bushes and watched and listened.

My next-door neighbour's wife opened the door.

"Could you let me 'ave a little scrapin' o' marge or drippin' for me piece o' bread, please, lady?" he said humbly, ending with his deep, heart-rending cough.

"Certainly," said Mrs Cleve. "Where's your bread?"

He felt in his pocket and his face dropped. The drop was cleverly done.

I muster lorst it, lady. It ain't 'ere. I muster lorst it. It muster dropped out of the 'ole in me pocket." He was almost weeping. "Sorry to 'ave troubled you, lady."

"Oh, that's all right," said Mrs Cleve compassionately. "I can let you have some."

She disappeared. He waited, coughing patiently till she reappeared with two thick slices of bread and butter and a golf coat of Cleve's to which I knew he was deeply attached. My friend returned. At the gate he dropped his cough and pathetic look and took back his steaming can and my boots.

"'Nother two bob," he said, looking with a professional eye at Cleve's golf coat.

Then he went across to the ditch and seated himself comfortably in it with his slices of bread and butter in one hand, his can in the other, and my boots and Cleve's golf coat beside him. He looked blissfully happy and at his ease. I almost envied him.

"What sort of fruit picking do you do?" I said.

His eyes behind his luxuriance of unkempt beard twinkled at me.

"Any sort o' fruit pickin' I does," he said, "isn't the sort o' fruit pickin' yer means when yer *sez* fruit pickin'."

He closed one eye at me, then attacked his meal with relish.

I went home to breakfast.

My wife ate very little.

"I feel too unhappy to eat," she said. "*Such* a poor old man came to ask for hot water and he hadn't even any tea. He looked *so* unhappy and he had *such* a cough and he was tramping to the fruit picking for work. I gave him your gardening boots, dear. If you'd seen his, you wouldn't have grudged them. I wish I'd given him something else. He was – oh, *so* pathetic."

The Riddle of the Heath
(London Opinion, 30/8/1924)

I think that something ought to be done about it. It is partly the fault of the police force and partly the fault of the Blackheath authorities and partly the fault of Angela. Angela is my cousin. I met her in town the other week and she said she was staying with friends at 30a Dartmouth Road, Blackheath, and asked me to call. She said Dartmouth Road quite distinctly. She sounded the final —d, —D as we used to call it in the kindergarten. You put your tongue on the roof of your mouth and let it jump off.

I set out for Blackheath a few days later. I did not know Blackheath then. I do now. If you ever get to the end of this article, you will know why. I took the train to Blackheath station. Fate was on my side – or appeared to be at first. Fate has a way of doing that, "To betray us to our ill", as Macbeth said. A policeman stood conveniently just outside the station.

"Can you tell me the way to Dartmouth Road?" I asked pleasantly.

"Row?" he said.

"No, Roa-Der," I replied.

He considered the matter deeply.

"There's a Dartmouth Road at Forest Hill," was the final result of his meditation.

I refused Forest Hill.

"There's one at Hampstead," he suggested brightly.

I spurned Hampstead.

"There's a Dartmouth Grove 'ere," he said, "an' there's a Dartmouth Place an' there's Dartmouth Row an'—"

"But why?" I said wildly. "I mean, what has it done? Why should it have no rest?" I had a vision of the Blackheath Urban District Councillors racking their brains over the name of a new road, and always falling back on Dartmouth. Dartmouth must have become a kind of habit, like drugs or catching the 9.15.

"I beg your pardon, sir?" said the policeman.

"With all the beautiful words in the English language," I began, warming to my subject, but he brought me back sharply to the matter in hand.

"Row," he said, "but not Roa-Der."

"She said 'Roa-Der'," I said firmly.

He looked depressed, then caught sight of a colleague and seemed to cheer.

"Wait a moment," he said.

He conferred with the colleague and then returned to me. He looked as if he bore good news.

"There is a Road as well," he said. "It's close to Row. Both across the heath."

"Which bus?" I asked.

"No bus," he said grimly. "You'll 'ave to walk."

I decided then that I didn't like Blackheath. But it was interesting to find that it really had a heath. I hadn't expected it. I begin to have hopes that there is a farm at Chalk Farm and a forest at Forest Hill. But I don't think I'll go to see, in case there isn't.

Blackheath heath is a large open space that takes a long time to walk across. It may have its picturesque moments, but it takes a long time to walk across. At the other end I found another policeman.

"Do you know the way to Dartmouth Road?" I said wearily.

"Did you say roa-Der," he said, "or Row?"

"Roa-Der," I said.

He shook his head.

"There's a Dartmouth Place this side the 'eath," he said, "an' a Dartmouth Grove an' a Dartmouth Row, but Dartmouth Road is the other side of the 'eath near the station."

"The other side—?" I repeated. "But I've just come—. Are you sure?"

"I know," he said with dignity, "all this here part. Dartmouth Road is the other side of the 'eath."

I looked round desperately.

"Is there a taxi place anywhere near?" I asked.

"No," he said with a certain grim triumph. "You'll 'ave to walk."

It was dusk. Again I set out on my lonely pilgrimage across the heath. At the other side I came across a dairy, and inside the shop I saw a man with a kind face. My spirit was broken. I went up to him and, between my sobs, I poured out my story. He gave me a glass of milk and a directory.

"There's Row, but there ain't no Roa-Der," he said. "See for yourself."

"She said 'Roa-Der'," I muttered feebly.

"I'd try Row," he said soothingly.

I wrung his hand.

"Thank you, thank you," I said unsteadily, setting out again into the night.

Half way across the heath I met the first policeman.

"Found it, sir?" he said cheerily.

Had I felt stronger I would have dashed his brains out, but my spirit was broken and my strength was spent.

"Not Roa-Der," I whispered brokenly. "I'm going to try Row."

I staggered on. I reached the other side of the heath. I passed by Dartmouth Grove and Dartmouth Place, and came to Dartmouth Row. Feebly, I rang at the door of 30a. As the door was opened I heard the sound of Angela's voice. Wild triumph came to my heart. I had beaten the heath. I had eluded Grove and Place and Road, the non-existent. I had run Row to earth.

"Well, you *are* late!" said Angela.

I sank down upon a chair and raised a weary hand to my brow.

"You said Roa-Der," I said.

"Did I?" said Angela. "I'm always doing that. Are you sure? Did I really say the d—?"

"You did," I said. "You said d—, *d*—, *d*—."

There is a certain satisfaction in the sound even when pronounced as we pronounced it in the kindergarten, if exploded with sufficient force.

Try it for yourself and see.

My nerves are still a complete wreck. I start from my sleep with frenzied cries of "No, *Roa-Der*, not *Row*." The sight of a bus bearing the sinister word "Blackheath" sends me into a cold perspiration. I feel that I ought to be able to claim legal compensation from someone, but I'm not sure whether I should claim it from the police force or the Blackheath Urban District Council or from Angela.

The Fall of David

(The Humorist, 1/11/1924)

My troubles began with the tennis weather. For John has an excellent tennis court and I have none.

But to reach John's house I must cross a field or walk a quarter of a mile round by the road. So I prefer to cross the field.

But in the field lives – David. Now David is very handsome. I am the last person in the world to deny his looks. He is excessively handsome, excessively vain and excessively arrogant. His gait puts you in mind at once of lord mayors' chains and turtle soup. In many ways I admire him. He so manifestly despises the inferior race of man.

But what David cannot understand, and what I find very difficult to explain to him, is that there exists through this field a public right of way.

Of course, if he never allowed me to use it, that would settle the matter once and for all, I should buy an aeroplane or use the road, But there are times when he allows me to use his field, when he merely stares at me coldly from a further corner of it. There are other times when he is waiting for me at the gate and I hastily pretend that I do not see him, but had meant to go round by the road all the time. I never deceive him.

The worst times are when he deliberately lets me get to the middle of the field and then advances upon me with manifestly hostile intent, his neck outstretched and ruffled up, his beak emitting threatening noises.

Now there may be strong silent men of blood and iron who can advance to meet an infuriated turkey who is advancing to meet them, but I am not one. I back. I back slowly but surely to the gate and the road.

Nothing stays his slow onward march upon me. The alleged power of the human eye simply amuses him. The use of his Christian name maddens him. He considers it too familiar. The humiliating spectacle can plainly be seen from the road, but this is not all. David is not content with driving me from his field. He cranes his neck through the bars of the gate and screams derisively at me as I set off along the road. I always pretend not to hear him, but he knows that I do, and he knows that I know that he knows that I do.

John sometimes comes to witness the sight. He says it gets funnier every time. That is possibly true. His description of it certainly seems to amuse people. It has won me the name of Goliath. David is my fly in the ointment of the tennis season.

But this morning something happened to change all that. In the window of the village shop a notice has appeared, and that notice for me has made life a different thing. Who is the transient being, this creature of the day, this lower animal, this David that I, the lord of Creation, should cower before him? This morning I entered the field with my head held high and stalked haughtily across it, slashing at the buttercups with my tennis racquet as I went, and humming nonchalantly.

Perhaps David had himself seen the notice, perhaps he instinctively felt my attitude. Anyhow, he merely watched me, dejectedly, from behind a tree. The reaction may set in. David may assert his tyrannical sway over me once more, but never again shall I be as before.

A notice of four words has quite definitely and finally put David in his right place in the cosmos.

The four words were "Join Our Christmas Club."

The Wager
(The Humorist, 20/6/1925)

I've forgotten exactly what Charles was talking about, but he said, "The thing is as impossible as it is to spend ten minutes in a church bazaar without buying something."

"How ridiculous!" I said. "There's no impossibility about that. I could easily do it. Any man could, unless he was exceptionally weak-minded."

"All right," said Charles. "There's one on at St Mark's tomorrow afternoon. I'll give you an entrance ticket, and I bet you a quid that you won't be in there for ten minutes without buying something."

"Done!" I said.

As soon as I entered the building, a girl came up to me carrying a tray of buttonholes.

"Will you have a buttonhole?" she said. "Only sixpence each."

I looked at her sternly.

"Certainly not," I said. "I'm the president of the S.P.C.F – the Society for the Prevention of Cruelty to Flowers. Look at them! You've torn them from their happy homes, away from all their friends and relations – to *die!*" I ended with a dramatic half sob. "It's murder. I'm going to introduce a bill into parliament making this an offence punishable by death."

She edged away, looking scared. I knew that she wouldn't come near me again.

I looked at the clock. One minute had gone. A girl came up with a tray of sweets.

"Will you buy a box of sweets?" she said. "Only two shillings."

I fixed her with a stern eye.

"Most certainly not," I said. "Don't you know how unhealthy those things are! They're responsible for all the decayed teeth and – er – the impaired digestions and – er – the weak mentality of – er – of everyone. The habit of consuming sweets at all hours has turned us from an A1 to a C3 nation. Why should I spend two shillings on poison? Tell me that."

She was moving off with a frightened look in her eye. I followed her.

"I tell you," I went on, encouraged, "it's these so-called sweets that are responsible for – er – for all I said before."

She darted behind a stall in sudden panic. I turned aside, wiping my brow, exhausted but triumphant. She wouldn't come near me again. I could see Charles watching me. I winked at him and looked at the clock. Four minutes had gone. A youth came up to me carrying a handsomely embroidered cushion.

"Will you buy a ticket for this cushion I'm waffling?" he said with a chinless smile. "Only a shilling."

I took out a notebook.

"Would you mind giving me a few particulars?" I said pleasantly. "I'm Secretary for the Anti-Raffling League. I'd like to be sure that this is strictly legal. I've prosecuted eighteen church bazaars in the last fortnight for raffling. I—"

But suddenly he was at the other end of the room, taking refuge behind the penny dip. I breathed again. I'd seen the last of *him*. I looked at the clock. Six minutes gone. I walked down the hall. Everyone except myself was wearing or carrying a buttonhole.

Then I saw Miss Masters. She was leaning against a pillar, looking bored and holding a little buttonhole of cornflowers. I'm a bachelor, and I've often thought I could do worse than Miss Masters. She somehow seems different from other women. I went up to her. She'd be a refuge, anyway. No one, seeing me in deep conversation with Miss Masters, would dare to interrupt me. There were three minutes left.

"Good afternoon," she said, smiling sweetly.

"Good afternoon." I looked down at her buttonhole. "So they've victimised you."

"Oh, I wouldn't exactly call it victimising," she said. "It's all in a good cause."

"Do you think so?" I said. "At present I'm working in a very good cause myself, and much harder than anyone else here."

"Are you really? You look awfully pleased with yourself."

"Yes. You see, I'm earning a pound. In two minutes now a man will come up and give me a pound. I shall have earned it in ten minutes."

She sighed.

"You must be *awfully* clever."

"I am," I said. Then I looked down at her buttonhole and grew expansive. "I say, that's just the colour of your eyes, isn't it?"

She shook her head.

"No. My eyes aren't as blue as that," she said. "It's more the colour of yours."

She held it up to my buttonhole. "It's just what you ought to wear with your blue eyes and that grey suit. Would you like it?"

"I'd love it."

She put it in for me. She has rather pretty hands. She patted it softly.

"Now it's yours."

"Now it's mine."

At that moment Charles came up.

"Half a minute left," he said. "How are you getting on?"

"Isn't he a dear?" said Miss Masters.

"He's just bought my last buttonhole. I've sold a hundred since the opening, but I was feeling almost too tired to sell this until the angel came and relieved me of it." She held out her hand to me. "Sixpence, please!"

I've changed my mind about Miss Masters. She's exactly like other women, after all.

The Pendulum Swings
(The Humorist, 14/11/1925)

Aunt Emma talked on and on and on....

She was discussing her married daughter, my pretty cousin Stella, and she looks on the dark side of Stella as she looks on the dark side of everything.

"She *would* shingle, of course," she said, mournfully, "the minute it came in. Nothing I said could stop her. She and Hubert go to those dreadful night clubs and they drink those awful cocktails and her skirts barely cover her knees and she smokes hundreds of cigarettes a day and she paints and powders as no decent girl would have done in my young days and...."

There is something soothing about Aunt Emma's voice when it goes on and on....

It was certainly Stella, but quite forty years older. She wore her grey hair still shingled. Cheeks and lips were still frankly reddened....

The other people in the room were at first shadowy, but gradually they became clearer and clearer. They were very young.

Stella walked out and softly, at first, they began to discuss her.

"Poor old Aunt Stella," said one, "isn't she hopelessly old-fashioned?"

"Isn't she?" said another. "Do you know, I saw her smoking a cigarette yesterday and she rouges, poor old thing. I'd sooner die than be seen with a cigarette or a powder puff. They're such hopelessly out of date affairs!"

"She drinks cocktails, too. She ordered one when she took us out to lunch. There were some awfully smart people at the next

table. *They* did *look amused when they heard her. One of them said, 'Cocktails! How sweetly old-fashioned!' We felt quite ashamed."*

A pretty girl arranged her flowing skirt about her feet. One dainty toe peeped out demurely.

"And she sticks to those dreadful old-fashioned skirts. She does *look absurd!"*

"Oh, I know," said another; "I've got a photograph of my mother when she was a girl wearing them. So ridiculous!"

"And the poor old thing goes to night clubs!"

"Are there any left?"

"Oh, yes, one or two. You see a few poor old dodderers dancing the most absurd old dances!"

"She doesn't even go in for Parish work."

"Doesn't she? Everyone *smart is doing that. I've got a duck of a slum for my district. When are you and Albert going to be married, dear?"*

"I'm not sure. I'm just making him a pair of those carpet slippers in woolwork. They're all the rage now. He came to tea yesterday. He was supposed to be coming the day before, but Mother had to go and I couldn't find a chaperon."

"They're so hard to get nowadays, aren't they? Elderly aunts are precious. It's so old-fashioned to go about without a chaperon!"

"Oh, but, my dear, I must tell you something. Albert and I are slowly collecting our furniture, you know, and we've got the loveliest thing – a genuine Victorian horsehair sofa. Martha and Edward have one, but theirs is imitation. We're going to have a Victorian drawing room. Everyone smart is having Victorian drawing rooms. Albert's mother is giving

us wax flowers in a glass case, and Mother is making antimacassars for us. We're looking round for an ormolu clock. Do come and see our things some day,

"I'd love to, but I've got such a lot of croquet arrangements. I'm playing at Wimbledon this summer so I must keep in practice."

"Poor old Aunt Stella still plays tennis!"

They laughed, tinkling girlish scornful laughter....

I sat up with a start and rubbed my eyes.

"She *must* be in the fashion," Aunt Emma was saying; "short skirts and cigarettes and paint and powder...."

She went on and on and on....

The Cruel Uncle

(London Opinion, Christmas 1925)

There are cruel uncles in fairy tales and there are cruel uncles in real life. I am one of the cruel uncles in real life. Or at least I am this Christmas. As a rule the twins score. But I certainly score this Christmas. The twins always come to stay with us in November. They are called Bunty and Billy and are sixteen years old. They bully me unmercifully.

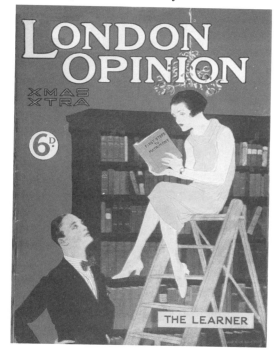

I took them to all the things they wanted to be taken to, and saw every play they wanted to see. They insisted on taking me to plays that called up a roseate blush to my middle-aged cheeks, but at which Billy (very much Oxford bagged) and Bunty (very much shingled) never turned a hair.

I gave myself agonising indigestion by going to strange restaurants with them. In vain I pointed out to them that my stomach is an English stomach, and likes English foods. It isn't a Chinese or Italian or French stomach. I think my stomach must be a particularly patriotic stomach. It simply hated that fortnight of the twins' visit. And that wasn't all. They wanted to go to a night club, so I took them to a night club and suffered excruciating torments of boredom. Take it from me there's about as much fun going to a night club as there is in St Paul's churchyard.

We spent the last evening of their visit at home. I hoped for peace, but there's never much peace where the twins are. They got me somehow on the chesterfield, with Bunty sitting on my head and Billy on my much-enduring stomach.

"Now," said Bunty cheerfully, "let's talk about Christmas presents."

"What Christmas presents?" I said as distinctly as I could.

"The Christmas present you're going to give us," said Billy.

"Billy," I said in a grieved voice, "surely someone in your distant childhood taught you that you mustn't ask for things. It simply isn't done."

"No – no," said Bunty. "We know. We're not actually going to ask for things. We're going to suggest."

"Just hint," said Billy.

"It's no use," I said. "I'm frightfully dense. It's simply no use hinting to me. I'm hint-proof."

"What shall we do, then?" said Billy.

"Get off my stomach," I suggested.

"Oh, no!" said Billy. "This is our position of advantage. We aren't going to give up till we've used it to the utmost. We're going to extort a promise from you."

187

"We're not going to *ask* for anything," said Bunty. "But – I know – I've got an idea. We'll write to you just before Christmas and we won't *ask* for anything, but you'll be able to gather from our letters what we need most. Now you must promise to give it us."

"We won't let you up till you do," said Billy sternly.

"You're doing my abdomen serious harm," I complained. "It hasn't got over the Chinese dinner it had last night yet, and you're simply aggravating the trouble."

"Promise – and we'll let you up," said Billy.

I felt the wall of my abdomen slowly giving way beneath Billy's weight, so I promised.

"I promise," I said solemnly, "to give to each of you the thing which I gather from his or her letter that he or she is most in need of."

Then they let me get up.

The letters arrived last night.

Bunty's is written in lines that slant down from the left-hand edge of the paper at an angle of 45. It is written in ink, and has evidently been folded up and put into the envelope as soon as written, without any ceremony (ceremony here being synonymous with blotting paper). You can just read the words through a blue-black haze. She has used quite good ink. Not the watery sort.

Dear Uncle,
I hope you will have a jolly Christmas. We enjoyed our visit to you awfully. I hope you've nearly got over it. I saw some ducky pearls in a shop window the other day. They just made me think how I'd love a string myself. They aren't
frightfully expensive – not the little ones.
Heaps of love, Bunty

And Billy's was –

Dear Uncle,
A friend of mine has just got a motor-cycle. Nearly everyone I know poseses one now. They seem to be looked upon as meer trifles but absolutely necessary. I should dearly love to posess one myself and hope to do so immediately,
Yours, Billy

I have just dispatched their presents to them by tonight's post. I promised to send them what I gathered from their letters they needed most, and I am a man of my word. I have sent Bunty a ruler and a piece of blotting paper, and I have sent Billy a dictionary.

The Give-Away

(London Opinion, 9/1/1926)

Have you ever given yourself away? It's ever so much more annoying than being given away by someone else.

When I was younger I used to take a cold bath every morning, and it gave me a reputation among my friends for hardiness and manliness and intrepid courage and Spartan asceticism and all that sort of thing. It's lady novelists who're responsible for it. As a matter of fact a cold bath's no proof of virtue at all. It's only a proof of lack of sensitiveness and appreciation of comfort that almost amounts to degradation.

Of course, I didn't look at it in this light when I took a cold bath. I mean a really cold bath – every morning. I thought I was a very splendid fellow indeed. And so did everyone else. As I said, it's lady novelists who're responsible for these distorted notions. They always make their heroes look "as if they took a cold bath every morning". It's a pretty mean thing to have done. I've never come across a lady novelist who takes a cold bath every morning. Yet they expect *us* to. But that's women all over.

But to return to my cold baths. People used to point me out to each other and say, "He takes a cold bath every morning right through the winter!" And they'd look at me with a faint shadow of the look with which people look at Rosita Forbes and Colonel Lawrence and the Mount Everest men and others who have performed exploits calling for unprecedented perseverance and endurance.

When I entered the club on a cold morning, shivering, men would look up from their armchairs by the fire and say with chattering teeth, "You didn't have one this morning, did you?" And I would throw out my chest and say, "Br-r-r-r-r-r! Yes, I did. Nothing like it. Glorious!"

Well, the years rolled on, and water provided by the London County Council (or the Worshipful Company of Watermen or whoever supplies the water in London) grew colder each year. So I began to put a little bit of hot in – not to heat it, you understand, but just to make it the right coldness for a cold bath. And gradually I began to put in more and more, but I still called it a cold bath because, after all, the term "cold" is a comparative term and, in conjunction with boiling water, you might call mine cold – well, coolish, anyway. But I liked people admiring me, and I liked feeling like the hero of a lady novelist's novel, so I never mentioned the hot water to anyone. Thus I kept my reputation and yet managed to instil a little comfort into my bleak early morning life.

This weekend I was staying with the Herberts. The Herberts are awfully proud of me. They tell their friends about me. They say, "He has a cold bath every day. Quite cold. All weathers. Has done for the last ten years. Right through the winter. Isn't it wonderful?" And their friends say, "Yes, isn't it?" or words to that effect.

Brown was staying with the Herberts, too. Brown plays a very posh game of golf, but I wasn't jealous of him because I had my cold baths to make up. The Herberts would say to Brown at breakfast:

"It was simply wonderful of you to do the eighth in one yesterday!"

And then they'd say to me:

"I say, did you *really* have one this

morning?"

And I'd rub my hands and say:

"Br-r-r-r-r-r-r! Yes! Glorious! Nothing like that first icy shock. And the icier the better!"

Brown didn't even pretend to have cold baths.

Now everything would have gone off as it always does if it hadn't been for a canary – a wretched little yellow canary that Mrs Herbert's mother gave her for a birthday present. (I never did like Mrs Herbert's mother, but she doesn't really come into the story.) Anyway, the creature lived in the drawing room, but in the early morning the maids used to put him in the bathroom while they "did" the drawing room, and the creature would watch me sardonically through the bars of its cage while I had my bath.

Well, yesterday morning I came down to breakfast as usual.

"Isn't it *cold?*" said Mrs Herbert. She looked at me admiringly. "I suppose you had one even today?"

"Br-r-r-r-r-r-r!" I said. "Rather! Glorious! Nothing like it. The first icy shock. Glorious!"

"I hope the canary doesn't worry you," she said.

"Oh, no," I said. "I think the little fellow quite enjoys it. He watches the steam with much interest."

"The st—" gasped Mrs Herbert.

"Yes," I said impatiently, "the steam – when I turn the hot tap on."

There was an awful silence, and then they began to talk about something else.

The Rival Garage
(London Opinion, 19/6/1926)

There are two garages in our village. One belongs to Mr Smith and is called the Ideal Garage, and the other belongs to Mr Brown and is called the Garage de Luxe. Both names are deceiving, and as a matter of fact there isn't much to choose between them. I patronised the Ideal Garage because it is next door to my house and the Garage de Luxe is nearly a quarter of a mile down the road.

Mr Smith of the Ideal Garage is large and red and perpetually smiling. Whenever he sees me coming to him, he says, "Well, and what's your little trouble *today*, sir?" He says it as though whatever my little trouble is, it will prove infinitely diverting to him. And whenever I ask him anything he says, "Fancy you not knowing *that*, sir!" and he says it as if he can hardly believe that there is anyone in the world who didn't know *that*.

Of course, there have been dark incidents in my traffic with Mr Smith of the Ideal Garage. There was the time when I rang him up from fifteen miles away because my car refused to move and I thought I must have broken what corresponds to the main spring; and he came and simply turned on my petrol tap. I don't think he's ever stopped laughing at that. Then there was the time when I'd left it outside a friend's house with its patent anti-thief gear-locking device nicely locked and found that I'd left the key at home and he had to come and tow me home. That amused him intensely. And always in the wide smile with which he utters his "And what's your little trouble *today*, sir?" I can see him thinking about the petrol tap and the gear-locking key. And other things.

Now Mr Brown of the Garage de Luxe would never laugh at anyone. He's thin and long and lugubrious. People's mistakes depress him; they don't amuse him. And he'd never tell anyone, because he never speaks unless it's absolutely necessary. I began to long for Mr Brown's silence and moroseness. I began to think how nice it would be to start fresh with someone who'd never heard of the petrol tap incident or the gear-locking incident. I began to feel that I'd go mad if I heard Mr Smith say once more "Well, fancy you not knowing *that*, sir!" or saw his broad smile so suggestive of petrol taps and switches and gear-locking as he said "And what's your little trouble *today*, sir?"

So I made a most momentous decision. I decided to change from the Ideal Garage to the Garage de Luxe in spite of the extra quarter mile. My self-respect demanded the change. So I wrote to Mr Smith and told him that I would not require his services any longer, and I set off to interview Mr Brown. I was revelling in the thought of Mr Brown's moroseness and silence and ignorance of the petrol tap incident, etc.

I entered the garage. Mr Smith came forward grinning from ear to ear. Petrol taps and switches and gear-locking keys were written all over his face.

"W-w-where's Mr Brown?" I asked.

"Sold 'is business," said Mr Smith cheerfully, "retirin' from the prerfession. I bought 'is garage, sir. Goin' to run the two, sir. Fancy you now knowin' *that*, sir. And what's your little trouble *today*, sir?"

Marigold's Double
(London Opinion, 3/7/1926)

Marigold is a fortune-teller and belongs to the Joneses. I don't know who christened her Marigold, but she's a large sort of circular cardboard thing divided into sections with a hole through the middle and a cord through the

hole, and you ask a question and twirl her round and then catch hold of a section and see what's written on it. Marigold is well-meaning, but not very intelligent. For instance, if you ask her "Who's going to win the Derby?" she will probably answer "Yes" or "No". And if you ask her "Shall I have any luck with those oil shares?" she will probably answer "His heart if false" or

"Await the time, you will find great love", or "Venture not far from home", or something equally illuminating. Or, if you just ask for general advice she will either play for safety and say, "If your desires are modest they will be satisfied", or else take cowardly refuge in "June" or "Saturday" or "The world is wide".

Jones made the thing for his wife's birthday present. A great friend of hers had one and she wanted one, so Jones borrowed it and laboriously copied it word for word, curve for curve....

He did it simply because she wanted it. That shows what marriage does to otherwise quite sensible men....

Jones hates Marigold, but Mrs Jones loves her. Mrs Jones never does anything or goes anywhere without consulting her, and Mrs Jones is an adept at twisting Marigold's meaningless phrases into whatever she wants them to mean. Mrs Jones can turn "Trust him not" into advice to have the furniture recovered, and "You will obtain this wish through a friend" into advice to go up to town for the sales, and "You will live in splendour" into advice to buy a new umbrella.

Jones would watch her on these occasions in amazement and admiration. On one of Marigold's sections is the legend "If you take this step you will regret it", and Jones was always wishing she'd get that, but she never did – till last week.

Last week she was going up to town to buy a new hat, though Jones assured her that she didn't need one.

"Just fetch Marigold, first, darling," she said to Jones, "and let's see what she has to say about it."

Marigold lives in Jones's study. Jones fetched her. I noticed a look of confidence on Jones's face that puzzled me.

Mrs Jones twirled it and caught hold of a section and read it aloud. "If you take this step," she read, "you will regret it." So she decided not to buy the new hat, after all....

Last night I was at the Joneses again. Mrs Jones wanted to go away for the weekend and Jones didn't.   Like all sensible men, Jones hates going away for the weekend. So at Mrs Jones's request he fetched Marigold, and Mrs Jones twirled Marigold and again read:

"If you take this step you will regret it."

So she decided not to go away for the weekend....

I followed Jones into his study.

"How do you do it, Jones?" I asked.

He shut the door carefully and handed Marigold to me. I examined her. Every section was inscribed: "If you take this step you will regret it."

"I made it," said Jones simply. "It's just like the other one to look at. I keep them both here and I bring this one out when she wants to do something I don't want her to do. I thought of it a week ago, and it's being a roaring success. She hasn't found out so far, and I don't expect she ever will.... What!... a genius?... Oh, I don't know....   Married life sharpens one's faculties, that's all!"

Next-Door Neighbours
(The Humorist, 17/7/1926)

The Joneses had been at The Laurels for two years before the Bessimers arrived at The Chestnuts next door.

The fame of the objectionableness of the Bessimers preceded them, because they'd once lived next door to a friend of Mrs Jones's, and she wrote to Mrs Jones to warn her about them. She said they borrowed everything borrowable and either did not return it or returned it broken, that they were always asking her in to meet Terrible People (for which occasions they "borrowed" most of the provisions and implements from her), and they invited themselves in to meals with her several times a week. She said that the Joneses must be Very Firm and Reject All Overtures, as if the Bessimers ever got in the thin edge of the wedge it would be hopeless.

The Joneses were consequently so Firm that even when the Bessimers had been there a whole year they hadn't succeeded in borrowing anything, and they'd only been in to The Laurels twice and the Joneses had only been in to The Chestnuts once.

Yet the Joneses' life was now completely darkened by the necessity of being Firm and Continually Rejecting Overtures. Continually Rejecting Overtures has a wearing effect upon the nerves of kind-hearted people. And the Joneses were kind-hearted people.

Mrs Jones began to look thin and worn, and Mr Jones's expression began to be one of chronic furtiveness, acquired by continually watching from the dining room window to make sure that Mr Bessimer had started for the station before he started for the station himself. Going to the station with Mr Bessimer would, of course, be the Thin Edge of the Wedge.

And then, to their great relief, the Joneses heard that the Bessimers were moving. They were going to live on the other side of London. The Joneses danced round the dining room table for joy when they heard the news. A great weight dropped from their hearts. Once more they would be able to walk out of their little front gate with head held high and look the whole world in the face, secure in the knowledge that the Bessimers were not lurking in ambush just outside to get the Thin Edge of the Wedge.

But, as I have said, the Joneses had kind hearts, and now that the Bessimers were actually going, Mrs Jones's kind heart began to trouble her. She made a very poor supper that night.

"You know, John," she said at last, "I can't help feeling that we haven't been really *kind*."

Mr Jones's kind heart was troubling him too.

"No," he said thoughtfully. "I don't see that we could have done any different in the circumstances, but – I quite understand how you feel."

Then she brightened.

"But John," she said, "now that they're going and it'll be quite *safe*, let's have them in for an evening. I – I'd sort of *hate* them to go away feeling that we'd been unneighbourly."

Mr Jones felt the same, so they invited the Bessimers in to supper the next week and did their very best to erase from the Bessimers' minds that hateful word "unneighbourly".

Mrs Jones said that they were so sorry that they were going before they'd really got to know them. Mr Jones, not to be outdone, said that he'd meant to put Mr Bessimer up for his club if they'd been staying any longer. Mrs Jones, being reckless and throwing caution to the winds, said that they might have had a jolly little summer holiday together somewhere if only the Bessimers hadn't been removing. And when the Bessimers had gone, the Joneses, exhausted but glowing with virtue, looked at each other across the *débris* of the feast and said, "Well, we did what we could, didn't we? I'm sure they won't think of us as unneighbourly *now*!"

And the next morning they heard that the Bessimers, who hadn't actually completed the sale of their house, had decided now to break off negotiations and stay where they were.

Mr Bessimer met Mr Jones on the way to the station and said how much they'd enjoyed last night, and it seemed silly to go away just when they were getting so jolly and friendly together, and he supposed he'd be put up for the club at the next meeting, and it would be nice to see a little more of each other than they'd been seeing lately.

In the afternoon Mrs Jones received a note from Mrs Bessimer asking for the loan of her coffee machine (and just a little coffee, too, dear, if you can spare it), and the mowing machine, and some milk (because they'd run out), and asking the Joneses in to supper that night to fix up the details of that jolly summer holiday they were going to have together, and *would* Mrs Jones be so angelic as to have them in to lunch on Sunday, as their maid would be out, and it would be rather nice to have some bridge this evening when they came in, so would Mrs Jones bring in some cards, as theirs were lost...?

So it was the Joneses who had to move.

They left The Laurels and went to live in a new garden city where there was company's water and main drainage but a nasty muddy road which made Mr Jones's boots so dirty every morning that he had to have them done again at Victoria.

The house can never be to them what The Laurels was.

And even there the Bessimers come to see them every Sunday and send them picture postcards during the week.

Making an Impression
(The Humorist, 24/7/1926)

Mind you, I refused to go to the Robinsons' picnic till I heard that Miss Tremayne was going to it, and then I accepted simply because I thought it would give me an opportunity of letting Miss Tremayne see what a capable sort of fellow I am, and what a good husband I'd make.

I've nothing to say in favour of picnics generally except that they do separate the goats from the wheat (if you'll excuse the biblical expression). I mean you can tell at once on a picnic who are the efficient, capable Admiral Crichton sort of men and who aren't, who'd make good husbands, and who wouldn't. A woman can take for granted, for instance, that a man who can open a ginger beer bottle with a penknife will be able to mend the window catch when it goes wrong, and that the man who confronts an angry flock of cows while the ladies get away in safety won't be afraid to give the cook notice.

So I went to the Robinsons' picnic solely to prove to Miss Tremayne what stuff I am made of. Others may surpass me at tennis (though I contend that I always happen upon badly balanced racquets), others may outshine me at the ukelele or Charleston, but I flattered myself that a crisis would display me in my true colours, and I thought that a picnic was the right place for a crisis.

One or two minor crises occurred early in the afternoon. A wasp stung Miss Green, and young Franks, in trying to slay it, fell over the milk bottle, so that no one could have any milk in their tea, and somebody else sat on an ant-heap, and somebody else on a piece of bread and honey thoughtlessly left unattended by the youngest guest (aged six), and somebody else tried to get Miss Smith's coat from the boat and dropped it into the water; but these were contretemps hardly worth mentioning.

At last, however, a real crisis occurred. Nobody had brought a tin-opener. Robinson said that he knew he'd asked somebody to do it, but he'd forgotten who it was, and there were a tin of sardines and two tins of peaches to be opened.

"Leave it to me!" I said in a quiet, cool sort of voice that I thought was rather effective. "I'll see to it."

So they left it to me. I hacked at it with stones and a penknife. I made my finger bleed. I crushed my thumb. I even tried my teeth on it and nearly dislocated my jaw. I spoilt a perfectly good suit of clothes over it. And Miss Tremayne watched me with a light in her eyes that might have been either amusement or admiration. I kept hoping that it was admiration.

I did get a bit of a hole in the sardine tin in the end, and we got a certain amount of sardine out with the help of a penknife and a fountain pen. I got a little hole in the peach tin, too, and all the juice poured out on to Miss Tremayne's dress. That was unfortunate. I frankly admit that that was unfortunate. But I hoped that my prowess as a human tin-opener would compensate for it.

Just as we were finishing tea, Robinson's brother arrived.

"You blighter!" said Robinson. "I remember now! It was *you* I told to bring the tin-opener!"

Robinson's brother pointed at me.

195

"I gave it to him to bring this morning." he said. "He put it in his pocket."

I put my hand into my pocket and there it was. And suddenly I remembered Robinson's brother giving it to me. Any psychologist will tell you that it was quite a normal and permissible and even interesting lapse of memory. But Miss Tremayne is not a psychologist. I think that women – even the best of them – are very lacking in sympathy. I've decided to remain a bachelor.

The Handy Man
(The Humorist, 23/10/1926)

I am what is generally known as a handy man.

I may here remark that in my family, at any rate, it is no great catch to be a handy man. All it means is that your relatives put off unpleasant jobs of every kind for your annual visit and pacify their consciences by pretending that you enjoy mending their coal shed roofs, and shimmying up their apple trees to cut off dead branches, and diving into their rain-tubs to find out where the leak is, and performing other desperate deeds of daring for no remuneration and very little thanks.

The minute I set foot in my sister's house on a long-deferred visit, she said:

"I've been so looking forward to your visit, dear. You're just in time to pick the plums."

I was taken aback, not by the blatant indecency of the greeting – for there's something about a handy man that kills all sense of decency in near-relations – but because I didn't know there were any plums in her garden. Mildly I mentioned the fact.

"No, I know there aren't," said Norah, "but the Joneses have gone away for all August and September, and they've kindly bequeathed us their plums. I said that, of course, I couldn't get them, but that you were coming to stay with us and would love to."

I swallowed.

"Kind of you," I murmured.

"Well, I know you like having little jobs like that to do," said Norah shamelessly. "I'll lend you a ladder."

"Is the place next door?" I asked hopefully.

"No," said Norah. "I'm afraid it's some little way off. In Rock Street, off High Street. But," with that determined cheerfulness that people can always bring to bear on other people's sorrows, "it will be a nice little occupation for you, and I'm *sure* you'll enjoy it."

I put it off till the last day of my visit, and then I sallied forth, my car loaded up with ladders and baskets for the spoils.

I worked hard all afternoon and then returned weary but triumphant with every plum that the garden had contained.

Norah seemed really grateful.

"How *lovely!*" she said. "I'd no idea that the Joneses had so many. What are you going to do now?"

"I'm going to rest, thank you," I said very firmly, ignoring the appeal in her eyes – she'd told me earlier in the day that the latch of the garden gate needed mending – and went upstairs.

I had quite a nice long sleep (gathering plums is awfully exhausting), and when I came downstairs again the aroma of plum jam in its earlier stages filled the house, and Norah was talking to two elderly ladies in the drawing room.

"John will see to it all for you," Norah was saying. "He's *awfully* good at seeing to things."

I entered, groaning inwardly.

"The Misses Tomkins have had their garden robbed," said Norah to me dramatically. "They're so upset. I'm just telling them that you'll go to the police station with them to give information about it."

So I led the Misses Tomkins to the police station and upheld them by my manly presence while the policeman took down particulars.

"What exactly was taken?" he asked.

"Plums," said the elder Miss Tomkins.

He wrote it down judicially.

"Only plums?" he said.

"There *are* only plums in the garden," said the elder Miss Tomkins with digity, "a *wonderful* yield of plums. We were out all afternoon and came home to find the trees *stripped*, the garden *rifled!*"

"We'll leave no stone unturned to find the thief, madam," the policeman reassured her, and we all went out.

The Misses Tomkins thanked me profusely and said they didn't know what they'd have done without me.

I was rather thoughtful on the way home.

"Norah," I said when I reached it, "where do the Miss Tomkins live?"

"In Rock Street," said Norah.

I thought some more.

"You did say the Joneses lived in the third house, didn't you?" I said at last.

"No, the fourth."

I thought still more.

"Norah," I said at last, "who lives in the third house?"

"The Miss Tomkins," said Norah.

Clarissa Changes a Wheel

(London Opinion, 23/10/1926)

"Will you come for a drive with me, Uncle George?" said my niece Clarissa.

Clarissa is very charming, but I doubted her competence as a driver of elderly uncles.

"Can you drive, my dear?" I said, doubtfully.

"I'm a beautiful driver," said Clarissa, with confidence and without modesty.

"Yes, but can you – deal with things if things go wrong?" I persisted. "I'm no use, you know. When motors came in I was too old to grapple with them."

"Oh, nothing could go wrong with it," said Clarissa, airily, "except perhaps a puncture or a burst tyre."

"And could you deal with that?" I said.

"Easily," said Clarissa, with a toss of her shingled head.

So I put my hat on my head and took my life in my hands and went out with Clarissa. She was, as she had said, a beautiful driver.

"I've misjudged you, Clarissa," I confessed. "I'd no idea that you could drive like this."

"Oh, I can," said Clarissa, airily, and at that moment there came a loud report.

"What's that?" I said as the car zig-zagged to a standstill.

"A tyre gone," said Clarissa.

"And – can you deal with a gone tyre?" I asked, apprehensively.

"Oh, easily. The wheel has to be changed, that's all."

"Can you change the wheel?"

As if for answer, Clarissa opened her handbag and took out a small mirror. She looked at her reflection with a business-like frown.

"I've never really thought that this hat suited me turned up like this," she said at last.

She whipped it off, detached a brooch from the brim, turned up the brim at quite a different angle, replaced the brooch, put the hat on again and once more studied her reflection thoughtfully.

"Yes – it's a great improvement," she said, slowly.

"Clarissa," I said, patiently, "hadn't you better be getting out your tools for dealing with the wheel?"

"I am doing," said Clarissa cryptically, taking a lipstick and powder-puff from her bag.

I waited while she frowningly examined her very charming reflection, and with a few deft touches made it more charming still.

"Clarissa," I admonished her gently, "this is not an appropriate moment for performing your toilet."

"Oh, yes, it is," said Clarissa, calmly replacing her little pots.

Then, and not till then, she descended from the car and went back to where the spare wheel was.

Before she had even touched it a passing car drew up and a personable young man descended.

"Can I be of any assistance to you?" he said with a deep blush as he took off his hat.

Clarissa looked up with a well-simulated look of surprise.

"Oh, I was just going to change the wheel," she said, with an adorable smile. "I've got a burst tyre."

"Let me do it for you," said the personable young man.

At this point another car drew up and another young man descended. The young man in possession received him coldly, but he insisted on helping. The two young men worked hard and glared at each other fiercely, while Clarissa stood idly by distributing her adorable smiles to them impartially. A third young man arrived, but the first two combined to freeze him off. Clarissa comforted him as he drove away by a specially adorable smile.

In a quarter of an hour it was done, and Clarissa, who hadn't done a hand's turn all the time, dismissed the two reluctant young men very firmly but with very charming smiles, and drove away leaving them gazing fatuously after her.

"There!" said Clarissa, "soon done, you see."

"Clarissa," I said sternly, "have you ever learnt how to change a wheel?"

"No," admitted Clarissa. "I suppose I shall have to when I'm about thirty, but I don't see why I need bother until then, do you?"

Vera Looks Out a Train
(The Humorist, 19/11/1927)

"How do the trains run back home, Vera?" I asked.

Vera took up the railway timetable and began to turn the leaves.

Now I'm only engaged to Vera, not yet married to her, so I couldn't take the timetable out of her hands and look up my train myself. During the engagement it is necessary to subscribe to the fiction that a woman knows how to look up trains in a railway timetable. All women think that they can do this, and are very touchy on the subject. I know of more than one engagement that has been broken off simply because the man hinted to the girl that she didn't know how to look up trains.

You may with impunity suggest to a woman that she is vain, unpunctual, or even deceitful, but you may not suggest that she does not know how to look up trains. I don't know why this is so. I only know that it is. After marriage, of course, it is different. At least, if you begin quite firmly, it is.

But as I said, I am only engaged to Vera, so I merely said, spiritlessly:

"Thanks so much, darling."

Vera opened the timetable.

"About what time must you go?" she said. "There's one at 9.40, but that's rather early, isn't it? Oh, and in any case, it seems to be going in the opposite direction, so it wouldn't do. What about the 10.10? Will that do?"

"What time does it get in?" I ventured.

"Let me see," said Vera, frowning. "The 10.10." Her fingers followed it down the page. "Oh, it doesn't get in at all. It seems to stop half way. So I suppose that wouldn't do either. Wait a minute. Here's one at 10.30. That would do, wouldn't it?"

"Is it an express?"

"I think so. Yes, it doesn't seem to stop anywhere till it gets to – oh, it's a Margate train. It's going in the wrong direction again."

"Er – may I look one minute?" I said, stretching out a hand.

Vera stiffened.

"I'm *quite* used to this timetable," she said, distantly. "I know my way about it blindfolded. Here's one at 10.25. Gets in at 11. Will that do?"

"Nicely," I said, trying to look grateful and confident and convinced that she knew her way about it blindfolded.

"Oh – one minute," said Vera. "It's a down train. You want an up one, don't you? Of course. I'm on the wrong page. I expect that's why all the trains were going in the opposite direction." She flicked over the pages. "*Here* we are. Oh, no, it's the wrong line. Wait a minute. I'll look at the index. *Here* we are. This really *is* right. There's a 10.30. And if you miss that, there's a 10.55. And if you miss that, there's an 11.15. I'll write them down for you, shall I?"

I said, "Thank you so much, darling."

She wrote them down.

We had a very nice evening, and then I went to the station.

I found that the 10.30 didn't exist at all.

The 10.55 didn't stop at my station.

The 11.15 was a "Saturdays Only".

There weren't any more trains, so I walked home.

Aunt Martha and the Doctor
(The Humorist, 11/12/1926)

Aunt Martha is the sort of woman who is never happy unless she is consulting a doctor. Whenever she goes to a new place – when other people would at once look round to find a nice dairy, or butcher, or garage, or even a nice walk or golf links – Aunt Martha gives her whole attention to finding a nice doctor.

If she only comes to stay with you for a week and is feeling perfectly well, she'll get you to ask your doctor to call so that she may see whether he says the same about her heart, or throat, or rheumatism as John's doctor said last week.

So we weren't surprised or unduly alarmed when on the first night of her visit she said she'd like to consult a doctor about her chest. She went on to tell us that she had had a cold on her chest in the early part of the year, and Fanny's doctor (she had been staying with Fanny the week before) had told her that every trace of it had disappeared, but she thought she might as well consult another doctor about it so as to be quite sure.

"Right," I said sympathetically, "I'll send for Dr Gordon."

"*Not* Dr Gordon, please," said Aunt Martha, impressively and mysteriously.

We were surprised. We were proud to possess a doctor like Dr Gordon in the village. He had been the star of his year at Bart's. It was rumoured that had his health been stronger he would have accepted a brilliant appointment in London. He had come to see Aunt Martha on her last visit to us about her neuralgia. We had rather swanked to her about being able to produce a doctor like Gordon.

"But you saw him when you were here before," I expostulated.

"Yes," said Aunt Martha, still more impressively and mysteriously, "I am only too aware of that."

"B-but," I gasped, "he's a splendid doctor."

"I," said Aunt Martha, magnificently, "happen to consider that he is *not*."

"Why?" I said, still amazed and aghast.

"I do not wish to undermine your faith in your medical adviser," she said. "I do not judge for others. I judge for myself. I have judged Dr Gordon as a doctor for myself, and I do not wish to put my health into his hands again."

"Do you mean to say that you weren't satisfied with him?" I asked, incredulously.

"I was *not* satisfied with him," said Aunt Martha with great vigour and primness.

She refused to give any details, but she refused to have Gordon, and she insisted on having a doctor.

There was a doctor in the next village whom I didn't know at all, but I set off to fetch him. It was a terrible nuisance. I had to wait an hour for him, and then I had to make an enormous detour to avoid passing Gordon's house. However, I got him at last and he examined Aunt Martha's chest, assured her there was no trace of her cold left, pocketed his fee, and departed.

His visit left Aunt Martha in a more genial mood.

"Now, Aunt Martha," I said, "do tell us what you objected to in Dr Gordon."

"Well," said Aunt Martha, "I think that after all it is my duty to tell you. I think that it is my duty to warn you against him. The man has no right even to pretend to be a doctor. You remember when I had him here for my neuralgia?"

"Yes."

"And he felt my pulse?"

"Yes," we agreed, breathlessly.

"Well, as he was feeling my pulse I looked at his watch, and he *couldn't* have been taking my pulse correctly because his watch was ten minutes slow!"

Simpson and the Baby

(The Humorist, 29/1/1927)

I ran into Simpson in the village grocer's at the rush hour. We clung together and edged our way with gentle and persistent force to the counter. I was buying butter for my wife, and he was buying potatoes and onions and lard and cheese for his.

When we finally emerged with our purchases I was not surprised to see Simpson begin to pack his into a pram containing a sleeping baby. Simpson is probably the best-trained husband in the world.

"I'll take the potatoes for you," I said kindly. "You seem to have as much as you can manage."

"Oh, thanks awfully," said Simpson.

So I took his bag of potatoes, and we set off to our two semi-detached villas, Simpson wheeling the pram.

Suddenly he smiled at me over his spectacles.

"Well, I've remembered to bring them back today," he said with pride.

"What?" I asked.

"The pram and the baby," he said, still smiling. "An awfully funny thing happened yesterday. A writer chap like you might make a good tale out of it. I went down to the shop for some bacon, and took baby, you know, as I sometimes do to give my wife a rest, and when I came home my wife said, 'Where's the baby?' and, upon my word, I'd completely forgotten it. I had to go back, and there he was in his pram still outside the shop."

I laughed.

"Well, you've remembered them today," I said.

We had reached the gate of Simpson's house.

"I'll bring the potatoes up to the door for you," I offered.

Together we went up to the front door. Simpson opened it. I noticed that there was a perambulator already in the hall.

"Here I am, dear," called Simpson gaily, "and I've remembered to bring baby back today!"

Mrs Simpson came into the hall. She was carrying the Simpson baby.

"But, John," she screamed hysterically, "you didn't *take* baby!"

Solving a Problem
(London Opinion, 29/1/1927)

"Are you," said Phyllida, "an expert on social problems?"

"More or less," I admitted, guardedly.

"Because I'm in a social difficulty."

"You ought to write to one of those papers that have a special column for that sort of thing," I said. "People write describing their social difficulties and the editor tells them what to do. I came across one once and found it excellent reading. One woman wrote to say that she was at a shooting-party and the man in the next butt to hers always missed, and ought she to make any comment or not, and the editor told her to say 'Hard lines!' or 'That was a near thing!' every time he missed. I watched the papers carefully after that, but I must have missed the actual murder, or else they managed to hush it up. I expect he shot her after the tenth 'Hard lines!' Of course, there's always the possibility that he missed her, too. I expect she'd say 'That was a near thing' in that case, unless it was the turn for 'Hard lines!'"

"Mine's a much more serious problem than that," said Phyllida.

"Cough it up," I said, vulgarly.

"Well, it was yesterday, and I was alone in the house, because Mother had gone up to town and it was Ethel's day out, and I was in the drawing room and saw the vicar and the vicaress and the master vicar. I knew they'd come to ask me to help at the bazaar, and I didn't want to, and I knew that they'd stay for hours and hours and I couldn't bear it, and I knew that as they came past the drawing room window they

could see the whole room except the bit of floor just under the window, and there wasn't time to escape, because they'd have seen me going across to the door. You see the dilemma, don't you?"

"Exactly," I said. "Quite a pedigree one. What did you do?"

"I did what seemed at the time for the best. I dropped on my hands and knees and flashed like lightning to the bit of floor just under the drawing room window, and I stayed there on all fours."

"Yes," I said. "So far so good."

"They passed without seeing me, of course. They rang at the front door about six times, and then I heard the vicar say, 'They must all be out,' and they turned to go. And then – this is the horrible part—"

"Yes?" I said, with interest.

"Then the boy vicar – I mean the vicar's son – he's eleven – popped his head through the drawing room window – it was open – and yelled out, 'I say, she's here all the time!' And they all came and looked at me. Standing right up to the window on the grass, you see, they could see me quite plainly. They looked at me for hours and hours – it seemed like hours and hours, anyway – and they didn't say anything and I didn't say anything. There didn't seem to be anything to say, you see. We just stared at each other. All their mouths were wide open with amazement. Through the window they looked like three goldfish in a glass jar. Then they went away, looking absolutely stunned with astonishment."

"No wonder," I commented.

"Well, what ought I to do? The tale will be all over the village by now. It's quite a social problem, isn't it?"

I agreed that it was.

"People will be saying I'm mad."

"I shouldn't be surprised."

"Do be sympathetic. I'm asking you for advice."

I considered the question in silence.

"The best thing for you to do," I pronounced at length, "is to provide a sort of counter-irritant."

"What do you mean?"

"Do something to make a new sensation about yourself so that they'll forget the old one of you on your hands and knees under your drawing room window."

"What sort of a new sensation?"

"You might leave your husband."

"Don't be silly. You know I haven't got a husband."

"That's a drawback," I admitted. "The first thing to do, then, is to get a husband. You can leave the leaving of him till you need yet another sensation."

We had reached the gate of her house.

"How does one set about getting a husband?" she said.

"They ask you," I explained.

Phyllida looked away.

"Well, you see, one hasn't asked me. Not a nice one, I mean.

"One's been wanting to for a long time," I said.

She sighed.

"A nice one?"

"*I* think he's nice," I said. "Don't go in yet. Let's go for a little walk and talk him over, shall we?"

"Yes," said Phyllida.

So that's what she did. The problem is solved. People haven't time to discuss Phyllida on her hands and knees under her drawing room window because they're so busy discussing what to give us for a wedding present.

The Smoker's Cure
(The Humorist, 26/3/1927)

I little thought what was in store for me when I set off on my long-deferred visits to John and Mary.

My sister Dorothy, who looks after me like a mother, packed for me and put in a box of my favourite cigarettes. I like cigarettes, but only if they are of particular quality, and even then I smoke but few.

"There's fifty in the box," she said. "That ought to last you for" – she closed her eyes – "four ones are four, carry one – four twos are eight, carry two" – she opened her eyes, looking pale but triumphant. "They ought to last you for about twelve days if you only smoke four a day. That's nearly a fortnight."

"You're shirking, Dorothy," I said, sternly. "You haven't brought it down to hours and minutes and seconds."

"Well, anyway, they ought to last you," she said, in a tone of finality.

I was going to stay with John first. John had a nine-year-old son called Jimmie. Jimmie wasted no time or breath on social greeting. He fixed me with a stern eye and said:

"What sort of cigarettes do you smoke?"

I told him. He looked still sterner.

"Dunno 'em," he said. "What series do they have?"

I gaped. "Series?"

"Yes," he said, impatiently. "Cards."

"Oh, cards," I said. "I see – cards. I get them by the box. I've got a box with me. They don't have cards."

He looked at me in horror and amazement.

"Don't—have—cards?" he said, incredulously.

"No," I said, guiltily.

His gaze made me feel as if I had been publicly detected in some horrible vice.

"Well," he said, in the tone of one who is more grieved than angry, but who is very deeply grieved, "I somehow never thought that you'd have come with cigarettes that don't have cards. I somehow never thought you'd come with any at all. I somehow thought you'd have waited to see what sort I was c'lecting. Most people do."

I was overwhelmed with shame and confusion.

"I'm so sorry," I said, penitently. "What are you collecting?"

"Wonders of the Deep," he said, promptly. "Pipkins. Gimme sixpence and I'll go'n' get a packet for you, shall I?"

I gave him sixpence. I could do nothing else. I saw that my name would be mud in that household henceforth if I didn't smoke Pipkins' cigarettes while I was there. He brought me back the packet and fell upon the card with a whoop. Then he looked at me again as if I had failed in some way to justify my existence.

"Got it!" he said, in disgust. "But" – relenting – "it'll do for a swop, an' p'r'aps the next one you get'll be luckier."

He offered them to me. I didn't want one, but I didn't dare refuse.

"I'll keep it for you, shall I?" he said kindly, retaining the packet, "an' then you won't have the trouble of gettin' it out whenever you want one."

For the rest of the morning he followed me about with the cigarettes. As I said before, I'm a discriminating smoker, and I only smoke, as a rule, about four cigarettes a day. The boy with this packet of Pipkins' was a nightmare. The minute I'd smoked one, he was there at my elbow with the wretched packet again.

"You are takin' a time gettin' through 'em," he commented. "Couldn't you smoke a bit quicker? P'raps the next packet'll have one I want."

I'd finished the whole packet before lunch. I'd suspected from the first that I didn't like the flavour of them, and by lunchtime I was sure.

Jimmie dashed off at once for another packet. He fell upon the card with a whoop and a yell of triumph. It was one he wanted. But, instead of assuaging him, it seemed to stimulate him yet further. He'd only seven of that series to get now – only seven. His eyes gleamed at me hungrily. Only seven. I smoked all the new packet before tea. His eye had completely broken my spirit.

I smoked two more packets after tea. Both were only swops. His manner implied again that I had proved myself deplorably incompetent. I tried to justify myself by smoking two more packets after supper. I went to bed feeling rather sick.

The next day was worse than the one before. I smoked seven packets of Pipkins' cigarettes beneath Jimmie's stern and impatient gaze, and I hadn't even the satisfaction of earning his gratitude, because only two were ones he wanted.

I went on to Mary's a broken man.

"Thank heaven!" I said, as I sank wearily into the train that was to carry me away from Jimmie. "Thank heaven, Mary has only girls!"

Mary received me hospitably.

"Here you are," she said. "We've been *so* much looking forward to your coming. The girls were *so* excited when I told them you smoked, because they're *so* keen on their cigarette card collection."

Then the girls came in.

"Oh, Uncle, darling," said Jane. "You *will* smoke Burnems' cigarettes while you're here, won't you, because I've only just begun the series, and I *do* so want to finish it."

"Oh, *no*, Uncle," protested Jill. "Do smoke Hayseeds'. It's 'Our Nation's Heroes', and they're ripping. I've got about half and I'll finish them, with luck, while you're here."

I had meant to stay a week, but I cut my visit short at the end of three days. During those three days I smoked ten packets of Burnems' and ten packets of Hayseeds', and they were the most nauseous things I've ever touched.

I went home a physical and spiritual wreck. Dorothy unpacked for me. She took out my box of cigarettes unopened and looked at me in joyful surprise.

"You've not smoked one," she said. "I believe you've given up smoking!"

"I have, Dorothy," I said, wildly. "I'm going to take up opium or cocaine."

"Wh-why?" gasped Dorothy.

"Because they don't have cards."

A Spring Walk
(The Humorist, 9/4/1927)

I met Angela at the corner of the street. Angela is my cousin, and has since childhood tried – unsuccessfully – to reform me.

"Isn't it a lovely day?" she said.

I suppose it was in its own way. The sky was a fierce kind of blue, and the sun was shining in a fierce kind of way, and a fierce sort of wind was blowing dust and paper about the street.

"There's nothing – *nothing* in all the world like these first days of spring," said Angela. "Where are you going?"

"To the club," I said.

"To fug over a fire this beautiful day?" said Angela, in horror.

"Yes, Angela," I said simply.

"How long is it since you went for a country walk?" she demanded sternly.

"My memory's a poor one, Angela," I pleaded. I don't remember anything before my fifth birthday, but I can give you my dear old nurse's address if you like, and you can find out from her."

"Well, I'm going for a country walk now," said Angela. "And you're coming with me."

"Spare me, Angela," I moaned. But she didn't.

"Look at the sun and the blue sky," she said, "and the birds singing and the buds bursting. There nothing – *nothing* in all the world like these first days of spring."

"You said that before, Angela," I murmured. "To return to it at this early stage in the conversation shows a deplorable poverty of thought."

But I knew that I couldn't escape. She

took me briskly up the road and over a stile and across a field and over another stile and across another field – all among singing birds and bursting buds and a nasty piercing wind. She talked all the time. But my spirit wasn't broken even by the singing birds and the bursting buds and Angela's talking.

I argued with her. She believes in the beauty of hard work, and I don't. She believes in the simple life, and I don't. I've met the simple life and I know that it means butter beans and a hard mattress and washing under a pump, and I don't like it.

She believes in sacrificing oneself for others, and I don't. Because, as I tell her, it's a far, far nobler thing to train others to be unselfish than to train them to be selfish. She believes in vegetarianism and I don't, because, as I tell her, I'm a kind-hearted man and I've learnt from Duse that the death agonies of a carrot are horrible to witness under a microscope.

So we argued and argued and argued as we tramped over a ploughed field which the sun, for all its appearance of fussiness, had omitted to dry after the last shower. Meantime, the sun had gone in and the blue sky had withdrawn itself to wherever blue skies do withdraw themselves to spend most of their time.

By the time we'd finished talking about the beauty of work, a drizzle had set in; by the time we'd finished talking about the simple life, a deluge had set in; by the time we'd finished talking about sacrificing oneself for others, hail was flinging itself upon us wildly from all directions; by the time we'd finished talking about vegetarianism, it was thundering and lightning, as well as hailing, and the sky was the colour of a London fog. The birds had ceased to sing and presumably the buds had ceased to burst. We got back as best we could in a tropical storm of rain and hail and thunder and lightning.

But it takes more than that to dampen Angela. At her gate she turned on me earnestly.

"If I've convinced you on one thing we've conversed about this afternoon," she said, "I shall not consider the afternoon wasted."

"That's all right, then, Angela," I said. "You may rest happy. Your afternoon has not been wasted. On one subject you've quite convinced me. One statement you made I believe now from the bottom of my soul."

"And what's that?" she said eagerly.

"That there's nothing – *nothing*," I said, bitterly, "in all the world like these early spring days."

And I turned up my dripping collar and went home through the hail and lightning to change.

The Car-Stealers

(The Humorist, 16/4/1927)

I came jauntily out of the wayside inn at Woodcombe, where I had had lunch, looked round for my brand-new occasional four, jumped into it and drove off. It was a pleasant day and the countryside looked just as the countryside ought to look on a pleasant day after a good lunch. I flitted along in a leisurely fashion, just touching thirty. Then I thought I'd get out the map and make sure of the exact road.

I stopped the car and put out my hand to the back seat for the case where I keep my maps. It wasn't there. I dismounted and examined the back seat. My case certainly wasn't there, but another case was. I opened it; then closed it quickly. It evidently belonged to a lady. I had caught a fleeting glimpse of a very natty little boudoir cap, a shingle brush, and a pot of rouge. I stood staring at it in amazement.

Then a horrible thought struck me. Slowly I went round to the back of the car to look at the number. It wasn't the number of my car. I went to look at the licence. It wasn't the number of my licence. No doubt at all about it. It wasn't my car. It was as like my car as one car can be to another, but – it wasn't my car. And I'd only had my car a week.

It's horrible to feel that you've lost your car after only a week, but it's worse still to feel that you've got someone else's. I looked guiltily up and down the road, half expecting to see a squadron of police already in pursuit of me. It's an awkward situation to be found in possession of a stolen car. Perhaps they wouldn't believe

that I'd got a car just like that one, and had taken that one by mistake. That, after all, must be the standard excuse of all motor thieves. They'd only smile when I said that.

Greychester was the next big town. Probably the owner had already notified the police of Greychester, and the entire local force would be awaiting me in ambush just inside the city. I decided not to go to Greychester just yet. It was about tea time, anyway, and I'd stopped just outside a picturesque little inn. So I decided to go in and have tea and think over the situation.

There was only one other person having tea in the lounge, and she was the prettiest girl I've ever seen in my life. And she was crying. I quite forgot my own trouble. It was terrible to watch her crying. I endured it till I'd finished the muffins. Then I approached her. All the best heroes of fiction, I knew, approach strange girls when they see them crying in the lounges of country inns. I've never yet met one who didn't. So I approached her and said:

"Excuse me, but – er – are you in any trouble?"

"Y-yes," she sobbed. "I'm in terrible trouble."

"Tell me," I said, sympathetically. "I may be able to help."

"Well," she began, "I started out from Bammingshott this morning—"

"Bammingshott?" I interrupted. "My sister lives at Bammingshott."

It turned out that she knew my sister very well. It was all most thrilling, and she grew more adorable every minute. I quite forgot the stolen car. She said that she was going to tea to my sister's next Sunday.

I said I'd be there. I decided to cultivate

my sister a little more than I'd been doing lately. After all, it's a brother's duty to go to see his sister frequently. I might put in a weekend with her occasionally.

Then we returned to the trouble. The dimples went and the tears came again. "And I had lunch at Woodcombe," she continued, "and was just coming along to Greychester when I found that my car wasn't my car. It looked just like mine, but it wasn't. The number was different, and there was a beastly little case full of maps instead of my case. I must have taken someone else's at Woodcombe – where I had lunch. And I don't know what to do about it. I only got it new last week and they'll think I stole it. And, oh, what shall I do? I ought to have been in Greychester hours ago, but I daren't go on because I'm so afraid of meeting a policeman. I daren't go back because I *know* they'll say I stole it."

I gaped at her. A light had dawned.
"What sort of car was it?" I said.
She told me.
The light dawned yet more.
"Where is the car?" I said.
"It's at the back door," she sobbed. "I *daren't* leave it at the front door. I *know* they'll say I've stolen it, and I shall so *hate* going to prison."

"Now you just leave all this to me," I said, assuming a very capable, business-like air. "I'll find your car for you, and get the other one back to its owner."
She stared at me, amazed.
"B-but how *can* you?" she gasped.
"Oh, quite easily," I said, with a swagger. "Just wait for me here." I went to the back door of the inn and drove my car round to the front next to hers. Then I fetched her.
"That's the one you lost, isn't it?" I said.

She gazed at me in admiration.
"Oh, how *wonderful* you are!" she said. "How *did* you do it? But the other – the one I stole without meaning to – how can you possibly find who it belongs to?"
I smiled a superior smile.
"Easily," I said. "Leave it all to me. It shall be with its owner before night."
She looked at me with increasing awe.
"I believe you're – you're a Scotland Yard detective," she gasped.
I smiled a mysterious smile, and tried to look like a Scotland Yard detective.
"Ah!" I said (it was rather a good "Ah!"). "Well, I suppose you want to get on to Greychester now. I'll see you on Sunday."
She drove off, turning round very precariously to wave to me as she took the bend at forty.
I may, of course, tell her all about it on Sunday. On the other hand, I may not.
It depends entirely how we get on, and whether I think it advisable to continue to be a Scotland Yard detective a little longer.

My Holiday

(The Humorist, 3/9/1927)

"Where are you going for your holiday?" said Simpkins sternly. Simpkins is one of those men who are generally referred to as "good organisers". He is not content with arranging his own holidays; he must arrange the holidays of every other man he knows.

As a matter of fact, I don't think that he ever has time to take a holiday himself, because he's always so busy arranging holidays for other people. He's a very noble character. Last year he sent me to the Lakes, and the year before that he sent me to Devonshire.

Now, I'm not an energetic man, and I find Simpkins' holidays tiring. However, I haven't the moral courage to defy him openly, so I said evasively:

"Oh, I – er – haven't quite decided yet."

You see, I'm not one of those methodical people who like to arrange their holidays months and months beforehand. I'm one of those people who like to decide where they're going after they've started out for it. In the day when people travelled by train I used to pack my bag, go down to the station and then see which of the posters looked the most attractive, or which of the booking office queues looked the shortest, or which train was just on the point of departure, and go there.

But since I've known Simpkins, of course, I've never been able to do that. In a way, it has been easier since I bought a car, because at least he can't get my ticket for me and see me off on the train to the right destination, as he used to. In a car I can cheat a little and leave out some of the places he puts down for me on my itinerary.

He looked at me very sternly (he's noted for standing no nonsense from people whose holidays he's arranging) and said:

"Going by car, of course?"

"Oh, yes," I said eagerly, because, as I said, you can always cheat a little by car and you can't by train.

"You ought to find the roads fairly clear in September. The August people won't be there."

"No," I murmured.

"Well, now," went on Simpkins briskly, "I'll tell you what would be the best thing to do. Go straight up by the Great North Road to Edinburgh. You might spend a day or two in Edinburgh looking round. Some fine historical spots. Then up to Aberdeen. Not a very good road, but passable. Good hotels. Then on to Inverness. Then down to Oban. Then home by Loch Lomond, Glasgow etc."

"It sounds rather a long way," I protested feebly. "I hadn't thought of going quite so far as that."

I knew, of course, that it was useless.

"Nonsense!" he said. "You'll do it easily in the time. Keep up a good average of, say, 130 miles a day. Start early in the morning. That's the secret."

It may have been the secret, but it wasn't a secret I wanted to know on my holidays. I opened my mouth to protest again, but he said very firmly, "I'll send you the itinerary properly made out."

So I just said "Thank you." It's all one can do with Simpkins. You may despise me, but you'd have done just the same thing in my place.

The next day he sent me a long itinerary most beautifully made out. The day after that there arrived what I can only describe as a library on a wholesale scale. There were three books on historical Edinburgh, another on the lakes of Scotland, three on the Scottish Highlands, four on the historical towns of Scotland, and some others.

On the next day arrived a detailed list of all the places of interest which I must stop at on my way, and on the next day a list of hotels that either Simpkins or his victims had sampled and approved. I felt at that stage that it was easier to go forward than to go back. Simpkins came to superintend my packing, because Simpkins is by this time an authority on what to take where.

"Plenty of rugs for Scotland," he said. "It isn't as if you were going to Devonshire."

I agreed that it wasn't.

Then I had to have a spare magneto and spare bulbs and two spare tyres and spare anything else that he could think of. He made out a long list and then came round to see that I'd got them all. I hadn't, of course, so he went out at once to get them for me.

He got up very early to see me off. I wouldn't have minded that if he hadn't got me up equally early to be seen off. He checked my belongings, told me that I ought to have another can of petrol in the car, hoped I'd get on all right, told me once more how and when to strike the Great North Road, and off I went.

I sauntered along at fifteen miles an hour just because Simpkins had told me to keep up an average of twenty-five. Then I found that I'd lost my way. It had just happened. It was obvious that I was not striking the Great North Road. I was meandering instead towards a tiny coast village about ten miles from my own home.

It seemed too late to change then. So I just went on and struck the village. I'd always thought it would be a jolly little place to spend a holiday in. I garaged the car and found rooms at a farmhouse on the top of the cliff.

I had a perfect holiday. I lay on the cliff or lay on the sand or, when I felt terribly energetic, I lay in the sea. The days passed like minutes.

Simpkins was on the look-out for me when I reached home.

"Splendid!" he said. "You look awfully fit. I always say there's nothing like getting right away from home and keeping on the move the whole time to bring a man home looking really fit. Change and movement. That's the secret. The hotels in Scotland are good, aren't they?"

I said that they were, because for all I know they are.

"Nothing like Scotland," he went on enthusiastically.

I said again that there wasn't, because I suppose that, strictly speaking, there isn't.

"You didn't have any difficulty with the hills?" he said.

"None," I said, with perfect truth.

"Any trouble with the car?"

"None," I said again.

"Not had to use any of your spares?"

"No."

"You've been exceptionally lucky," he said, "in a journey of – let's see – how many miles?"

He looked at my speedometer. He'd looked at it just before I'd started off. He gaped. His eyes bulged. But I was equal to the occasion.

"That's out of order."

"Oh, yes," he said, "they do get out of order sometimes. I'll come round and see if I can put it right tomorrow."

So I went home to put the speedometer

out of order so that Simpkins might put it right tomorrow.

The problem of my life was solved. Every year Simpkins will draw out elaborate tours for me and every year I shall go to the little village on the cliffs and laze my holiday away as a holiday should be lazed away. And every year I shall come back with my speedometer out of order. And every year Simpkins will come in the next morning to put it right for me.

Of course, he'll begin to smell a rat sooner or later, but it's too early to worry about that.

Alexander
(The Humorist, 12/11/1927)

I didn't really mean to buy him, but I've never seen tortoises being hawked on the pavement before, and I stood looking at them for those few fateful moments too long that mean you have to buy one.

I didn't quite know what to do with him, so I wrapped him in my evening paper and took him to Victoria with me. Either he likes travelling or he was interested in the League of Nations (he was wrapped in a very stirring article on the League of Nations) because I hadn't any trouble with him on the journey at all. I thought more than once of putting him on the luggage rack and leaving him there, but it seemed a coward's solution of the problem.

Then I thought of handing him to the porter with the evening paper, but at the critical moment my courage failed me. I somehow didn't like to take him straight home, because I had an idea that they'd make a fuss of him, so I took a bus to Miss Merridew's.

I went to Miss Merridew's because she has two tortoises of her own – Moses and Aaron – and I thought she'd be sympathetic and give me good advice about Alexander. I'd christened him Alexander while waiting for the bus. I'd also tried to make friends with him, but he was a bit stand-offish, and evidently thought a good deal of himself.

I'd hoped to find Miss Merridew alone. This time Dawson and Montford were both with her. It is well known that both Dawson and Montford want to marry Miss Merridew, who, by the way, is rather nice.

I've always liked Dawson, and I've never had any use for Montford, who is one of those big, handsome chaps who go about thinking that they are Douglas Fairbanks' double.

I slipped Alexander into my pocket and I thought I'd wait till they'd gone before I told Miss Merridew about him. I thought that she'd be more sympathetic alone. Besides, Montford would be sure to try to be funny about him.

They were just going to have a race between Moses and Aaron. Dawson had backed Moses and Montford favoured Aaron.

They set them off from the gate and then went in to look at Miss Merridew's chrysanthemums.

"We're going to give them ten minutes and then go out and see which has got the farthest up the hill," said Miss Merridew. "We're not going to watch them, because it makes them nervous."

A moment later Montford went out to see how they were getting on.

"Both about equal, so far," he announced when he came back, and we went on looking at chrysanthemums.

At the end of ten minutes we all went out to see who had won.

Only Aaron was in sight. Evidently Moses had wandered off the course into a ditch or somebody else's garden.

"My candidate's won," said Montford, with his complacent smile.

Suddenly I saw a good opportunity of getting rid of Alexander, and taking Montford down a peg or two at the same time.

I shaded my eyes.

"Wait a minute," I said. "I think I can see Moses right up there."

I hastened on ahead, neatly slipped Alexander from my pocket to the road and then held him up for them to see.

"Here he is," I said. "Won by lengths and lengths."

Miss Merridew came up to identify him. He really is exactly like Moses. They may, of course, be related. She measured the distance with her eye. I had perhaps rather overdone the distance but I'd wanted to be secure from observation when I took Alexander from my pocket.

"It's – it's amazing, isn't it?" said Miss Merridew, weakly.

I agreed that it was.

The others were coming up. Miss Merridew looked at Dawson, who had backed Moses, and murmured to me: "It seems like an omen, doesn't it? A sort of leading—"

I was just assuring her that it did, when Montford came up and accused me of cheating.

He hadn't seen me put Alexander down, but he knew I must have done something like that, because he'd pinched Moses when he came out to see how they were getting on. He took him out of his pocket to convict me of guilt.

Miss Merridew and Dawson got engaged the next day and are going to be married next month. It is rumoured that Montford is going to give them a butter-dish. This may not, of course, be true, but it is well known that there are no depths of revenge which a vain man piqued may stoop to.

As for me, I think I shall give them Alexander. It seems an excellent way of getting rid of him.

Retribution

(The Passing Show, 18/2/1928)

They both deserved it – both Jim and the woman with red hair.

Jim had no right to let me in for the thing, and the woman with red hair had no right to exist.

Jim had said quite distinctly:

"Do go with Agatha. She doesn't want to go alone. I believe it will be quite a decent show. I'll follow as soon as I can get off."

I had a vague idea that it was either a cinema stunt or a mannequin parade or exhibition dancing. Certainly I'd no idea that it was going to be a lecture on the Vegetation of Central Asia.

If I'd known that it was going to be a lecture on the Vegetation of Central Asia, I'd never have gone within ten miles of it, and if I'd known the woman with red hair – or anyone even remotely resembling her – was going to speak I'd have climbed Mount Everest, if necessary, to escape it.

But having gone there I had to stick it – with Agatha drinking in every word eagerly by my side. Though Agatha is my brother's wife we do not see eye to eye in many things. For instance, Agatha can take a deep, deep interest in the Vegetation of Central Asia and I can't. Some people are made one way, and some another, and I'm glad that I'm made the way I am, and not the way Agatha is.

But it was a horrible experience. I had to sit on a hard chair and listen to hard facts about the Vegetation of Central Asia, and watch the hideous facial contortions of the red-haired woman for hours and hours and hours. I suffered as deeply as only those who are finely tuned to suffering can suffer.

At the end of hours and hours and hours of mortal agony on my part the red-haired woman stopped talking and the group broke up and tea came in. And then I saw Jim. He'd just come in. He'd funked the meeting but had turned up for the meal. Just like Jim.

I looked round me cautiously. The red-haired woman was standing unattended by the fireplace. Agatha was nowhere to be seen. She was probably in the further room. I walked up to the red-haired woman.

"Excuse me," I said courteously, "but could I bring a friend of mine to speak to you?"

"Certainly," said the red-haired woman.

"He's a Lithuanian," I went on.

"A Lith—?" said the red-haired woman, startled.

"A Lithuanian," I said calmly. "A native of Lithuania."

"Oh yes," said the red-haired woman, still rather taken aback. "Er – does he talk English?"

"Not *spoken* English," I said. "He speaks it only in deaf and dumb language. He can't pronounce it or understand it pronounced. But he can talk it by signs quite fluently."

I saw with relief that she possessed what I consider to be one of the most beautiful virtues in the world, credulity. She possessed that rare and precious characteristic of believing everything she was told.

"I can talk and understand that language, of course," she said proudly. "I consider that every public speaker ought to master it. This is the first time I've been called upon to use it but I dare say I shall get on all right."

"He wants you to tell him as much as you possibly can about the Vegetation of Central Asia," I said. "He's passionately interested in it, but of course he couldn't understand your speech. I'll go and fetch him."

I found Jim behind a screen where he was trying to edge himself near a plate of savoury sandwiches.

"Hello, Jim," I said, "come at last?"

"Couldn't get away before," said Jim. "What was it like?"

"Fine."

"Who spoke?"

"That woman with black hair."

"Not the red-haired one?"

"Goodness, no. The poor red-haired one's deaf and dumb. No one here can talk to her and she's dying to talk to someone. I knew you could talk deaf and dumb language, so I said I'd find you. Come on."

"But, I say! I've had no tea."

"Never mind. You mustn't keep her waiting. She's longing to talk to someone."

I drew him gently but firmly across the room and planted him in front of the red-haired woman.

Then I withdrew to the other end of the room and watched them. The red-haired woman was doing her best, and most nobly, and so was Jim.

He was very pale and occasionally he mopped his brow. He was hearing all about the Vegetation of Central Asia in the deaf and dumb language and trying to make adequate comment. I watched them for five blissful minutes. Then I went quietly home.

My Seat

(The Humorist, 3/3/1928)

I don't know why I'm so fond of that particular end of that particular seat, but the fact remains that I am. For years I've always sat on it when waiting for my train. No one else has ever dreamed of taking it.

For more years than I can count, the same people have always gone up to the city from our garden suburb by the 8.35, and they all know that particular end of that particular seat is mine.

Sometimes, of course – on January 1st or July 1st – I find a female sitting on it with a sale catalogue, but I don't mind that so much because, after all, it's only two days a year, and I rather like to think that the poor thing spent her last lucid moments on my seat.

From the seat you have the whole station under your eye. You can see the waiting room and the steps and the bridge. You can see people tearing across the bridge about half a minute before a train goes out, and you can have little bets with yourself as to whether they'll catch it.

Also it is a comfortable seat for reading the paper on. I've made it comfortable, I've moulded it to my back by long usage.

So you can imagine what I felt like when I came down to the platform, having allowed myself the usual five minutes to sit watching the bridge and reading the paper, to find a man in a brown hat sitting there on my seat and reading his newspaper.

I'd never seen him before. And there he was, sitting at my particular end of my particular seat. I sat down at the other end (the other end is very draughty, and you can't see the steps or the bridge or the waiting room from it) and looked at him.

He went on reading his newspaper just as if I wasn't looking at him. People grossly exaggerate the effect of the human eye. It had no effect at all upon the man in the brown hat.

The next morning I set off for the station a few minutes earlier, and got my seat as usual. The man in the brown hat, I thought contentedly, would now know whose seat it was. But he didn't. When I got down to the station the next morning at the usual time he was in it again.

I saw that I'd have to make an early start every morning for a bit till I'd finally got it into his head that it was my seat. So the next morning I went early again, and it was all right. I got there first, and the man in the brown hat just hovered round disconsolately. But the morning after that I went early and it wasn't all right. The man in the brown hat had gone yet earlier, and was in the seat reading his newspaper.

Then began a struggle to the death.

The next day I went so early that I caught the train before the one I usually catch. The office wasn't open and I had a nasty cold wait, but still I got my seat. The next day, however, I didn't. The man in the brown hat got there so early that he, too, caught the earlier train. But evidently his office wasn't open either, because after that, however early he got there, he waited, like me, for the 8.35.

This has been going on for nearly a fortnight now. Every day we get there earlier and earlier, but we always wait for the 8.35. Sometimes the man in the brown hat gets the seat; sometimes I get it. Yesterday I got there at 7.30 and found him there. Today I am feeling triumphant because I got it. I reached the station soon after seven o'clock. I now buy two or three papers to fill in the time.

So if you ever pass a garden suburb station and see two men lining up in a queue just after the station has been closed for the night – and one of them in a brown hat – you'll know all about it.

A Super-Tax
(The Humorist, 24/3/1928)

"I hear they're going to tax bachelors," said my sister-in-law Angela. There was a gleam in her eye that I knew well. It meant that she'd found a "nice girl" for me.

Ever since Angela married Jim she has been finding "nice girls" for me. The path of my life is literally strewn with "nice girls" found by Angela and rejected by me.

"They often say that, Angela," I replied, "but they'll never do it really. You see, parliament consists solely of people who either are married or aren't. Those who aren't married naturally won't want to tax themselves, and those who are married – well, they're human after all. They wouldn't want to exert ruthless economic pressure to make other men surrender all the joy and peace and freedom of life, and to enter—"

But I saw that Angela wasn't listening to me. She has a gift for not listening to me that amounts almost to genius. She just waits till I've stopped talking and then says what she was going to say before I began.

So I stopped talking because it didn't seem any use going on, and she said:

"I want you to come to tea tomorrow. I've got *such* a nice girl coming over for the day."

"Which one?" I said, apprehensively, "the one who wears dibjas, or the one who sings, or the one who talks about Einstein's Theory of Relativity?"

She had tried all those on me.

"None of those," she said coldly. "Quite a new one. Very pretty and full of charm."

They're all very pretty and full of charm when Angela tells me about them. But I

217

knew that I'd get no peace at all till I'd met her, so I went to tea with Angela the next day.

The nice girl turned out to be very different from Angela's other nice girls. In fact, she wasn't what I should call a "nice girl" at all.

She had dimples, and she could do all the dances Angela disapproves of, and she'd been fined twice that year for exceeding the speed limit. And she was in every way as charming as most of Angela's nice girls aren't.

In fact, she was so charming that I took her out to the greenhouse after tea to show her the blight on Angela's boronias. It's rather a picturesque sort of blight and we stayed looking at it for some time and talking about – oh, we talked about heaps of things. I found her very easy to talk to. At the end she looked at me and dimpled.

"Has Angela been trying to frighten you by telling you there'll be a tax on bachelors?"

"Yes, she has," I admitted.

"Well, don't worry. There'll *never* be a tax on bachelors. And you can feel quite safe with me if she's been frightening you about me. You see, it's Leap Year, and so you can't propose to me. It wouldn't be valid. And I promise not to propose to you. So, you see, you're *quite* safe."

"Are you sure it wouldn't be valid if I proposed to you?" I said.

"Quite."

"What would happen?"

"I'd say 'no'. Try it."

I tried it.

"Honoria, will you marry me?"

"No, James. And my name's Joan."

So I told her what my name was, and we arranged to go to a dance together the next night. Then we went back to Angela.

When she'd gone I said to Angela in a hollow voice:

"Well, Angela, I proposed."

"You *didn't!* screamed Angela.

"I did," I said, in a still hollower voice. "I thought I'd better get it over."

"And what happened?"

"She r-rejected me," I sobbed. "I'm going out to Central Africa to shoot kangaroos."

I went out into the cold, dark night.

And that put Angela out of it altogether.

But Joan and I continued to meet – unknown to Angela, of course.

Nearly every night I took her to an expensive restaurant to dinner, and after that to expensive seats at a theatre, or to an expensive night club, or to expensive dances. It was all very expensive altogether. Once or twice I hinted to Joan that something cheaper might do. But she said:

"Oh, that's so dull. I mean, it's all right for a lot of stuffy married people, but not for *us!*"

Then I took Jim into my confidence and told him all about it. He looked very serious and said:

"Oh, no, of course you can't do the thing cheaply. I mean, it's all right spending quiet evenings together and going to quiet places when you're married or even engaged, but – hang it all, man, if you aren't even engaged to the girl you've got to do her proud."

This has been going on for three months and I'm just on the point of bankruptcy.

"Don't take her out any more?" you say? No, that's out of the question. You see, I've formed a sort of habit of her and I don't think I could break myself of it.

But I know what she meant when she

said parliament would never tax bachelors. It won't because it knows that they already are taxed. Up to the hilt.

What I don't understand is what she meant by saying that she wouldn't propose to me.

What else has she been doing during these three months?

And it certainly does seem the simplest way out of it….

Left in Charge
(The Passing Show, 7/4/1928)

It was really most awkward that Julia had to go to her mother's for that weekend because it was just the time that April would come out with measles if she were going to come out with them at all. You see, April had been in contact with measles and had been enjoying a mild quarantine ever since.

"But it's not in the least likely that she'll come out with them," said Julia carelessly, "because she's had them. It really needn't worry you at all, dear. Nurse will know just what to do if she *should* come out with them."

April is only six and I am April's father. A heavy load of responsibility had descended on me when I heard that I was to be left in charge of her over the fateful weekend.

I took Julia's advice and didn't worry about it till Nurse rang me up at the office and said that she'd been sent for to *her* mother's, because her mother had broken her leg, and it was Ellen's day off and what should she do? I flung myself into the breach, of course, like a true Briton and said that I'd come home at once. And I came. I found Nurse standing on the doorstep with her box packed and the cab at the door.

I felt a little nervous, of course.

"What about this – I mean these measles, Nurse? Isn't today the crucial day? What do I do if she comes out with them?"

"Oh, don't you worry about that, sir," said Nurse, as she stepped into her cab and drove off.

I went slowly up to the nursery where

April, bedecked in a jazz feeder, was making merry with a glass of hot milk and an egg.

She greeted me hilariously through a mouthful of egg.

"Hello, Daddy! Isn't it fun! Just you and me! My egg's all loose and runny. I'm going to pour it out on my plate and play rivers with it."

"Does Nurse let you do that?" I enquired, feebly.

"No," said April, simply, "but she's not here."

I looked at her anxiously. Wasn't the child rather flushed?

"Do you feel quite well, April?" I said apprehensively.

"Yes. I'm going to pour it all out like this for a sea and have little bits of bread for ships."

"Are you *sure* you feel quite well, April?"

"Yes," said April. "The sea's all yellow because a ship full of butter has just been wrecked in it. Against this rock. The captain didn't see it because he was asleep—"

I suddenly remembered that Julia always kept a thermometer in the top drawer of her dressing-table. *That* was the thing to do, of course. Take her temperature. It would settle the horrible doubt. I ran for the thermometer.

When I came back, April had temporarily abandoned her sea piece and was almost totally eclipsed behind her glass of milk. I tore the glass from her lips and clapped the thermometer into her mouth. If she had the measles there wasn't a moment to be lost, of course. She gurgled happily.

I left it in for the prescribed three minutes and then took it out. It was 101. There was no doubt about it.

I couldn't help feeling that it was a good thing that I was in charge instead of any of those casual women. I must act at once, of course. There wasn't a minute to be lost. I hurried downstairs to the telephone and rang up the doctor.

The doctor was out. I've never been able to discover where doctors spend their time, because they're never anywhere to be found when you want them. I suppose there is a doctor's club somewhere where they go to play billiards. That put me in a quandary. I won't pretend I wasn't getting rattled.

It's terrible to have your only child attacked by a virulent disease under your very eyes, so to speak, and not to know what to do. Too late I realised that we ought to have a book on measles so as to be prepared for this contingency. Everyone ought to have a book on measles.

And then, just as I was beginning to feel really desperate, I saw Jones passing the window. Now Jones is a thoroughly useful little chap. He always knows what's won the two-thirty, and what the weather forecast is, and where you have to change to get to Bournemouth and things like that. I felt sure that he'd know all about measles.

So I flung up the window and called:

"*Hi!* Jones!"

He stopped.

"Hello!" he replied. "What is it? House on fire?"

"No," I said, "April's down with measles and they're all away except me, and the doctor's out. What ought I to do?"

He looked a little taken aback.

"Well, I'm awfully sorry, old chap," he said. "I've never had 'em myself. And my wife and the maids are all out. But," he brightened, "I tell you what. We've got a book at home about diseases. I'll get it."

"Are you sure it's got measles in?" I said anxiously.

"Sure?" said Jones.   "I know it's got

hydrophobia and *delirium tremens* in, so it's sure to have measles."

"You'll fetch it along at once, won't you?" I called, and drew down the window.

I'd got April to bed by the time he returned with it. At first she didn't want to go to bed, but when I suggested that we'd play a game that she'd got measles, she went quite gaily. Then Jones arrived with his book.

According to the book the patient must be put to bed at once in a darkened room with a bronchitis kettle. Well, we'd got her to bed all right.   The next step was to darken the room. This was more difficult than you'd think.

First we tried drawing the curtains but they didn't really darken the room properly because they were cretonne curtains and some light came through. Then we looked for some darker stuff to hang over the windows but we couldn't find anything that would do. We tried the dining room rug but it was too heavy and brought the

curtain-rod down. And then Jones had one of his brilliant ideas. He said that he'd got a pot of dark green paint at home and that if we put that over the window it would completely darken it. It was, in its way, of course, a drastic step but desperate ills call for desperate remedies and there wasn't a moment to be lost with the poor child stricken down like this by a virulent disease and no help at hand.

So Jones ran home to fetch his green paint and I began to look for a bronchitis kettle.   I knew that Julia had one somewhere. I found it at last and was just filling it when Jones returned with his green paint.

He began on it at once. It certainly did seem splendid stuff for darkening but, of course, I couldn't watch him very carefully because I was busy with my bronchitis kettle. The thing kept catching fire and I had the very greatest difficulty in putting it out. I thought that perhaps I was putting the paraffin in the wrong place but I wasn't used to the thing, which made it very difficult.

And then quite suddenly Julia came home. It seems that her mother had recovered from whatever she'd sent for Julia about. Julia stood in the doorway for some seconds watching us, literally paralysed by amazement.

I explained what we were doing. She looked at Jones (who was working like mad to get the room darkened) with a very strange expression.   Certainly he was making rather a mess over the carpet, but then he knew that there simply wasn't a moment to be lost. I was just putting a bronchitis kettle fire out when she came in.

"Isn't it *lovely*, Mummy!" said April blissfully. "I'm pretending to have measles and Daddy's making lovely fireworks for me and Mr Jones is making lovely fountains and waterfalls with green paint!"

"She looks perfectly well," snapped Julia, turning her eyes at last to April.

"She isn't," I said. "She's got a temperature of 101."

"I don't believe that she's got a temperature at all," said Julia.

"Take it yourself and see, then," I advised her.

So she did, and – you'll hardly believe it – the child's temperature had gone down to normal.

She packed Jones off without any ceremony at all. (She was only *just* polite to him) and then turned to me. She wasn't even *just* polite to me. But how on earth could I be expected to know that if you take a child's temperature just after it's swallowed a mouthful of hot milk it goes up to 101? There was nothing about that in Jones's book.

And how could I know that you don't put paraffin in a bronchitis kettle?

I still contend that I acted for the best.

And it's some slight consolation that April thoroughly enjoyed the whole thing. In fact she is continually asking me to play that game again.